CONCISE ENCYCLOPEDIA OF THE
OCEAN

RED LEMON PRESS

First published in the UK by:
Weldon Owen
King's Road Publishing
2.07 The Plaza
535 King's Road
Chelsea, London, SW10 0SZ
Weldon Owen Pty Ltd

Much of the text in this book is taken from *The Illustrated Atlas of the Sea*, originally published by Weldon Owen Pty Ltd in 2009. All the information in this edition has been completely revised and updated.

Authors and consultants:

Dr. Stephen Hutchinson, Senior Research Fellow, National Oceanography Centre, Southampton, UK

Professor Johann R. E. Lutjeharms, Department of Oceanography, University of Cape Town, South Africa

Beverly McMillan, Science Writer and Author, Virginia, USA

Dr. John Musick, Marshall Acuff Professor Emeritus in Marine Science, Virginia Institute of Marine Science, College of William and Mary, Virginia, USA

Dr. Bernard Stonehouse, Emeritus Associate, Scott Polar Research Institute, University of Cambridge, UK, and Honorary Research Fellow, Maritime Historical Studies Centre, University of Hull, UK

Dr. Matthias Tomczak, Emeritus Professor of Oceanography, Flinders University, South Australia

Project Editor Claudia Martin
Designer Natalie Schmidt
Managing Editor Hazel Eriksson
Publisher Donna Gregory

ISBN 978-1-7834-2430-6

A CIP catalogue for this book is available from the British Library.

Printed and bound in Malaysia.

10 9 8 7 6 5 4 3 2 1

Weldon Owen is a division of Bonnier Publishing.

www.bonnierpublishing.com

Blue hole (right)
Forming an almost perfect circle a quarter-mile (0.4 km) in diameter, the Great Blue Hole of Lighthouse Reef in Belize is one of the most dramatic diving destinations in the world. Several such sinkholes exist, all in coastal areas where rising seas flooded a limestone cave system and caused the roof to collapse.

CONTENTS

⚡ Hawaiian monk seal (left)

The shy, critically endangered Hawaiian monk seal (*Monachus schauinslandi*) is native to the tropical waters of the northwestern Hawaiian islands. Its numbers have declined dramatically due to several factors, including coastal development encroaching on its habitat.

Cinnamon clownfish (left)

The cinnamon clownfish (*Amphiprion melanopus*) spends much of its life amid the protective tentacles of an equally colorful sea anemone (*Heteractis crispa*) in the tropical waters of the western Pacific Ocean. Its food includes algae and plankton.

Golden jellyfish (left)

Endemic golden jellyfish (*Mastigias c.f. papua etpisoni*) fill Jellyfish Lake, a marine lake on Eil Malk island, Palau, in the western Pacific. Jellyfish Lake is connected to the ocean through narrow cracks in an ancient reef but is isolated enough for these jellyfish to have evolved into a substantially different subspecies from those in nearby lagoons.

Great Barrier Reef (left)

This is the world's largest coral reef system and possibly the largest single structure made by living organisms. It is made up of some 3,000 individual reefs and 900 tropical islands. It lies off northeast Australia and supports a great diversity of flora and fauna.

FOREWORD

Producing an encyclopedia is a daunting undertaking that requires an incredible breadth of knowledge, great attention to detail, creative skill in illustrative design and, of course, an ability to convey essential information with a well-written narrative. Indeed, producing an encyclopedia of the oceans creates additional challenges in that the topography of the seafloor and of the ocean surface must be sensed remotely, and the marine life that inhabits the waters can be understood only from painstaking scientific research, much of which may not be widely available to the general public. Not only are the waters, the ocean floor, and the marine life complex and varied, but together they represent a coupled system with threads of connections that run throughout both time and space.

The Concise Encyclopedia of the Ocean is an amazing publication. It is more than an encyclopedia in a traditional sense: it has nuggets of recent scientific research, ranging in scale from global to molecular that are embedded within the chapters. It contains stunning photographs to illustrate the diversity of marine environments and marine life and it offers much that is relevant in our lives through the inclusion of forays into climate change, pollution, natural resources, hurricanes, tsunamis, threatened sea life, and conservation. It is also more than a standard encyclopedia in that it is comprehensive, easy-to-read, and offers an introduction to the casual scientist—yet contains much of interest to the more sophisticated scientific adventurer.

The Concise Encyclopedia of the Ocean is divided into twelve chapters, the first six of which provide an overview of the water, its composition, circulation, and never-ending motion from waves and tides; its physical environments extending from the dynamic coastlines to the frigid dark plains of the deep sea; and its marine habitats, forms of life, and rich natural resources. The next five chapters, written by experts in their respective fields, are structured around the five oceans: Arctic, Southern, Atlantic, Indian, and Pacific. It is here that the maps of the oceans can be found with color-coded bathymetric depths that are superimposed with hundreds of geographic names to depict the shoals, plateaus, ridges, basins, trenches, and other features that together make up 70 percent of Earth's surface. Each of these chapters is presented in a similar format that also includes, interspersed throughout the pages, dozens of helpful insets to convey ocean basin statistics, patterns of ocean currents, and the distribution of natural resources within the basins. A final reference chapter provides an encyclopedic factfile, glossary, and gazetteer.

Humans have always had a fascination for the oceans, and you will surely enjoy reading about them in this compelling reference. It brings together in one volume all of the attributes that provide this fascination, ranging from the intensity of the ocean's physical processes, to the incredible diversity of marine life that lives in the waters, to the shape and structure of the basins that hold both the waters and the life. *The Concise Encyclopedia of the Ocean* will surely be a lasting contribution.

Dr. John T. Wells
Dean and Director, Virginia Institute of Marine Science

HOW TO USE THIS BOOK

This encyclopedia is arranged in two main sections. The first section provides a historical and physical overview of the global sea. Photographs, diagrams, and mapping illustrate information about different marine environments and species. The second section is a chapter-by-chapter cartographic survey of the world's major oceans and the sea divisions they encompass. It includes details of seafloor topography, maps that show the key currents, and photographs and information about animal life and human activity in the region. A reference section completes the book and consists of a detailed factfile on the oceans and their subdivisions, a glossary, a gazetteer, and an index.

Thematic pages

The thematic pages include detailed world maps accompanied by illustrations, diagrams, charts, graphs, and photographs. They cover topics as diverse as the origins of water on Earth, exploration of the seas, ocean ecosystems, and conservation.

Thematic maps
Thematic maps show a range of data such as wildlife distribution, physical features, and sea depth.

Scale
The scale of the main map, plus a scale bar and projection information are included here.

Thematic map key

Introduction
This text gives a clear, concise overview of the most salient facts about the featured topic.

Informative photography
Current photographs of the sea, marine life, and resources are included with captions.

Diagrams and illustrations
These highlight relevant topics such as geological processes, ecosystems, wildlife, and oceanographic research equipment.

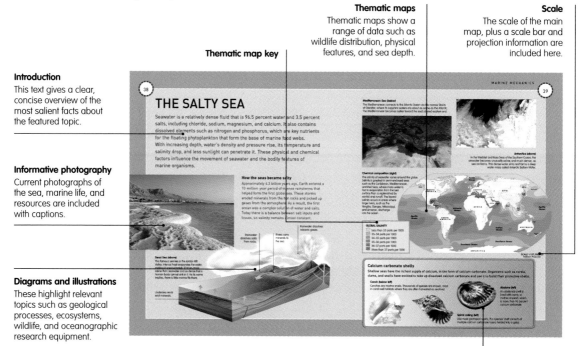

Feature box
Special-interest subjects are shown in a feature box, with their own introduction and selected photographs or illustrations.

Cartographic pages

These pages show detailed maps of the world's oceans and seas, accompanied by illustrations, diagrams, charts, graphs, and photographs. The text describes the nature of each sea and its major currents and climatic influences.

Conservation icons

The conservation status of endangered and critically endangered animals, as determined by the IUCN Red List of Threatened Species, is indicated by a red or yellow icon.

⚡ Critically endangered   ⚡ Endangered

Locator map
This map indicates the location of the ocean.

Pie chart
Facts about each ocean are presented in a pie-chart.

Oceans (left)
The introduction page for each chapter provides an overview of physical geography, natural resources, statistical information, and typical ecosystems.

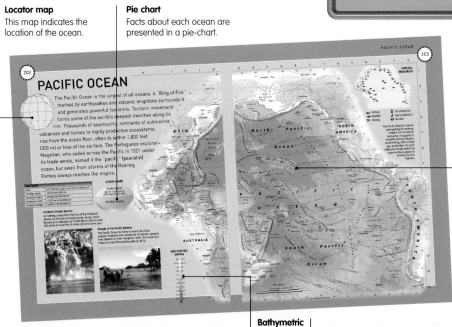

Cartographic map
Each chapter opens with a large map of the entire ocean.

Three-dimensional view of seafloor
A computer-generated map reveals details of ridges, canyons, and other seafloor features.

Bathymetric depth scale

Seas (right)
These pages take a close-focus look at a particular sea. A large-scale map shows the seafloor features in detail. Smaller supporting maps and images show key currents, natural resources, wildlife, and human activity.

Pie charts, tables, and graphs
Additional details about regions, or the animal life found there, are provided in the form of tables, charts, or graphs. This at-a-glance information adds to captions and photographs.

Wildlife photography
Photographs from wildlife and undersea specialists show the animal life in the region.

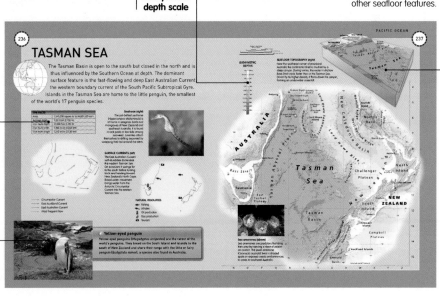

A GUIDE TO THE MAPS

The maps in this encyclopedia contain a variety of labels, symbols, and other graphic devices to provide detailed information such as ocean floor depth and topography, and the location of undersea mountains, trenches, and volcanoes, rivers, cities, and country borders. A grid allows you to locate all these features using the gazetteer on pages 264–78. In addition, throughout the book, thematic maps provide information about features of interest, such as ocean currents, natural resources, physical geography, and temperature.

Cartographic map

Each map shows details of the seafloor, including variations in depth, topography, and named features.

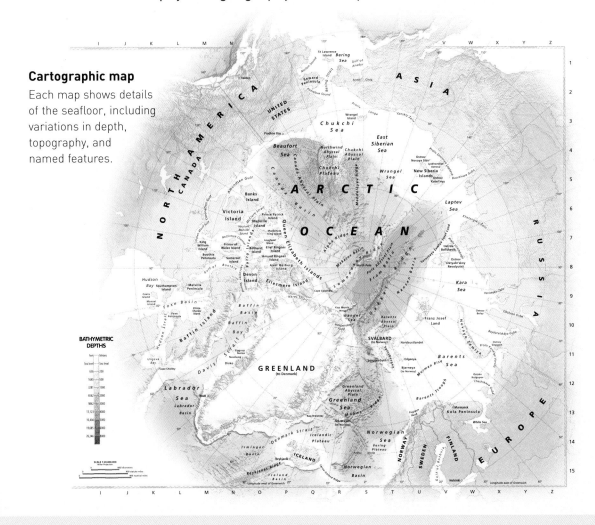

Thematic mapping

Marine life maps

Maps display marine life topics such as wildlife species range, migratory paths, and coral distribution.

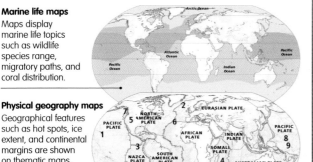

Physical geography maps

Geographical features such as hot spots, ice extent, and continental margins are shown on thematic maps.

NASA and NOAA maps

Maps display data and information gathered using the latest satellite and sonar technology.

Natural resources

A small map carries icons to denote the natural resources to be found in each ocean area.

NATURAL RESOURCES

- Fishing
- Shellfish
- Mining
- Oil production
- Gas production

Currents

A diagrammatic map shows the prevailing surface currents in the area.

SURFACE CURRENTS

- → East Greenland Current
- → East Spitsbergen Current
- → Irminger Current
- → Norwegian Atlantic Current

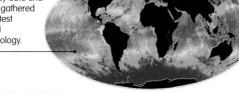

Map legend

BATHYMETRIC DEPTHS

Feet	Meters
Sea level	Sea level
656	200
1640	500
3281	1000
6562	2000
9842	3000
13,123	4000
16,404	5000
19,685	6000
26,246	8000

SCALE AND PROJECTION

SCALE 1:20,000,000
Miller Projection

400 kilometers

400 statute miles

400 nautical miles

Every map has a scale bar that includes nautical miles and also shows map projection details.

WATER FEATURES

Ocean	*PACIFIC OCEAN*
Sea	*Bering Sea*
Bay/gulf	*Gulf of Alaska*
Channel/strait	*Bering Strait*
Lake	*Lake Nasser*
River	*Nile*
Canal	*Suez Canal*
Seamount	▲ Zheng He Seamount 6,263ft (1,909m)
Bathymetric feature	Madagascar Basin

PHYSICAL FEATURES

Geographical feature	*Baja California*
Peninsula	**Cape York Peninsula**
Cape/point	**Beachy Head**
Island group	**Solomon Islands**
Island	**Isla Santa Maria**
Pole	**North Pole**

PLACE NAMES

Country name	**F R A N C E**

CITY SYMBOLS

■ Los Angeles	Over 5 million inhabitants
● Houston	1 million to 5 million
○ Miami	100,000 to 1 million
Bangkok	National capital
Hanoi	National capital
Riga	National capital

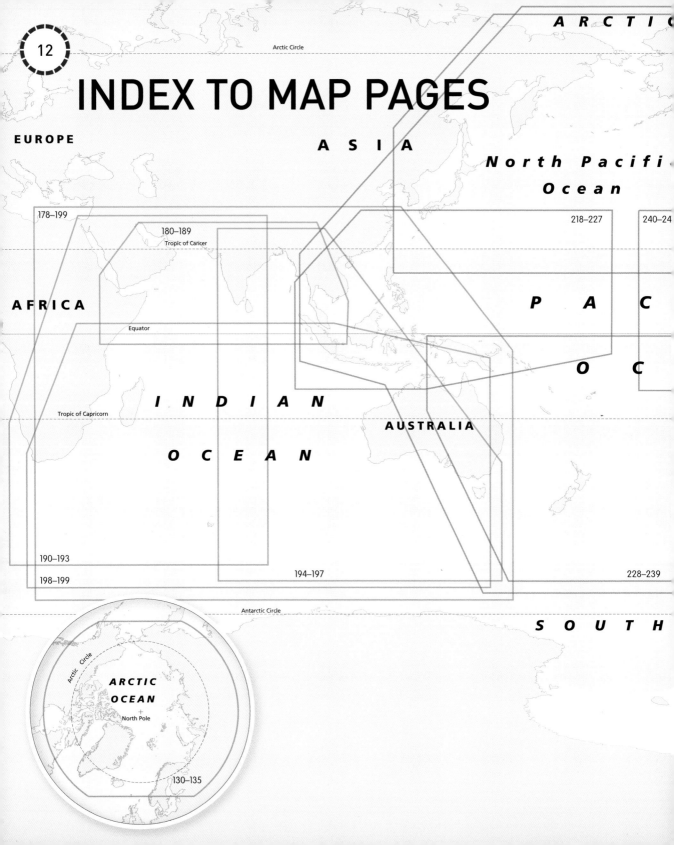

INDEX TO MAP PAGES

Arctic Circle

EUROPE

A S I A

North Pacific
Ocean

178–199

180–189
Tropic of Cancer

218–227

240–24

AFRICA

P A C

Equator

190–193

198–199

I N D I A N

O C E A N

Tropic of Capricorn

AUSTRALIA

O C

194–197

228–239

A R C T I C

Antarctic Circle

S O U T H

ARCTIC
OCEAN
+
North Pole

Arctic Circle

130–135

O C E A N

146–175
148–167

Arctic Circle

NORTH AMERICA

North Atlantic Ocean

EUROPE

ATLANTIC

Tropic of Cancer

AFRICA

204–217

I F I C

E A N

SOUTH AMERICA

OCEAN

Equator

Tropic of Capricorn

South Pacific Ocean

South Atlantic Ocean

246–249
202–249
168–175

Antarctic Circle

ERN OCEAN

A N T A R C T I C A

S O U T H E R N

Antarctic Circle

+ South Pole

138–143

O C E A N

CHAPTER ONE

WATER ON EARTH

Rocky shore

A sculpted and eroding rocky shore hints at the changeable physical features of the undersea world beyond. Like ecosystems on land, the marine environment is dynamic and varied. It encompasses an array of geological forms as well as changing physical and chemical conditions that establish the wide array of habitats where communities of marine life may survive.

THE GLOBAL SEA

Liquid water covers more than 70 percent of the world's surface and is the defining feature of our planet. Salt water makes up 97 percent of this watery domain, forming a global sea that is subdivided into five oceans: the vast Atlantic and Pacific Oceans, the Indian Ocean, the Southern Ocean, and the small, polar Arctic Ocean. For much of recorded history, this global sea has been an enigma. Its currents and weather patterns have challenged seafarers, while its undersea landscape and marine life have largely been hidden beneath the waves. Only within the last two centuries have mariners and scientists begun to uncover the mysteries of Earth's oceans.

GLOBAL SEA FACTS	
Total area	139 million square miles (361 million km²)
Total volume	310,000,000 cubic miles (1,347,000,000 km³)
Average depth	12,230 feet (3,730 m)
Greatest depth	35,840 feet (10,900 m)
Mean ocean crust thickness	4.04 miles (6.5 km)
Longest mountain range	10,000 miles (16,000 km)

Ocean depths (below)
For each ocean basin, the long colored bar shows maximum depth. The shorter bar indicates the basin's average depth.

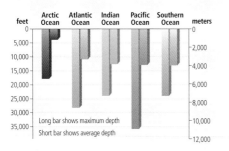

Long bar shows maximum depth
Short bar shows average depth

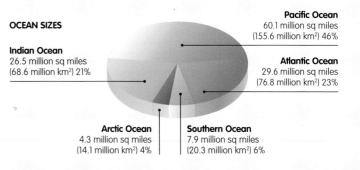

OCEAN SIZES

Pacific Ocean
60.1 million sq miles
(155.6 million km²) 46%

Atlantic Ocean
29.6 million sq miles
(76.8 million km²) 23%

Indian Ocean
26.5 million sq miles
(68.6 million km²) 21%

Arctic Ocean
4.3 million sq miles
(14.1 million km²) 4%

Southern Ocean
7.9 million sq miles
(20.3 million km²) 6%

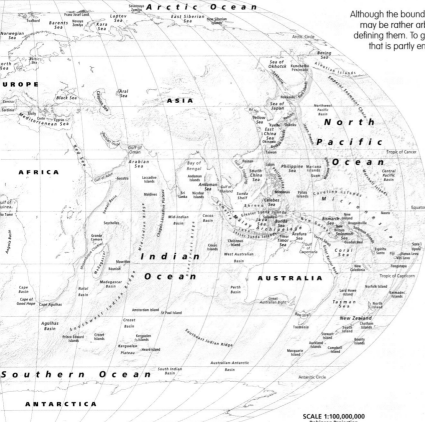

The marine map (left)

Although the boundaries between oceans and their subdivisions may be rather arbitrary, geography and size are key factors in defining them. To geographers, a "sea" is a large area of ocean that is partly enclosed by land. It may include a smaller arm called a gulf. Bays are smaller still.

The sea in motion

Waves underscore the constant motion of the sea. Globally some of the largest waves wash the shores of the Hawaiian Islands.

Island outposts

Island chains punctuate vast reaches of the Pacific. Shown here is Ulithi, one of a collection of coral islands in the Pacific known as Micronesia.

A multitude of fish

Marine life comprises an estimated 25,000 species of bony fish, including this striking longnose hawkfish (*Oxycirrhites typus*).

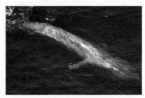

🔊 Marine mammals

Whales and other marine mammals occur in every ocean. This is a blue whale (*Balaenoptera musculus*)—the largest animal on Earth.

A world of oceans (below)

As this series of maps shows, although apparently separated by continents, the oceans interconnect to form a continuous swath of seawater on Earth's surface. Thus they form a single, unified global sea.

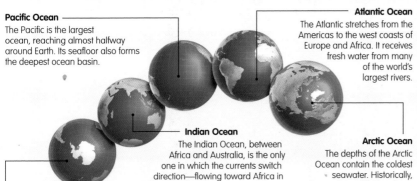

Pacific Ocean

The Pacific is the largest ocean, reaching almost halfway around Earth. Its seafloor also forms the deepest ocean basin.

Atlantic Ocean

The Atlantic stretches from the Americas to the west coasts of Europe and Africa. It receives fresh water from many of the world's largest rivers.

Indian Ocean

The Indian Ocean, between Africa and Australia, is the only one in which the currents switch direction—flowing toward Africa in winter and toward India in summer.

Arctic Ocean

The depths of the Arctic Ocean contain the coldest seawater. Historically, portions of it have been ice-covered all year round, a situation global warming is changing.

Southern Ocean

In winter as much as 7.7 million square miles (20 million km²) of the Southern Ocean is covered by ice.

WATER AT WORK

Water's chemical properties were crucial in the evolution of the seas and eventually of life itself. One is a high heat capacity, the ability to absorb a great deal of heat before water warms appreciably. As a result, temperatures in watery environments, including oceans and the bodies of organisms, remain remarkably stable. Water also dissolves many other substances, and it has surface tension—the cohesiveness that keeps individual molecules connected to one another in raindrops, rivers, and in the vast global sea.

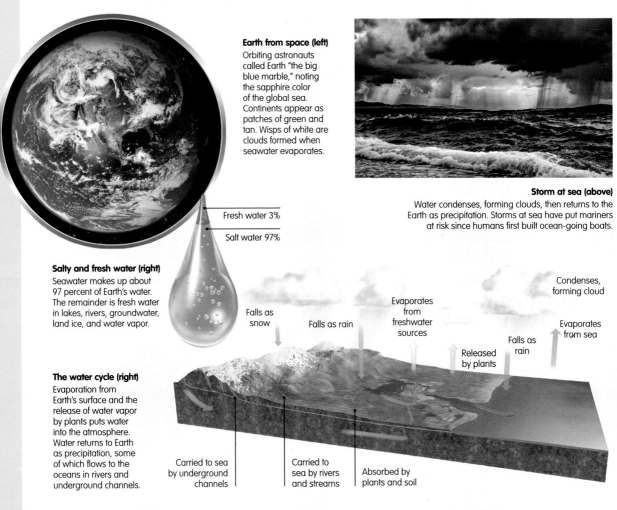

Earth from space (left)
Orbiting astronauts called Earth "the big blue marble," noting the sapphire color of the global sea. Continents appear as patches of green and tan. Wisps of white are clouds formed when seawater evaporates.

Storm at sea (above)
Water condenses, forming clouds, then returns to the Earth as precipitation. Storms at sea have put mariners at risk since humans first built ocean-going boats.

Fresh water 3%

Salt water 97%

Salty and fresh water (right)
Seawater makes up about 97 percent of Earth's water. The remainder is fresh water in lakes, rivers, groundwater, land ice, and water vapor.

The water cycle (right)
Evaporation from Earth's surface and the release of water vapor by plants puts water into the atmosphere. Water returns to Earth as precipitation, some of which flows to the oceans in rivers and underground channels.

Condenses, forming cloud

Evaporates from freshwater sources

Falls as snow

Falls as rain

Released by plants

Falls as rain

Evaporates from sea

Carried to sea by underground channels

Carried to sea by rivers and streams

Absorbed by plants and soil

Properties of water

Water's properties make it one of the most extraordinary substances on Earth. Links between water molecules called hydrogen bonds cause water to lose or gain heat slowly, so temperatures in watery environments are quite stable. Water also is relatively dense, providing physical support for floating and swimming organisms. Yet water's solid form, ice, is less dense than liquid water, so ice floats—allowing aquatic life to survive beneath it.

Making a water molecule (right)

A water molecule has an oxygen atom sandwiched between two hydrogen atoms, giving the molecule two arms with opposite electrical charges. This difference spurs the formation of hydrogen bonds that give water unique properties.

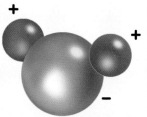

THE WATER TABLE	
Boiling point	212°F (100°C)
Freezing point, pure water	32°F (0°C)
Freezing point, seawater	Around 28.6°F (-1.9°C)
Weight of 1.75 gallons (1 L) at 68°F (20°C)	2.2 pounds (1 kg)
Seawater salt content	Average 3.5%
Fresh water salt content	Less than 0.1%
Pressure increase with depth	14.7 pounds (6.7 kg) per each 33 feet (10 m)
Average speed of sound in water at 46°F (8°C)	4,721 feet (1,439 m) per second
Greatest supply of fresh water	Antarctic ice (90%+)

SOLID

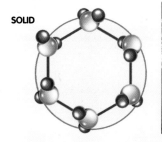

Solid water

Below 32°F (0°C), bonds between water molecules form a rigid, open lattice, which makes ice less dense than liquid water.

LIQUID

Liquid water

Liquid water is called a universal solvent because salts and many other substances can readily dissolve in it.

GAS

Gas

Water vapor is the gaseous phase of water. Water is the only substance on Earth that naturally exists as a solid, liquid, and gas.

ORIGIN OF A WATERY WORLD

The newly formed Earth was a turbulent, volcanic planet. No liquid water—and no life—could exist on its searing surface, but gases vented from volcanoes included water vapor that accumulated in dense, hot clouds. More steam rose from ice evaporating from comets that bombarded Earth's surface. As early Earth rapidly cooled, however, the clouds of steam began to condense into rain—the source of the first liquid water on the planet's surface.

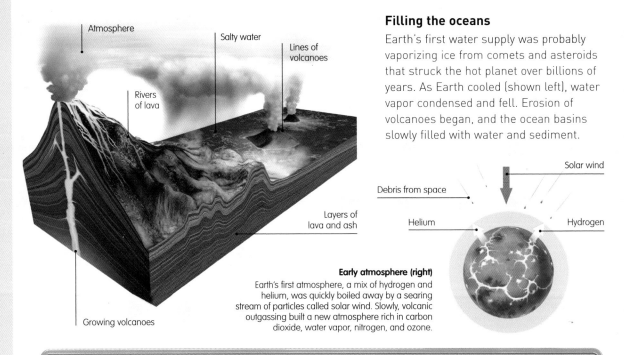

Atmosphere

Salty water

Lines of volcanoes

Rivers of lava

Layers of lava and ash

Growing volcanoes

Filling the oceans

Earth's first water supply was probably vaporizing ice from comets and asteroids that struck the hot planet over billions of years. As Earth cooled (shown left), water vapor condensed and fell. Erosion of volcanoes began, and the ocean basins slowly filled with water and sediment.

Solar wind

Debris from space

Helium

Hydrogen

Early atmosphere (right)

Earth's first atmosphere, a mix of hydrogen and helium, was quickly boiled away by a searing stream of particles called solar wind. Slowly, volcanic outgassing built a new atmosphere rich in carbon dioxide, water vapor, nitrogen, and ozone.

Evidence for early beginnings

Zircon crystals from ancient streambeds, such as Jack Hills in Western Australia (shown left), form when water is present around melting granite. Dated to about 4.4 million years ago, zircons are remnants of Earth's first rocky crust, which was later destroyed by meteorite impacts. Their age strongly implies that conditions required for life—including liquid water—may have developed much earlier and faster than once thought.

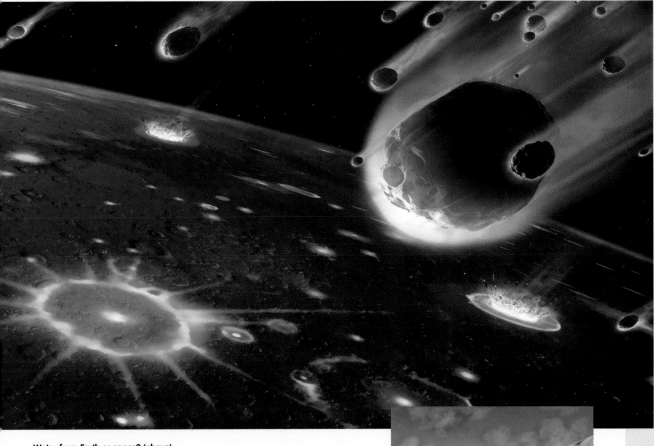

Water from Earth or space? (above)

At one time most scientists believed that Earth's first liquid water condensed from water vapor spewed by volcanoes along with other gases. Further study has supported the "heavy bombardment" theory that, over billions of years, ice-rich comets and asteroids brought water with them when they collided with Earth's atmosphere. Quite possibly, some combination of processes generated the planet's water supply.

UV light

Hydrogen

Water

Oxygen and ozone

Nitrogen

Carbon dioxide

Earth's first ozone layer (left)

Intense sunlight interacted with oxygen in the early atmosphere. This chemical reaction formed an ozone layer that protected Earth's surface from further harmful solar radiation. The ozone barrier paved the way for the evolution of more complex life.

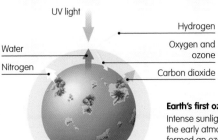

Land and sea (above)

Rain, formed by condensing water vapor, fed the oceans. The emerging waters lapped the volcanic granite that formed the first continents.

THE EVOLVING SEA

As Earth cooled, a crust formed over its molten interior. As water vapor in the atmosphere condensed into droplets, torrential rain filled what would become ocean basins. Runoff from land areas contained eroded minerals, the beginnings of the salty sea and a seafloor blanketed by sediments. Several times during Earth's early history, the heat from asteroid impacts boiled away the oceans and any life they may have contained. By about 3.8 billion years ago, however, primitive cells became established, and the evolution of life was under way.

Millennia of change and loss (below)

Earth's ecosystems and the types of organisms in them have changed as climate shifts correlated with ice ages and fluctuating sea levels. Different factors have also triggered at least five mass extinction episodes, in which more than half of animal species were lost. Many ecologists today fear that a sixth mass extinction is under way.

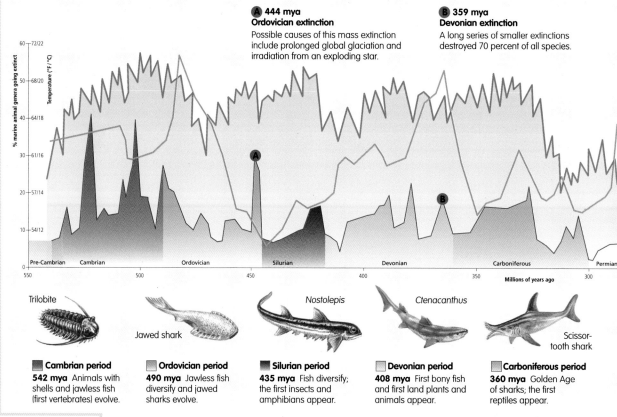

**A 444 mya
Ordovician extinction**

Possible causes of this mass extinction include prolonged global glaciation and irradiation from an exploding star.

**B 359 mya
Devonian extinction**

A long series of smaller extinctions destroyed 70 percent of all species.

Trilobite

Jawed shark

Nostolepis

Ctenacanthus

Scissor-tooth shark

Cambrian period
542 mya Animals with shells and jawless fish (first vertebrates) evolve.

Ordovician period
490 mya Jawless fish diversify and jawed sharks evolve.

Silurian period
435 mya Fish diversify; the first insects and amphibians appear.

Devonian period
408 mya First bony fish and first land plants and animals appear.

Carboniferous period
360 mya Golden Age of sharks; the first reptiles appear.

— Temperature
— Sea level (present at 0)
— Extinction rate
● Mass extinction event

Evolving life

Bacteria were among the first lifeforms to evolve in early Earth's shallow seas. Some of these single-celled species, called cyanobacteria, carried out photosynthesis as plants do, using sunlight to manufacture their own food. Over time they formed domed mats—known as stromatolites—that hardened into limestone as sediments and minerals accumulated in them.

Stromatolites (right)

Fossil stromatolites have been dated radiometrically to about 3.5 billion years old. Shark Bay (shown right) in Western Australia is home to Earth's only living stromatolites. These specimens may be up to 1,000 years old.

Stromatolite structure (right)

Growth The mat of bacteria grows, mounding above the accumulating sediment.

Mineralization The bacteria secrete calcium carbonate, or limestone. The mineral secretions trap sediments that form darker layers.

Interior The interior of the stromatolite reveals concentric layers formed during previous growth.

Base The base of the stromatolite is firmly attached to the surface upon which the mound was originally established.

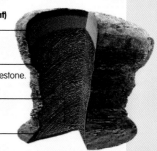

C 251 mya
Permian extinction

Loss of 96 percent of marine species followed global warming caused by volcanism and shifts in sea chemistry.

D 208 mya
Triassic extinction

About 20 percent of major marine groups and the last large amphibians vanished at this time.

E 65 mya
Cretaceous extinction

An asteroid impact and massive volcanism plunged Earth into years of "impact winter," killed off the non-avian dinosaurs and half of marine species.

Sea level (ft/m)

980/300
660/200
330/100
0
-330/-100
-660/-200

Quaternary

Last ice age

Pangea

Triassic   Jurassic   Cretaceous   Tertiary

250   200   150   100   50   0

River-dwelling shark, *Xenacanthus*

Reptile with webbed toes, *Nothosaurus*

Relative of angel and saw sharks, *Protospinax*

Relative of the great white whark, *Cretoxyrhina*

Megalodon

☐ **Permian period**
286 mya Mass extinctions occur both on land and in the seas.

☐ **Triassic period**
248 mya Early dinosaurs, mammals, and marine reptiles appear.

☐ **Jurassic period**
208 mya First modern sharks and rays evolve; mass extinctions in seas take place.

☐ **Cretaceous period**
144 mya Sand tigers and some other modern shark lineages; the first birds appear.

☐ **Tertiary period**
65 mya to today Mammals, birds, and flowering plants diversify.

Into the future:

A dramatic increase in extinctions began in the Quaternary around 1.8 million years ago. These human-caused losses continue today.

EARTH'S TECTONIC PLATES

Earth's crust is divided into about a dozen sections, or plates, that move in different ways atop semi-fluid material underneath. Some contain all or part of the modern-day continents, while others, such as the Pacific Plate, lie entirely beneath the sea. By way of the process once called continental drift and now known as plate tectonics, plate movements slowly reposition continents, push up mountains, and recycle the crust of ocean basins. Such changes have been reshaping the seas for more than half a billion years.

Making ocean basins (below)
Ocean basins form over millions of years as magma upwelling from Earth's interior gradually splits continental crust, creating an opening into which water can flood. That process is occurring today in parts of eastern Africa.

Birth of a rift valley
As a landmass begins to split apart, the land tilts and begins to subside, creating a wide valley.

Flooding the new ocean basin
When the valley floor subsides below sea level, seawater fills the depression. The formation of seafloor pushes the landmasses further apart.

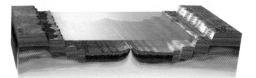

Seafloor spreading
The ocean widens as spreading continues. As the seafloor moves outward it settles and sinks, leaving a ridge on either side of the rift.

Geological features (below)
Earth's constantly moving tectonic plates are responsible for many of the planet's large-scale geological features, including those all or partly submerged under the sea.

Undersea collision
Arcs of volcanic islands occur where two ocean plates collide and one slides beneath the other.

Mid-ocean ridge
Where plates meet at mid-ocean ridges, new seafloor forms as crust material wells up from the mantle underneath.

Hot-spot volcanoes
Areas of unusually hot mantle beneath the interiors of crustal plates give rise to hot-spot volcanoes.

Coastal collision
Arcs of volcanic mountains occur where an oceanic plate collides with a continent and subducts beneath it.

Plate boundaries (right)

Heat rising by convection from Earth's mantle drives the movement of crustal plates. The plates may slide past each other, spread apart, or collide. Volcanism and mountain building are common where plates collide.

Convergent boundary
When plates collide, the heavier one is often subducted into the mantle, slipping under the lighter one.

Divergent boundary
When plates move apart, new seafloor forms at oceanic spreading centers, or rifts, in continental crust.

Transform fault boundary
Where crustal plates mainly slide past each other, they form a transform fault boundary.

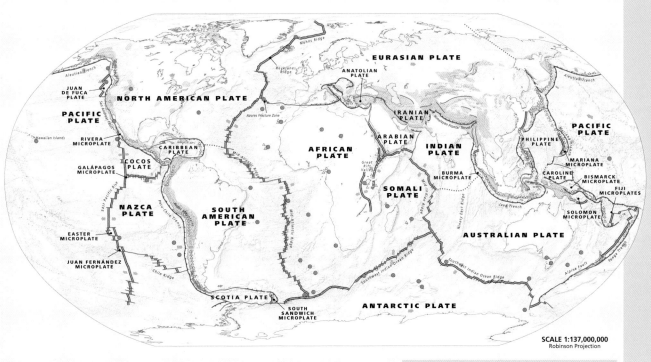

Aleutian Trench
Mohns Ridge
Reykjanes Ridge
EURASIAN PLATE
ANATOLIAN PLATE
Aleutian Trench
JUAN DE FUCA PLATE
NORTH AMERICAN PLATE
IRANIAN PLATE
PACIFIC PLATE
PACIFIC PLATE
Hawaiian Islands
RIVERA MICROPLATE
Azores Fracture Zone
Himalayan Frontal Thrust
ARABIAN PLATE
INDIAN PLATE
PHILIPPINE PLATE
CARIBBEAN PLATE
AFRICAN PLATE
Great Rift Valley
MARIANA MICROPLATE
COCOS PLATE
Mid-Atlantic Ridge
BURMA MICROPLATE
CAROLINE PLATE
BISMARCK MICROPLATE
GALÁPAGOS MICROPLATE
SOMALI PLATE
FIJI MICROPLATES
East Pacific Rise
Peru-Chile Trench
Mid-Indian Ridge
Ninety East Ridge
Java Trench
SOLOMON MICROPLATE
NAZCA PLATE
SOUTH AMERICAN PLATE
Mid-Atlantic Ridge
AUSTRALIAN PLATE
EASTER MICROPLATE
JUAN FERNÁNDEZ MICROPLATE
Chile Ridge
Southwest Indian Ocean Ridge
Alpine Fault
Tonga Trench
SCOTIA PLATE
SOUTH SANDWICH MICROPLATE
ANTARCTIC PLATE

SCALE 1:137,000,000
Robinson Projection

Sliding plates
Transform faults occur where plates move past each other. Earthquakes occur where fault zones intermittently lock up, then release.

Continental rift
The tectonic splitting of a continent forms a deep valley. If the valley floor continues to thin, seafloor spreading forms a new ocean basin.

Folding crust
Colliding continental plates cause the crust to thicken and crumple, which produces high mountains.

TECTONIC FEATURES

▨	Earthquake zone
△	Volcanic zone
●	Prominent hot spot
↤↦	Convergent margin
═	Divergent margin
—	Transform fault
⋯⋯	Diffuse or uncertain
⇨	Direction of movement

Earth's tectonic plates today (above)
The red lines mark actively spreading ridges. Earthquake-prone areas correlate with subduction zones—for example, along the west coast of South America where the Nazca Plate is sliding under and pushing up the South American Plate.

CHANGING OCEANS

As ancient continents moved, the lifeforms on them were carried along, and researchers have been able to use fossil discoveries and the global distribution patterns of living species to help confirm hypotheses about continental movements. Today's continents have occupied the same general positions for about 10 million years. Even so, they are still on the move—on average, about 2 inches (5 cm) a year—as the age-old shifting of Earth's crustal plates continues.

The supercontinent Pangea
About 260 million years ago, a single supercontinent called Pangea was essentially a gigantic island surrounded by sea. The geological changes that created Pangea would later break it apart, forming the modern position of continents and seas.

Moving continents

Earth's crust is divided into movable rocky sections called tectonic plates that essentially float on the upper mantle. Over geological time, moving plates have carried continental landmasses along with them in a process known as plate tectonics. When continents separate, the populations of species inhabiting them may also be separated, a phenomenon that helps explain the global distribution of certain plants and animals.

Today, the unusual plants called cycads occur on several continents. This ancient group first arose on Pangea and evidently cycads were carried around the globe as the supercontinent broke up.

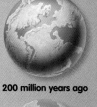

200 million years ago

90 million years ago

Present day

60 million years from now

Pillow lava (above)
As lava flows undersea, it quickly cools and forms a skin, creating a characteristic "pillow-like" shape. This pillow lava formed recently off Hawaii. As pressure builds within, new pillow will burst through the skin.

Changing ocean floor (below)
This computer-generated image shows the relative ages of seafloor areas, with the youngest (red) clearly aligned along mid-ocean spreading centers.

Million years

0 20 40 60 80 100 120 140 160 180 200 220 240 260 280

Last ice age

Ice today

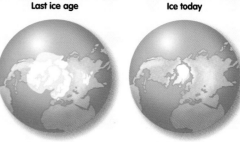

Icy times (above)
During an ice age, extensive ice sheets develop in certain regions, as in Antarctica and Greenland today. By this measure, Earth is still in an ice age that began 2.6 million years ago. Sea level falls as large amounts of water become locked up in ice. The process continues during colder ice-age periods when glaciers advance. Sea level rises when glaciers retreat, a trend that accelerates as the overall ice age wanes.

Sedimentary basins

Where tectonic events are actively producing new seafloor, surface sediments are usually thin. In contrast, at the "rise" where a continental shelf tapers to the deep ocean floor, deep blankets of soft sediments can develop. Sediment blankets about 75 percent of the ocean basins and much of the continental shelves. Some of these sediments enter the marine environment as weathering rock and eroding soil washed or blown into the sea or carried there by rivers. Some form muddy deposits while others are converted to sticky clays. Still other sediments are soft "oozes" consisting of the decomposing remains of marine organisms.

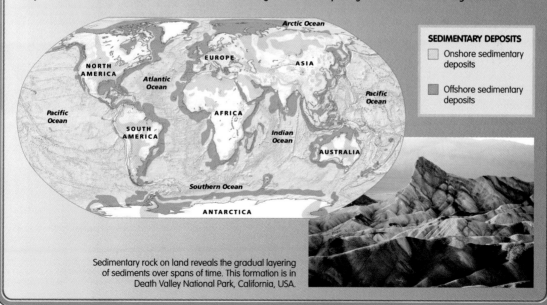

SEDIMENTARY DEPOSITS

Onshore sedimentary deposits

Offshore sedimentary deposits

Sedimentary rock on land reveals the gradual layering of sediments over spans of time. This formation is in Death Valley National Park, California, USA.

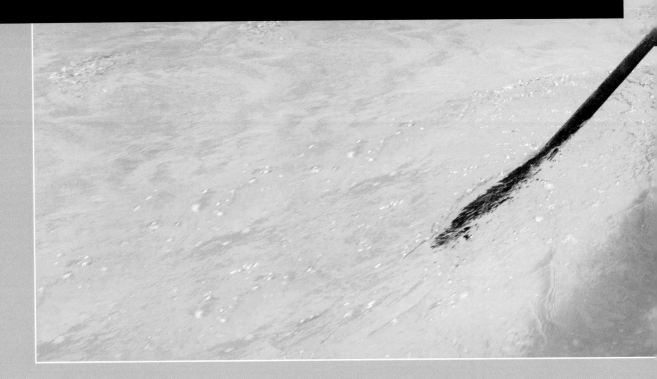

EXPLORING THE OCEANS

Outrigger

An outrigger is a float rigging extending beyond a boat's gunwale. In outrigger canoes and sailboats, an outrigger is a thin, long hull. Its weight reduces the risk of capsizing in one direction, while its buoyancy reduces the risk in the other direction. Among the earliest outriggers were those used for sea travel by Austronesian-speaking peoples of Southeast Asian islands.

HISTORIC EXPLORATION

Humans have taken to the waves for thousands of years, seeking food, commerce, new lands, treasure, and scientific understanding. The first intrepid mariners included Polynesians in dugout canoes and Egyptian traders in watercraft fashioned from bundles of reeds. By the 1400s, larger, sturdier vessels were expanding the range of ocean travel, transforming the seas into highways that could carry seafarers across whole oceans. Some coastal nations created navies that could extend their military might and support voyages of conquest.

Finding the Northwest Passage

The search for a Northwest Passage from the Atlantic to the Pacific beckoned a long line of explorers willing to challenge the harrowing conditions of the Arctic. Vitus Bering, James Cook, and Sir John Franklin all mounted unsuccessful expeditions, Franklin's ending in catastrophe. Eventually it was the savvy and meticulously prepared Norwegian explorer Roald Amundsen who discovered a route through the Arctic Ocean in 1906, after a four-year effort.

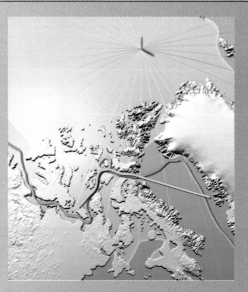

THE NORTHWEST PASSAGE, THE ARCTIC

▭ **Franklin's route**
Sir John Franklin and his crew were last seen in Lancaster Sound in July 1845. Expedition remains were found on Beechey Island five years later.

▭ **Amundsen's route**
Initially following Franklin's route, Amundsen had the good fortune to attempt the Passage when conditions in the Arctic were more favorable.

Vessels equipped to plow through ice and withstand its pressure have been essential to travel and exploration in polar seas. Early icebreakers were wooden sailing ships with an iron-sheathed hull. A modern icebreaker's hull is broad for added stability and its steel bow is reinforced. Rather than ramming through ice, the heavy bow slides over it and crushes it.

Historic sea routes (below)

Early records describe the intrepid journeys of an Egyptian explorer who sailed to Arabia in 2750 BCE. Polynesians used outrigger canoes and celestial navigation to reach Tonga and Samoa in 1000 BCE. Later, and European, Chinese, and Muslim mariners all helped chart the oceans. By the eighteenth century, only the inhospitable seas of Antarctica remained unknown.

➤ Columbus and the *Santa Maria* 1492

The *Santa Maria*, a bulky cargo ship, was the flagship of Columbus's fleet during his voyage across the Atlantic, from Spain to North America. The ill-fated ship foundered off Haiti on Christmas Day, 1492.

➤ Viking mariners

Ancient Vikings braved the North Atlantic in sleek ships powered by oars and a sail. Archeological discoveries reveal that they reached North America more than 1,000 years ago, long before Columbus arrived.

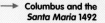

➤ Polynesian expeditions	➤ Portuguese expeditions
➤ Viking expeditions	➤ English expeditions
➤ Chinese expeditions	➤ French expeditions
➤ Spanish expeditions	➤ Dutch expeditions

SCALE 1:119,100,000
Robinson Projection

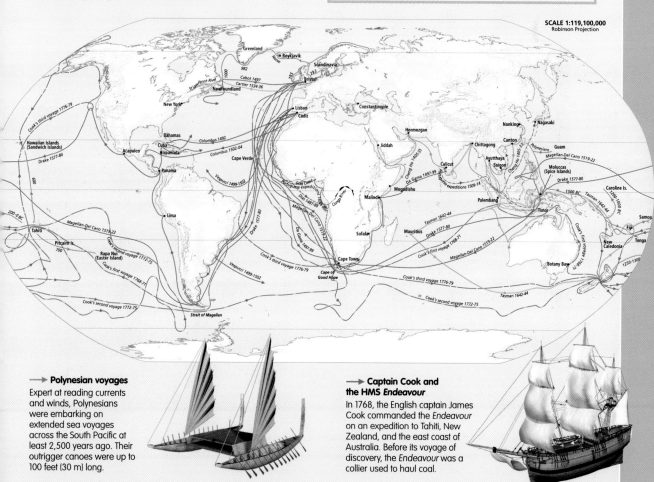

➤ Polynesian voyages

Expert at reading currents and winds, Polynesians were embarking on extended sea voyages across the South Pacific at least 2,500 years ago. Their outrigger canoes were up to 100 feet (30 m) long.

➤ Captain Cook and the HMS *Endeavour*

In 1768, the English captain James Cook commanded the *Endeavour* on an expedition to Tahiti, New Zealand, and the east coast of Australia. Before its voyage of discovery, the *Endeavour* was a collier used to haul coal.

SHIPPING TODAY

Initially employing oars and sails, and later increasingly sophisticated engines, shipbuilding knowledge and technology advanced steadily over the centuries. Likewise, navigation tools evolved from devices such as the cross staff and astrolabe to the finely tuned chronometers developed by European watchmakers. For today's sophisticated diesel-powered ships, nearly every corner of the globe is accessible. About 90 percent of world trade is carried by the shipping industry. Every year, around 18 million containers make 200 million trips across the world's oceans.

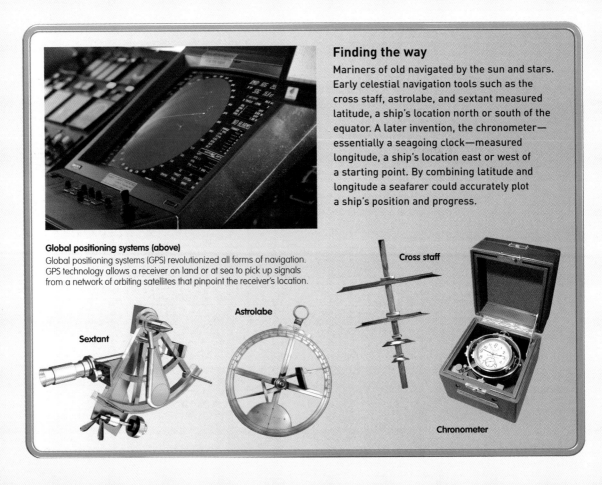

Finding the way

Mariners of old navigated by the sun and stars. Early celestial navigation tools such as the cross staff, astrolabe, and sextant measured latitude, a ship's location north or south of the equator. A later invention, the chronometer—essentially a seagoing clock—measured longitude, a ship's location east or west of a starting point. By combining latitude and longitude a seafarer could accurately plot a ship's position and progress.

Global positioning systems (above)
Global positioning systems (GPS) revolutionized all forms of navigation. GPS technology allows a receiver on land or at sea to pick up signals from a network of orbiting satellites that pinpoint the receiver's location.

Cross staff

Sextant

Astrolabe

Chronometer

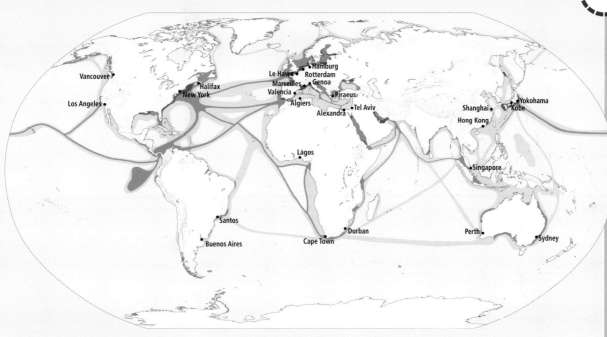

Very heavily frequented shipping routes
Heavily frequented shipping routes
Moderately used shipping routes
• **Major port**

Shipping routes today (above)

Today's large ships need not follow routes dictated by wind patterns or the sinuous contours of continents. The opening of the Panama Canal in 1914 dramatically shortened travel time between the Atlantic and Pacific. The 1923 opening of Egypt's Suez Canal did the same for ocean travel between Europe and Asia. These changes also made sea transport safer and less costly.

Shanghai port (left)

Shanghai, China, has the world's busiest container port, the Yangshan deep-water port, which handles over 35 million standard-sized containers in a year.

Modern cargo transport (right)

Modern container ships are among the largest of all seagoing vessels. They carry manufactured goods inside stackable containers sized to fit on trucks or railroad cars when the ship reaches port.

SURVEYING THE SEAS

For most of human history, the ocean depths remained inaccessible. This changed in the 1800s with the advent of diving gear, as well as motorized winches and strong steel cables which enabled deep-sea sampling. Today, underwater cameras, sonar, and sampling tools are transforming understanding of the marine landscape and its lifeforms. From space, satellites gather data about seasonal changes in ocean temperatures. Some of the most exciting discoveries have come from expeditions using remotely operated vehicles, which have revealed caches of mineral resources and details of the deep abyss.

GYRE, JAPAN

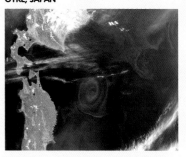

Historical study

Long before oceanography was a recognized science, scholar-naturalists surveyed marine life and deepened understanding of currents and ocean basin features. The American Benjamin Franklin published a chart of the Gulf Stream in 1777. Later, Matthew Fontaine Maury did extensive research on currents and winds.

In 1873, scientists aboard the British vessel *Challenger* launched the first major voyage to study marine life and the seas. Traveling more than 79,000 miles (127,000 km) over three years, the expedition covered large areas of the Atlantic and Pacific Oceans.

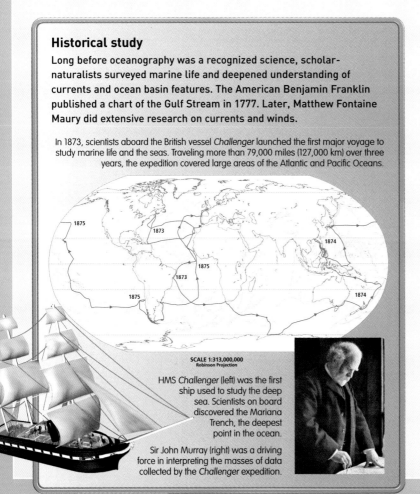

SCALE 1:313,000,000
Robinson Projection

HMS *Challenger* (left) was the first ship used to study the deep sea. Scientists on board discovered the Mariana Trench, the deepest point in the ocean.

Sir John Murray (right) was a driving force in interpreting the masses of data collected by the *Challenger* expedition.

Mapping the sea surface (above and below)
Satellites allow scientists to observe and compare ocean conditions on a global scale. Using advanced sensing technology, satellites relay data that is converted into computerized images. Among other benefits, the vivid map-like images provide previously unavailable information about shifts in ocean currents that affect climate. They also allow monitoring of ocean chemistry and phytoplankton—the foundation for sea food webs.

SEAFLOOR OFF LOS ANGELES

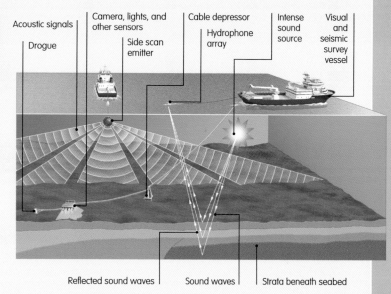

Acoustic signals

Drogue

Camera, lights, and other sensors

Side scan emitter

Cable depressor

Hydrophone array

Intense sound source

Visual and seismic survey vessel

Reflected sound waves

Sound waves

Strata beneath seabed

Mapping the seafloor (above and right)
Ship-based sonar devices allow scientists to map the seafloor. Pulses of sound waves directed at some part of the seafloor bounce off submerged objects and surfaces. Aboard ship, instruments convert these echoes into an image of the undersea landscape and objects, such as sunken ships, that might be there. In seismic surveying, sound waves directed into the seabed yield computer-generated images of the seafloor interior.

Global oceanographic research

Governments continue to invest in new centers of oceanographic research, equipped with the latest facilities and vessels. Their discoveries have applications not only for improving understanding of the marine world, but also for naval operations and locating potential mineral resources such as oil and gas reserves.

Investigating marine ecosystems (left)
Research into marine ecosystems includes studies of the kelp forest at Point Lobos State Reserve, California.

Monitoring endangered species (right)
A marine biologist removes an old tag from a sea turtle at Turtle Cove, Diego Garcia, in the Indian Ocean. It is a nesting site for both hawksbill and green turtles.

CHAPTER THREE

MARINE MECHANICS

Blue waves

In seawater, light wavelengths corresponding to different colors are absorbed or scattered. Red light is absorbed quickly, so the sea surface usually appears blue. Ocean water appears bluest where it holds less organic material. Increased material, including phytoplankton containing the green pigment chlorophyll, makes water appear greenish, as in estuaries or along coasts.

THE SALTY SEA

Seawater is a relatively dense fluid that is 96.5 percent water and 3.5 percent salts, including chloride, sodium, magnesium, and calcium. It also contains dissolved elements such as nitrogen and phosphorus, which are key nutrients for the floating phytoplankton that form the base of marine food webs. With increasing depth, water's density and pressure rise, its temperature and salinity drop, and less sunlight can penetrate it. These physical and chemical factors influence the movement of seawater and the bodily features of marine organisms.

How the seas became salty

Approximately 4.3 billion years ago, Earth entered a 10-million-year period of intense rainstorms that helped form the first global sea. These storms eroded minerals from the hot rocks and picked up gases from the atmosphere. As a result, the first ocean was a complex solution of water and salts. Today there is a balance between salt inputs and losses, so salinity remains almost constant.

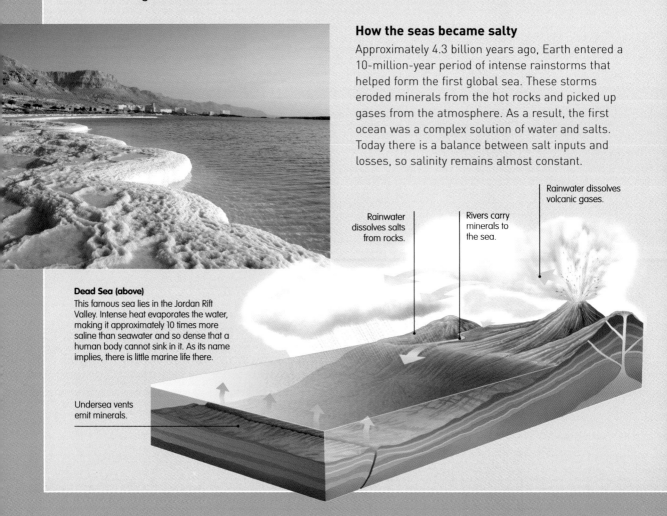

Rainwater dissolves volcanic gases.

Rainwater dissolves salts from rocks.

Rivers carry minerals to the sea.

Dead Sea (above)
This famous sea lies in the Jordan Rift Valley. Intense heat evaporates the water, making it approximately 10 times more saline than seawater and so dense that a human body cannot sink in it. As its name implies, there is little marine life there.

Undersea vents emit minerals.

Mediterranean Sea (below)

The Mediterranean connects to the Atlantic Ocean via the narrow Straits of Gibraltar, where its sapphire waters are about as saline as the Atlantic. The Mediterranean becomes saltier toward the sea's closed eastern end.

Antarctica (above)

In the Weddell and Ross Seas of the Southern Ocean, the seawater becomes unusually saline, and much denser, as sea ice forms. This dense water sinks and forms a deep water mass called Antarctic Bottom Water.

Chemical composition (right)

The salinity of seawater varies around the globe. Salinity is greatest in semi-enclosed seas such as the Caribbean, Mediterranean, and Red Seas, where more water is lost to evaporation from the sea surface than is replenished by rainfall and runoff. The lowest salinity occurs in areas where large rivers, such as the Yangtze, Ganges, Mississippi, and Amazon, discharge into the ocean.

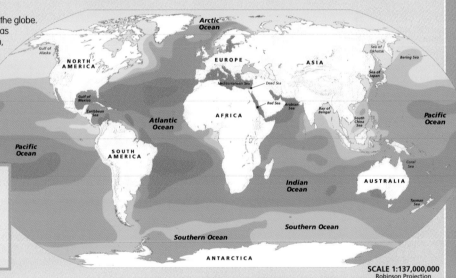

GLOBAL SALINITY

 Less than 33 parts per 1000
 33–34 parts per 1000
 34–35 parts per 1000
 35–36 parts per 1000
 36–37 parts per 1000
 More than 37 parts per 1000

SCALE 1:137,000,000
Robinson Projection

Calcium carbonate shells

Shallow seas have the richest supply of calcium, in the form of calcium carbonate. Organisms such as corals, clams, and snails have evolved to take up dissolved calcium carbonate and use it to build their protective shells.

Conch (below left)

Conches are marine snails. Thousands of species are known, most in coral reef habitats where they are often harvested as seafood.

Abalone (left)

An abalone's shell is lined with nacre, or mother-of-pearl, which is more than 95 percent calcium carbonate.

Spiral coiling (left)

Like most gastropod snails, this species' shell consists of multiple calcium carbonate layers twisted into a spiral.

CURRENTS & CIRCULATION

Currents are streams of moving water. Wind creates sea surface currents. Relatively warm water flows in some of these, including equatorial currents, while at higher latitudes water flows are much colder, such as the Labrador Current. In the largest oceans, surface currents include looping gyres in which water may be as much as 6.6 feet (2 m) higher in the center than at the edges. The combined effects of gravity and Coriolis forces drive the current in a horizontal spiral. The Gulf Stream, off the eastern United States, and other boundary currents move along the edges of continents. Seawater also circulates in thermohaline currents, in which differences in temperature or salinity push water masses past one another, usually vertically.

Surface and deep ocean circulation

While dozens of small and large surface currents rapidly circulate upper ocean waters, deep-water masses simultaneously travel slowly around the global sea by thermohaline circulation. The North Atlantic Deep Water forms as water in the northern hemisphere sinks. Over an estimated 275 years it flows to the Antarctic, then onward to the deepest parts of the Indian and Pacific Oceans before upwelling returns it to the surface.

In the two great Atlantic Ocean gyres, a cooler current flows from the east toward the equator, crosses west as a warm current, then returns east at higher latitudes.

Due to the Coriolis effect, currents on either side of the equator tend to move apart. This divergence causes upwelling in the open ocean.

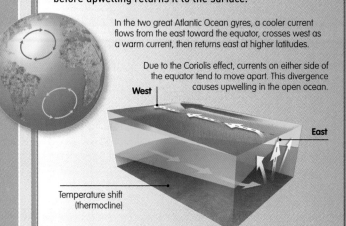

West

East

Temperature shift (thermocline)

Thermohaline circulation (below)

Seawater becomes denser when it cools and less dense as it warms—changes that move immense water masses. Dense cold water near the poles sinks and travels toward the equator. These deep-water masses eventually rise again.

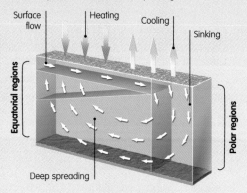

Surface flow

Heating

Cooling

Sinking

Equatorial regions

Polar regions

Deep spreading

The Great Ocean Conveyor (below)

The Great Ocean Conveyor is a slow-moving thermohaline system that links the Pacific, Atlantic, and Indian Oceans. It transports oxygen from the surface to deeper waters.

Above 86°F (30°C)
77–86°F (25–30°C)
68–77°F (20–25°C)
59–68°F (15–20°C)
50–59°F (10–15°C)
41–50°F (5–10°C)
Under 41°F (5°C)
··· Summer pack ice limit
··· Winter pack ice limit
→ Warm current
→ Cool current

SCALE 1:109,600,000
Robinson Projection

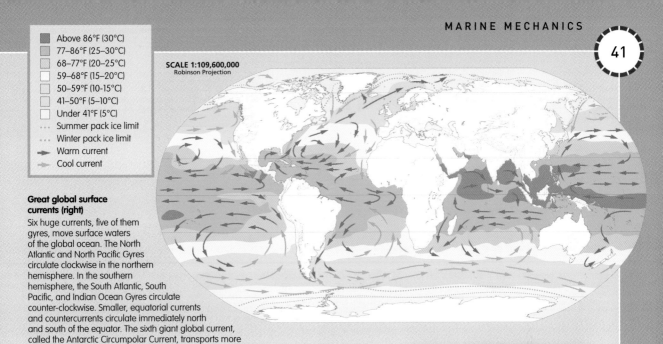

Great global surface currents (right)

Six huge currents, five of them gyres, move surface waters of the global ocean. The North Atlantic and North Pacific Gyres circulate clockwise in the northern hemisphere. In the southern hemisphere, the South Atlantic, South Pacific, and Indian Ocean Gyres circulate counter-clockwise. Smaller, equatorial currents and countercurrents circulate immediately north and south of the equator. The sixth giant global current, called the Antarctic Circumpolar Current, transports more water than any other.

Upwelling and downwelling

Vertical thermohaline water movements, also called upwelling and downwelling, are vital for marine ecosystems. Sinking surface water replenishes oxygen in the deepest parts of all ocean basins, while rising deep-water masses return valuable sunken nutrients to the surface. Most of these vertical water movements occur along continental coasts.

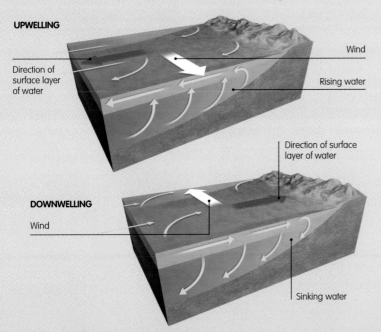

UPWELLING

Direction of surface layer of water

Wind

Rising water

DOWNWELLING

Wind

Direction of surface layer of water

Sinking water

The Amazon Plume (above)
Where rivers empty into an ocean, they can produce strong surface currents—the Amazon Plume shown here is a well-known example.

Ocean eddies (above)
This false-color radar image of the Weddell Sea near Antarctica shows two eddies roughly 25–37 miles (40–60 km) in diameter.

CLIMATE AND THE SEA

A region's climate is the long-term pattern of weather conditions there. The sea strongly influences climate all over Earth through its interactions with the atmosphere, where sunlight first reaches Earth. About 49 percent of incoming sunlight is reflected back to space; the remaining 51 percent is absorbed. In response to the combined effects of solar heating and Earth's rotation on its axis, air in the atmosphere warms, rises, cools, and descends in masses known as cells. This general scheme of atmospheric circulation produces the global water cycle, and influences climatic patterns of seasonal temperatures and precipitation. It also translates into the wind patterns that drive surface ocean currents, and it affects long-term movements of water masses between the surface and the depths of ocean basins.

The global energy equation (below)
About 30 percent of the Sun's energy beamed toward Earth is immediately reflected back to space. Clouds and the lower atmosphere absorb another 19 percent. The remaining 51 percent of solar energy is absorbed by the sea and land, including a small amount that is temporarily captured by photosynthesizing plants. Over time, however, all solar energy that reaches Earth's surface is radiated back to space.

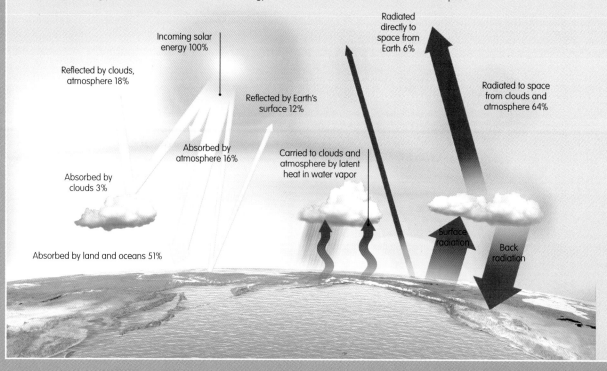

Incoming solar energy 100%

Reflected by clouds, atmosphere 18%

Reflected by Earth's surface 12%

Radiated directly to space from Earth 6%

Radiated to space from clouds and atmosphere 64%

Absorbed by atmosphere 16%

Carried to clouds and atmosphere by latent heat in water vapor

Absorbed by clouds 3%

Surface radiation

Back radiation

Absorbed by land and oceans 51%

Arctic Ocean

NORTH AMERICA

EUROPE

ASIA

Atlantic Ocean

AFRICA

Pacific Ocean

Pacific Ocean

SOUTH AMERICA

Indian Ocean

AUSTRALIA

Southern Ocean

ANTARCTICA

°F	°C
86	30
77	25
68	20
59	15
50	10
41	5
32	0
23	-5

Monitoring sea surface temperature (above)

Satellite-based instruments allow researchers to precisely measure the surface temperature of the world sea. The data used to generate this image was gathered over a period of 20 days in early spring. The coolest areas, around both the polar regions, show up as purple, while the warmest ocean regions show up as a red-orange band around the equator. A succession of such images allows scientists to monitor temperature shifts in different areas over time.

Atmospheric fireworks (below)

As on land, a thunderstorm at sea can trigger the dramatic atmospheric discharge of electricity known as lightning. Bolts of lightning can travel an estimated 136,000 miles per hour (220,000 km/h).

RETREATING LARSEN ICE SHELF

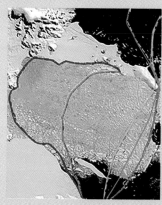

Ice shelf collapse (below)

In mid-March 2002, after shrinking steadily for 40 years, 1,255 square miles (3,250 km²) of the Larsen ice shelf collapsed, shattering into icebergs. The sudden event loosened 720 billion tons of ice into the sea.

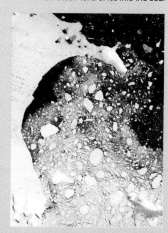

▬ 1947   ▬ 1961   ▬ 1993
▬ January 2002   ▬ March 2002

Retreating ice shelf (above)

Over the years the extent of Antarctica's Larsen ice shelf has increased and decreased. In about 1960, however, the shelf began retreating due to prolonged global warming. Lines show ice shelf extent in 1947, 1961, 1993, and 2002.

EL NIÑO AND LA NIÑA

In a roughly four-year cycle that unfolds along the coast of Peru, a tropical Pacific wind shift called the Southern Oscillation slows or reverses major currents. It also halts normal upwelling of cold, nutrient-rich water there. Spanish fishermen named this phenomenon El Niño (the Christ Child). It may last 18 months or longer. In the Americas and Southeast Asia, the abnormally warm, nutrient-poor El Niño current may mean disaster for fish and other wildlife that rely on seasonal upwelling for food. Increased evaporation of the warm surface water fuels an increase in severe storms that affect agriculture and other human activities. In an opposite phenomenon, La Niña, the sea surface remains uncharacteristically cool. It, too, produces abnormal weather patterns that extend around the globe.

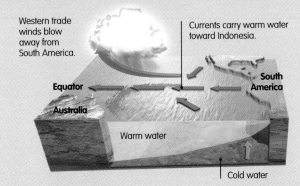

Western trade winds blow away from South America.

Currents carry warm water toward Indonesia.

Equator

South America

Australia

Warm water

Cold water

Normal wind and current patterns (above)
Normally in the tropical Pacific, surface winds blow westward, away from South America. Currents push warm water toward Indonesia, and upwelling replenishes nutrients and helps maintain normal weather patterns.

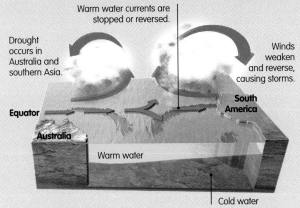

Warm water currents are stopped or reversed.

Drought occurs in Australia and southern Asia.

Winds weaken and reverse, causing storms.

Equator

South America

Australia

Warm water

Cold water

From normal to El Niño (above)
El Niño weather pattern begins when air pressure rises over the Indian Ocean and declines over the Pacific. This shift weakens trade winds, and coastal upwelling of the Peru Current ceases.

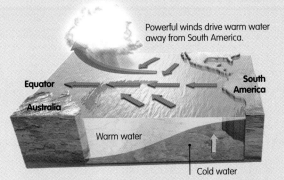

Powerful winds drive warm water away from South America.

Equator

South America

Australia

Warm water

Cold water

From El Niño to La Niña (above)
Eventually the El Niño wind pattern reverses and winds again drive warm water away from South America. Unusually powerful winds trigger stronger than normal upwelling of the Peru Current, setting La Niña in motion.

Satellite monitoring of El Niño and La Niña

The TOPEX/Poseidon satellite monitors conditions in the oceans. Normal wind and current patterns were present in 2003. In 1997, however, satellite instruments tracked the development of El Niño. By October the mass of warm water (white area) had spread along the whole west coast of North and Central America. One year later, wind and current conditions had reversed and La Niña's cold water was upwelling.

NORMAL CONDITIONS

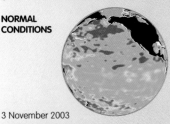

3 November 2003

EL NIÑO

18 October 1997

LA NIÑA

8 November 1998

Shifting El Niño weather patterns

During El Niño, the arrival of an abnormal, large mass of warm water in the eastern Pacific may dramatically change precipitation patterns. Along the west coasts of North and South America, downpours and tornadoes may wreak havoc in areas that are usually drier, while drought develops in parts of Australia, Africa, and elsewhere.

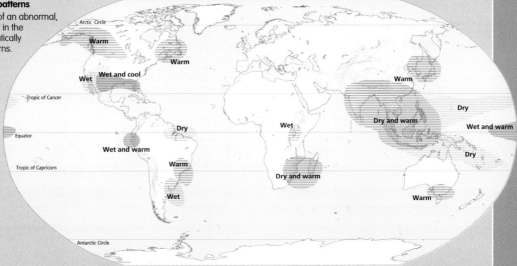

Arctic Circle

Warm

Warm

Wet and cool

Wet

Warm

Tropic of Cancer

Dry

Dry and warm

Wet and warm

Equator

Dry

Wet

Wet and warm

Warm

Dry and warm

Tropic of Capricorn

Wet

Dry and warm

Warm

Antarctic Circle

☐ Dry and warm
☐ Warm
☐ Dry
☐ Wet and warm
☐ Wet
☐ Wet and cool

Starving seal
The 1997–98 El Niño had a serious impact on the marine food web along the west coast of the Americas. With its normal food supply of small fish diminished, this South American sea lion (*Otaria flavescens*) is starving.

Coastal storm
Unusually frequent and severe storms and tornadoes are common during El Niño years. Coastal California has suffered huge losses in human life and property as storms trigger flooding, mud slides, and other damage.

Eye of the storm
Typhoon Fengshen slammed into coastal China, Macau, and the Philippines, causing over 1,400 deaths in the 2008 La Niña year.

WIND

Overall, air moves in patterns set by incoming solar energy. At lower latitudes, where sunlight is more intense, air warms, expands, and rises. At the poles, air cools, contracts, and falls. Earth's rotation shifts winds and currents to the right (clockwise) in the northern hemisphere and to the left (counter-clockwise) in the southern hemisphere. This shift is called the Coriolis effect. In addition, gravity pulls air from areas of high pressure, where the air mass is relatively cool, to areas of low pressure, where the air mass is warmer. An anticyclone develops over areas of high pressure and often correlates with fine weather.

WIND PATTERNS

Foehn
Burga
Bora
Etesians
Chinook
Santa Ana
Mistral
Norte
Bise
Seistan
Sirocco
Símoon
Papagayo
Brisa
Shamai
Sulawesi
Harmattan
Haboor dust storms
Berg
Brickfielder
Virazon
Brisa
Southerly
Zonda
Pampero
Fremantle Doctor
Buster
Williwaw squalls
Canterbury Northwester

Spinning planet (right)
On our spinning planet, freely moving objects including weather systems appear to follow a curved path. They turn to the right in the northern hemisphere and to the left in the southern hemisphere.

North Pole

60°N

30°N

Equator

30°S

60°S

South Pole

The Coriolis effect (above)
The Coriolis effect can be understood by imagining that someone sitting at the center of a moving roundabout (point A) throws a ball to someone sitting at a point on the rim (point B). By the time the ball reaches B, the person on the rim will have moved to point C. To this person, the ball will appear to have curved away from them.

Land and sea breezes (below)
Coastal sea breezes develop early in the day when cooler air over the ocean rushes in to replace rising, warmer air over land. Overnight the process reverses, and land breezes develop.

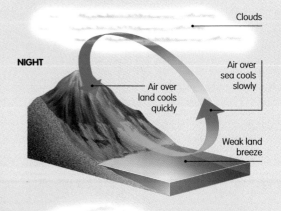

Clouds

NIGHT

Air over land cools quickly

Air over sea cools slowly

Weak land breeze

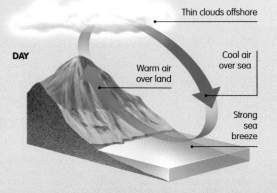

Thin clouds offshore

DAY

Warm air over land

Cool air over sea

Strong sea breeze

SUMMER   **WINTER**

Seasonal monsoons (right)
In summer, winds carry moist air across the Indian Ocean. The resulting monsoon rains begin in the south and spread northward. Monsoon season ends as winter cooling causes the wind direction to reverse.

Airflow around the globe

Due to the Coriolis effect, air masses in the northern and southern hemispheres circulate in different directions. In each hemisphere, moving air travels in three circulation cells, one around the pole, another at mid-latitude, and the third in the tropics bordering the equator. Among other effects, the circuits generate prevailing easterly winds in the tropics and high latitudes, and prevailing westerly winds in middle latitudes.

Becoming becalmed (left)
Mariners once dreaded becoming trapped in the doldrums, a belt of light winds in the tropics. A sail-powered ship might languish for days or weeks as supplies of food and drinkable water dwindle.

Polar cell
Cold air at the poles sinks and travels toward the equator before rising upon meeting the Ferrel cell.

Ferrel cell
Some air from Hadley cells continues toward the poles before rising at about 60° north and south. These cells are named after William Ferrel, who identified them in 1856.

Hadley cell
Warm air rises from the equator and spreads toward the poles before sinking at around 30° latitude north and south. These cells are named in honor of the English scientist, George Hadley, who first described them in 1753.

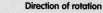

Direction of rotation
Earth rotates from west to east.

Polar easterlies
Cold easterly winds blow from the poles to 60°.

Northeast trade winds
These winds blow toward the equator.

Doldrums
The area at the equator where winds are typically light.

Westerlies
Warm, moist winds blow from the west.

WAVES

Ocean waves are set in motion by external energy. Most are wind waves that form as wind blows across the sea surface, its kinetic energy curling seawater up and forward. At a wave's crest, gravity pulls the water downward into a cuplike trough. Wind waves usually travel steadily across the surface, finally releasing energy when they reach the shore.

A shore thing (above)
A shoreline's structure helps determine the characteristics of the waves that wash it. Towering, curling breakers develop where waves arrive at a steep shore, as here, in Waimea Bay off the Hawaiian island of Oahu.

Wave features (below)
Wavelength is the distance between crests, while wave height is the vertical distance between a trough and a crest. Wave steepness is the angle from the bottom of a trough to the top of the neighboring crest.

PARTS OF A WAVE

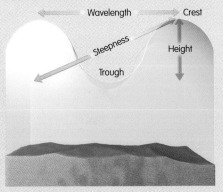

Wavelength · Crest · Steepness · Height · Trough

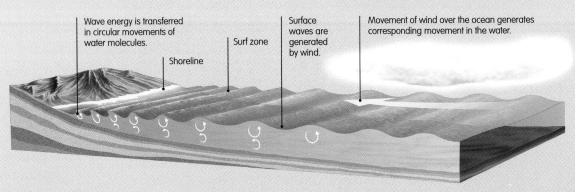

Wave energy is transferred in circular movements of water molecules.

Shoreline

Surf zone

Surface waves are generated by wind.

Movement of wind over the ocean generates corresponding movement in the water.

Making waves (above)
Wind moving over the ocean generates corresponding movement in surface water. Steady wind over great distances tends to generate long, smooth undulations called swells. In the surf zone close to shore, water particles move in circles that become larger closer to the surface. When the orbiting water particles strike bottom in the shallows, they flatten out. The forward thrust near shore forms crests and breakers.

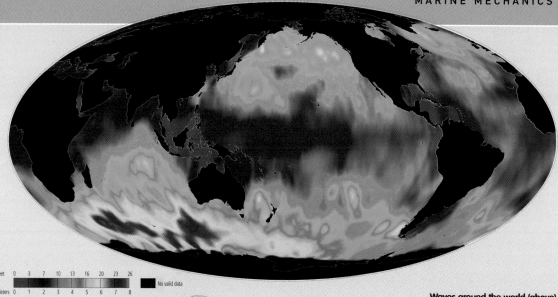

Feet | 0 | 3 | 7 | 10 | 13 | 16 | 20 | 23 | 26
Meters | 0 | 1 | 2 | 3 | 4 | 5 | 6 | 7 | 8

No valid data

Waves around the world (above)
This map shows the typical wave height in various regions of the global sea. Wave heights are color coded, from magenta for waves that are less than 3 feet (1 m) high, through blue, green, and yellow, to red for waves of 20–25 feet (7–8 m). The largest waves occur in the southern Indian Ocean and the Southern Ocean near Antarctica.

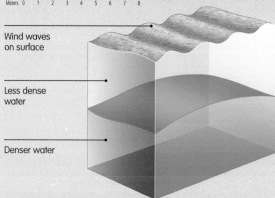

Wind waves on surface

Less dense water

Denser water

Internal wave (above)
Waves can form below the sea surface, often at the bottom of a thermocline where a layer of warm water abuts a layer of colder, denser water. Generated by currents, tides, or winds, such internal waves can be more than 100 feet (30 m) high.

FIVE DIFFERENT WAVES	
Capillary wave	A tiny ripple-like wave that carries only a little amount of wind energy.
Plunging wave	A breaking wave whose crest curls into a tube as the wave advances toward a steeply sloping shore.
Deep-water wave	A wave traveling through water deeper than half the wave length.
Spilling wave	A breaking wave whose crest crumbles onto the wave base as the wave advances up a gently sloping shore.
Forced wave	A wave that persists because the energy that generated it continues.

Sea swell
The gently rising and falling ocean surface motion called "swell" consists of longer-period waves that do not break. The arrival of swell in calm waters can indicate a storm is coming.

Storm-battered shores
Storm waves crashing on a Nova Scotia coast transfer their considerable energy to the shore. Many shorelines are regularly reshaped by the pounding force of storm waves.

Gentle waves
The slope of the bottom effects the way waves break over it. On this Micronesian shore, the reef structure offshore disperses the wave energy, so the waves lap the shore.

STORMS

Storms are atmospheric disturbances that develop when a region of high pressure envelops an area of low pressure. At sea, storm winds generate large, potentially dangerous waves, often reaching 20 feet (6 m). In areas such as the North Atlantic Ocean, winds and currents may produce rogue waves of 110 feet (33 m) or more.

Stormy weather (below)
Around the world, search and rescue services put to sea to rescue ships at risk during stormy weather. Here a coastguard patrol boat rides the waves.

Storm waves (below)
As a storm builds, strengthening winds transfer a great deal of energy to the sea surface. Waves also interact with one another. This chaotic energy infusion may produce waves with a variety of wavelengths, heights, directions, and other physical characteristics, a phenomenon oceanographers term a wave sea. Rare rogue waves develop when many chaotic wind waves converge in a single spot.

1. Wind blowing across the sea surface produces small waves with rounded crests, narrow troughs, and a short wavelength.
2. As the waves continue to grow larger, the wave crests become more pointed and the troughs rounder.
3. Finally, the wave crests become less stable as gravity pulls them downward. Whitecaps form when the waves break.

Wind

Wind

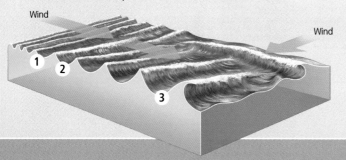

The Bermuda High

A large, permanent region of high atmospheric pressure in the North Atlantic shifts with the seasons between the Azores and Bermuda. Air in this high picks up moisture from areas to the east. As the moist air circulates clockwise, it helps fuel the development of tropical storms and hurricanes that strike the Caribbean and the southeastern US during the summer and fall.

HURRICANE STRIKING NEW ENGLAND

HURRICANE MOVES INTO GULF OF MEXICO

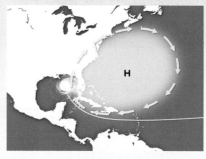

Beaufort wind scale

The Beaufort wind scale ranks the force of wind at sea on a scale from zero (calm) to 12 (hurricane). The wind force determines how high wind-driven waves will be. It was devised to measure wind force on sailing ships.

BEAUFORT WIND SCALE		
Force	Wind speed [mph (km/h)]	Description
0	Below 1 (below 2)	Calm
1	2–3 (3–5)	Light air
2	4–7 (6–11)	Light breeze
3	8–12 (12–19)	Gentle breeze
4	13–18 (20–29)	Moderate breeze
5	19–24 (30–38)	Fresh breeze
6	25–31 (39–51)	Strong breeze
7	32–38 (52–61)	Near gale
8	39–46 (62–74)	Gale
9	47–54 (75–86)	Strong gale
10	55–63 (87–101)	Whole gale
11	64–74 (102–120)	Storm
12	Above 74 (120)	Hurricane

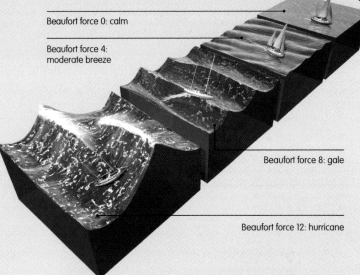

Beaufort force 0: calm

Beaufort force 4: moderate breeze

Beaufort force 8: gale

Beaufort force 12: hurricane

Waterspouts

A tornado is a funnel of air rapidly spiraling upward into a cloud. It is the most violent of all climatic phenomena. Waterspouts are tornadoes that develop or pass over warm, shallow water, sucking up a whirling column of water that may rise as high as 300 feet (100 m). Waterspouts usually develop during tropical storms when masses of cold and warm air interact with the sea surface.

Mariners of old recounted frightening encounters with waterspouts. This nineteenth-century painting (left) depicts multiple waterspouts threatening the sailing ship *Trombes*.

When descending cold air meets warmer air below (right), the interaction creates low pressure that draws the warm air upward—and with it, surface water.

Falling cold air causes low pressure.

Wind circulates in a column around a central core.

Strong winds develop as warm air travels upward.

Not all waterspouts develop at sea. Some begin to form over land and then move to warm coastal waters offshore (above).

HURRICANES

Called hurricanes in the Atlantic and eastern Pacific and typhoons in the western Pacific, tropical cyclones generally develop over tropical seas where warm air soaks up evaporating surface water. Over several days, the air mass starts spinning counterclockwise in the northern hemisphere, attaining hurricane status when the wind reaches 74 miles per hour (118 km/h). Air in the calm center or "eye" of a hurricane is warmer and under lower pressure than in the spiraling rain bands farther out. The greater the pressure difference between the inner and outer regions, the greater a hurricane's intensity.

Pressure systems (right)
In a low-pressure system, surface air converges counterclockwise toward the center, then rises and diverges in the opposite direction. The reverse happens in a high-pressure system. Air flows from high to low pressure, creating wind.

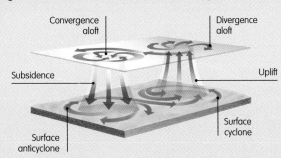

Convergence aloft

Divergence aloft

Subsidence

Uplift

Surface anticyclone

Surface cyclone

How a hurricane works (below)
A hurricane forms when rising humid air begins rotating counterclockwise. As the air rises, it creates intense low pressure that essentially sucks in additional air over the sea surface. The circulating warm air typically holds a great deal of water vapor—a large hurricane can dump 20 billion tons (18 billion t) of rainwater in a day. Paired with high winds, the deluge can cause severe damage on land.

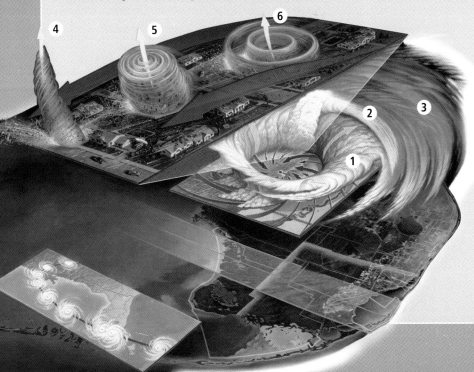

1. **Eyewall**
   The calm eye of a hurricane is surrounded by an eyewall—massive, dark storm clouds that produce the heaviest rain and strongest winds.

2. **Spiraling air**
   An upward spiral of warm, moist air is drawn into the central area of low pressure. Moisture sustains the formation of the storm clouds.

3. **Rain bands**
   As the storm builds, spiraling bands of rain clouds form. The outer bands may be more than 200 miles (320 km) from the eye.

4. **Approaching land**
   The eye forms and the hurricane is at its most dangerous approaching land.

5. **Over land**
   Without moisture from the sea, the hurricane starts to lose some of its energy.

6. **Hurricane dies**
   Farther inland, the hurricane dissipates.

Eye of a hurricane (left)

In 2005, Hurricane Hernan developed into a huge storm off California and northwestern Mexico. Maximum winds measured 165 miles per hour (266 km/h). This satellite image clearly shows its eye, the calm area at a hurricane's center.

Southern hemisphere hurricane (right)

A satellite tracks Hurricane Monica, building strength off northeastern Australia in April 2006, the southern hemisphere autumn. Its winds eventually peaked at 215 miles per hour (370 km/h). Colored areas correlate with rainfall, with red being the heaviest.

Measuring hurricane intensity

Climatologists use the Saffir-Simpson scale (shown at bottom) to categorize hurricane intensity. The most powerful hurricanes typically develop in the western Pacific, which has tallied the most category 4 and 5 storms. Hurricanes are virtually unknown in the South Pacific and southern Atlantic, where cold currents translate into cool air. The largest tropical cyclone on record is Super Typhoon Tip, which struck Japan in 1979. Measuring 1,380 miles (2,220 km) in diameter, Tip generated winds of 190 miles per hour (305 km/h).

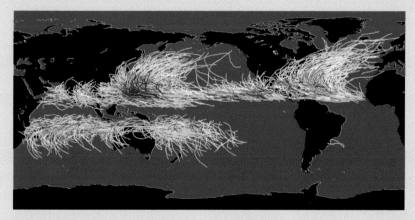

Destruction caused by Typhoon Haiyan, Philippines, 2013

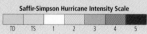
Saffir-Simpson Hurricane Intensity Scale

TD TS 1 2 3 4 5

Distribution and paths (above)

Hurricanes develop in the North Atlantic, North and South Pacific, and Indian Oceans, in latitudes between 5° and 20°, where there is ample evaporation of water from warm currents and a strong Coriolis effect can start them rotating.

THE SAFFIR-SIMPSON SCALE			
Category number	Wind speed [mph (km/h)]	Storm surge [ft (m)]	Damage
1	74–95 (118–152)	4–5 (1.2–1.6)	Minimal
2	96–110 (153–176)	6–8 (1.7–2.5)	Moderate
3	111–130 (177–208)	9–12 (2.6–3.7)	Extensive
4	131–155 (209–248)	13–18 (3.8–5.4)	Extensive
5	More than 155 (248)	More than 18 (5.4)	Catastrophic

Shrimp boats blown ashore by Hurricane Katrina, 2005

TSUNAMIS

The Japanese word tsunami roughly translates as "harbor wave." A tsunami is a speeding wall of water that can reach heights of 100 feet (30 m) or more and travel at a speed of 500 miles per hour (800 km/h). It is caused by a seismic shift such as a seafloor earthquake or an erupting undersea volcano. Typically, the triggering event launches a succession of huge waves as much as 45 minutes apart. Such waves may be imperceptible in the deep open ocean, but as a tsunami nears shore its height increases dramatically.

TSUNAMIS AROUND THE WORLD

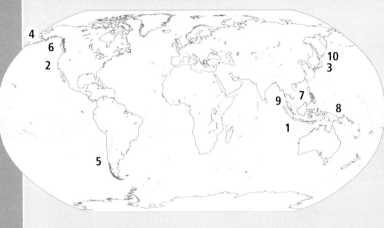

TEN WORST TSUNAMIS		
1	1883	Krakatau erupts and a tsunami sweeps over Indonesia. 36,000 people die.
2	1896	A tsunami hits Los Angeles on the Californian coast.
3	1896	The Sanriku tsunami strikes Japan and kills more than 26,000 people.
4	1946	Alaskan quake generates a tsunami. Hours later it kills 159 people in Hawaii.
5	1960	A tsunami kills 1,000 people in Chile, 61 people in Hawaii, and 180 people in Japan.
6	1964	Waves from an Alaskan quake sweep down the west coast, killing 122 people.
7	1976	A tsunami kills more than 5,000 people in the Philippines.
8	1998	A tsunami strikes the north coast of Papua New Guinea, killing 2,000 people.
9	2004	A powerful earthquake triggers waves that travel thousands of miles to crash onto the coastlines of at least 14 Asian and African countries. More than 225,000 people die.
10	2011	An earthquake off the Pacific Coast of Japan triggers a tsunami with waves up to 133 feet (40 m). More than 15,800 people die.

Progress of a tsunami (below)

After a shock launches a tsunami, it can travel across an ocean in less than a day. At the shore, the tsunami arrives as a series of wave crests and troughs 10 to 45 minutes apart.

Calm surface
On the surface all seems calm. The tsunami may be less than 40 inches (1 m) high and is hardly noticed by sailors.

Submarine shock
Most tsunamis develop when an earthquake occurs deep in the ocean. Seafloor tectonic plates shift against one another, producing powerful shock waves. The energy of these waves then is transferred to the sea above.

At the shore
As the waves near the shore, their speed decreases and their height increases.

Spiraling forces
The powerful shock waves of energy spread outward.

Pre-tsunami (below)

The Indonesian province of Aceh took the brunt of the December 2004 Indian Ocean tsunami. This aerial view shows the town of Lhokna in 2003.

Washed away (above)

The tsunami washed away most buildings and vegetation in Lhokna, drowned nearby agricultural areas, and removed sand from the beaches.

2004 INDIAN OCEAN TSUNAMI

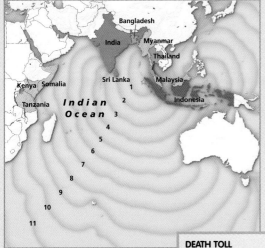

Path to destruction (above)

The Richter magnitude 9.2 or 9.3 earthquake that occurred on December 26, 2004 caused movement along a fault to the west of Sumatra. The sudden displacement in the sea floor sent a shock wave across the ocean. This map shows the hour-by-hour progress of the wave over 11 hours.

DEATH TOLL
- \> 100,000
- 10,000–100,000
- 1,000–10,000
- < 1,000
- No data
- 2 Hours after event

The tsunami hits (below)

Throughout coastal Indonesia, the morning of December 26, 2004 held no sign of impending danger from the tsunami. Shortly before the first wave struck, however, the ocean off Aceh receded as water was pulled out toward the growing wave offshore. Then a series of waves up to 50 feet (15 m) high rushed toward the shore, crashed upon the beach, and pushed inland with massive force.

Before the tsunami

Water retreats

Disaster strikes

TIDES

In each tide cycle, the sea surface rises then falls in conjunction with the shifting pull of gravity from the Moon and the Sun as Earth rotates on its axis. Lunar gravity exerts the strongest pull, so the sea bulges below the Moon's position above Earth. A corresponding bulge occurs on the planet's opposite side.

As Earth rotates through the bulges, the result is a pattern of shallow, planet-sized waves that are visible as rising and falling water levels along the shore. The Moon rises 51 minutes later each day, so a tide cycle lasts 24 hours and 51 minutes and high tide occurs 51 minutes later each day.

Spring and neap tides (below)
The highest and lowest tides, called spring tides, occur year-round at two-week intervals corresponding to the full and new moon. "Neap tides"—the lowest high and highest low tides—occur during the Moon's first- and third-quarter phases. Spring tides result when Earth, the Moon, and the Sun all align. The combination of their gravitational effects increases both high tide height and low tide levels. Neap tides occur when Earth, the Moon, and the Sun form the points of a triangle. In this configuration, the Moon's gravitational pull is at right angles to that of the Sun and the Sun's gravity partly cancels it out.

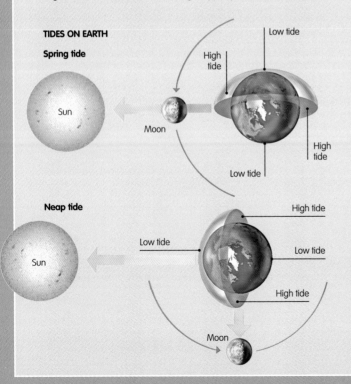

TIDES ON EARTH

Spring tide

Low tide

High tide

Sun

Moon

High tide

Low tide

Neap tide

High tide

Low tide

Sun

Low tide

High tide

Moon

Highest high tide (above)
The shape and depth of the Bay of Fundy, on Canada's east coast, give it perhaps the greatest tidal range in the world—56 feet (17 m). This photograph shows Hopewell Rocks at high tide, when the rock bases are submerged.

Lowest low tide (above)
At low tide, Hopewell Rocks are completely above the water line and the shore is a mudflat. Tidal action has scoured out the rocks' bases and eventually will erode them away completely.

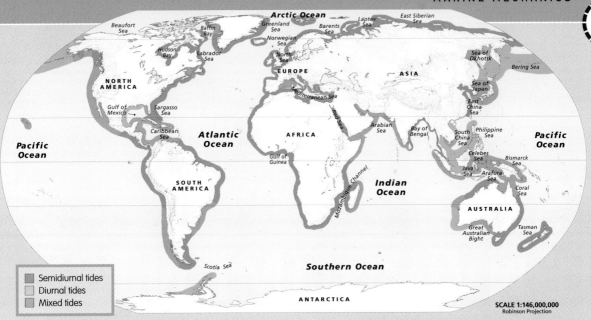

Semidiurnal tides
Diurnal tides
Mixed tides

SCALE 1:146,000,000
Robinson Projection

Tides around the globe (above)

Three general tide patterns occur along Earth's coastlines. Most coastal areas experience semidiurnal, or twice daily, tides in which the levels of high or low tides are about equal. Also common are mixed tides—semidiurnal tides in which the levels of highs or lows are unequal. Along some coastlines, tides follow a simpler diurnal pattern of one high and one low a day.

Bright red tide (right)

A "red tide" is a "bloom" of millions of rusty-hued phytoplankton called dinoflagellates. Toxic to fish or shellfish and other marine life, red-tide organisms can also cause poisoning and allergic reactions in humans.

Tide curves (below)

These graphs plot how water levels fluctuate during different types of tides over a 48-hour period. Although the water levels are unequal in mixed tides, the shifting pattern repeats about every 12 hours 25 minutes.

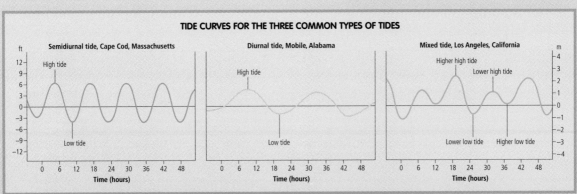

TIDE CURVES FOR THE THREE COMMON TYPES OF TIDES

Semidiurnal tide, Cape Cod, Massachusetts
High tide
Low tide
Time (hours)

Diurnal tide, Mobile, Alabama
High tide
Low tide
Time (hours)

Mixed tide, Los Angeles, California
Higher high tide
Lower high tide
Lower low tide
Higher low tide
Time (hours)

CHAPTER FOUR

SEA ENVIRONMENTS

Coral polyps

This photograph shows colonies of coral animals, each a polyp that resembles a slender stalk. The polyps grow, they are nourished, and they reproduce as they undulate with the current in tropical shallows. The catalog of marine life encompasses a striking array of animals, plants, and microorganisms, each with structures and functions suited to survival in a particular undersea environment.

SEA DEPTHS

All forms of life are profoundly affected by their surroundings. In the sea, two of the most crucial physical factors are light and temperature at different depths. Oceanographers divide the three-dimensional marine environment into the pelagic zone of open water and the bottom or benthic zone. The layers of the pelagic zone are defined by the amount of sunlight reaching them: the upper sunlight zone, the less populated "twilight" zone, and the cold, dark depths.

Surface to deep (left)
Sperm whales (*Physeter macrocephalus*) must surface to breathe, but they may dive as deep as 3,300 feet (1,000 m) in search of their giant squid prey.

Fast swimmer (right)
The blue, golden, and green mahi mahi (*Coryphaena hippurus*) closely match the hues of the upper ocean waters where these speedsters live and pursue darting flying fish.

The food-rich surface

The upper two percent of the global sea contains more living organisms than the rest of the ocean combined. Here sunlight fuels the growth of vast pastures of plant-like phytoplankton that sustain themselves by photosynthesis. They are the foundation for a global food web that includes zooplankton, tiny drifting animals preyed upon by species ranging from shrimps to whales. Food-rich surface waters also sustain a tremendous variety of fish species.

This species of krill (*Euphausia superba*) and the sea butterfly (*Clione limacina*) are types of zooplankton that drift or swim weakly with surface sea currents.

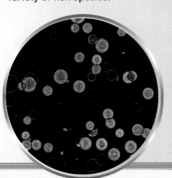

Diatoms (left), here magnified under a microscope, are mostly single-celled phytoplankton with a hard, shell-like casing of silica that often forms an intricate pattern characteristic of each species.

Krill

Sea butterfly

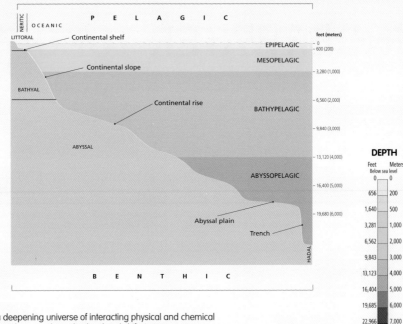

P E L A G I C

NERITIC

OCEANIC

LITTORAL

Continental shelf

BATHYAL

Continental slope

Continental rise

ABYSSAL

Abyssal plain

Trench

HADAL

B E N T H I C

EPIPELAGIC
MESOPELAGIC
BATHYPELAGIC
ABYSSOPELAGIC

feet (meters)

0
600 (200)

3,280 (1,000)

6,560 (2,000)

9,840 (3,000)

13,120 (4,000)

16,400 (5,000)

19,680 (6,000)

Ocean zones (right)

Ocean waters are subdivided broadly into a nearshore neritic realm and the oceanic realm. The pelagic realm encompasses the sunlit epipelagic and dimmer mesopelagic zones, where marine life is most abundant; the darker and less populated bathypelagic and abyssopelagic zones; and the hadal zone of seafloor trenches, a frigid, dark world where relatively few organisms survive.

DEPTH

Feet Below sea level	Meters
0	0
656	200
1,640	500
3,281	1,000
6,562	2,000
9,843	3,000
13,123	4,000
16,404	5,000
19,685	6,000
22,966	7,000
26,247	8,000

Environments for life (below)

Away from shore, the sea becomes a deepening universe of interacting physical and chemical factors. Vertically, each ocean has layered zones where depth-related shifts in temperature, salinity, and other conditions set the ground rules for survival of marine species.

SCALE 1:143,100,000
Mercator Projection

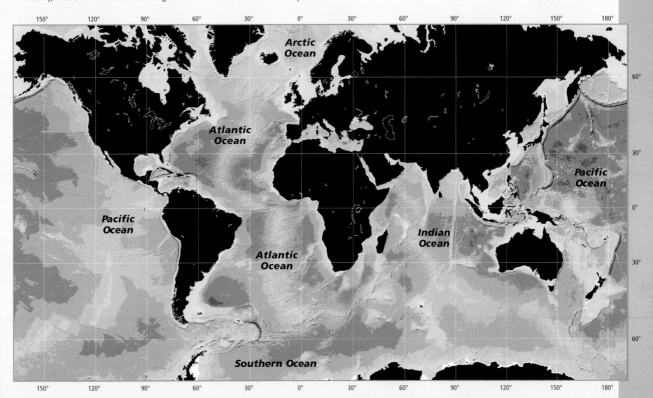

Arctic Ocean

Atlantic Ocean

Pacific Ocean

Pacific Ocean

Indian Ocean

Atlantic Ocean

Southern Ocean

UNDERWATER TOPOGRAPHY

Marine scientists have given us a remarkable picture of the sea's major topographic features. This physical portrait includes: the submerged, sloping margins of the continents; scores of submarine canyons; the vast plains of the deep abyss; plunging ocean trenches; approximately 20,000 inactive volcanoes that form structures known as seamounts and flat-topped guyots; and about 40,400 miles (65,000 km) of sinuous undersea mountain ranges marking the submerged seams of crustal plates. Similar diversity marks the seafloor surface, which may be rocky, sandy, or a blend of sand and mud.

Kali Ghandaki Gorge
21,000 feet (6,400 m)

Mariana Trench
35,826 feet (10,920 m)

Deepest trench (above)
The Mariana Trench, the deepest part of the world seas, is more than 14,800 feet (4,500 m) deeper than the deepest land trench, Nepal's Kali Ghandaki Gorge.

Mauna Kea
33,000 feet (10,000 m)

Mount Everest
29,029 feet (8,848 m)

Highest mountain (above)
The marine volcano visible above the sea surface as Hawaii's Mauna Kea rises about 4,000 feet (1,200 m) higher than the tallest mountain on land, Mount Everest.

CRATER LAKE, OREGON, USA

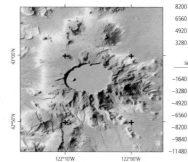

feet	meters
8200	2500
6560	2000
4920	1500
3280	1000
sea level	
−1640	−500
−3280	−1000
−4920	−1500
−6560	−2000
−8200	−2500
−9840	−3000
−11480	−3500

WEST ROTA, MARIANA ARC

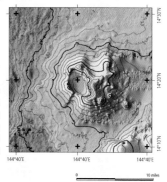

Volcanic legacy (above)
Researchers have ample evidence of past undersea volcanoes. These images compare the crater of an extinct land volcano, Crater Lake in the US state of Oregon, and the crater of an extinct marine volcano in the western Pacific.

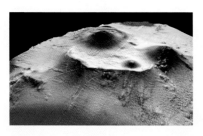

feet	meters
−1640	−500
−3280	−1000
−4920	−1500
−6560	−2000
−8200	−2500

Seamount (left)
A seamount is an undersea peak or volcano that is at least 0.6 miles (1 km) high. This image shows Denson Seamount in the Gulf of Alaska. The channel to its right is approximately 10,500 feet (3,200 m) deep.

Active marine volcano (left)
Hundreds of active volcanoes exist in the sea. This one, the Nikko submarine volcano, is part of the Mariana Trench arc. Nikko's summit is about 1,280 feet (391 m) below the surface.

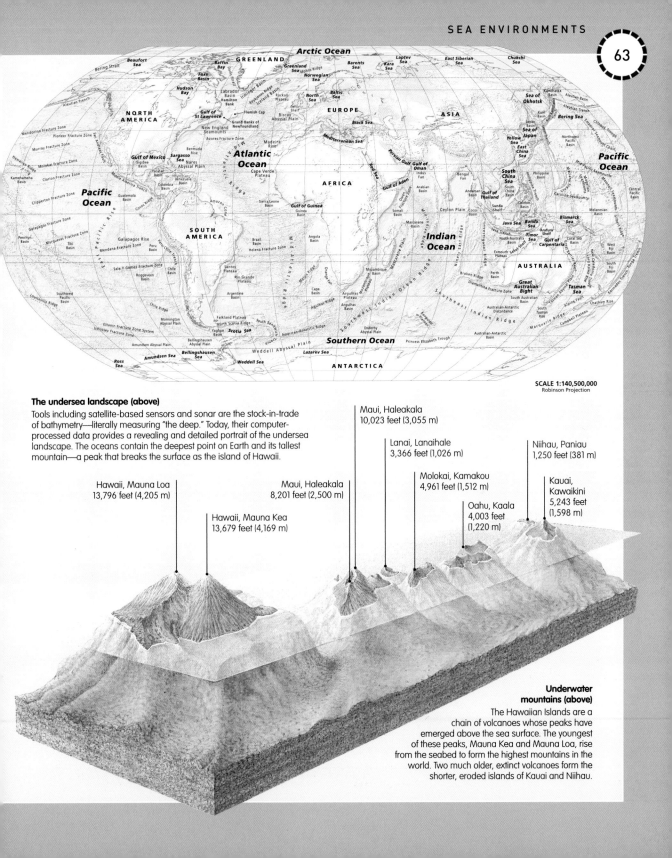

SCALE 1:140,500,000
Robinson Projection

The undersea landscape (above)

Tools including satellite-based sensors and sonar are the stock-in-trade of bathymetry—literally measuring "the deep." Today, their computer-processed data provides a revealing and detailed portrait of the undersea landscape. The oceans contain the deepest point on Earth and its tallest mountain—a peak that breaks the surface as the island of Hawaii.

Maui, Haleakala
10,023 feet (3,055 m)

Lanai, Lanaihale
3,366 feet (1,026 m)

Niihau, Paniau
1,250 feet (381 m)

Hawaii, Mauna Loa
13,796 feet (4,205 m)

Hawaii, Mauna Kea
13,679 feet (4,169 m)

Maui, Haleakala
8,201 feet (2,500 m)

Molokai, Kamakou
4,961 feet (1,512 m)

Oahu, Kaala
4,003 feet
(1,220 m)

Kauai,
Kawaikini
5,243 feet
(1,598 m)

Underwater mountains (above)

The Hawaiian Islands are a chain of volcanoes whose peaks have emerged above the sea surface. The youngest of these peaks, Mauna Kea and Mauna Loa, rise from the seabed to form the highest mountains in the world. Two much older, extinct volcanoes form the shorter, eroded islands of Kauai and Niihau.

DEEPEST DEPTHS

Deep ocean basins make up more than half of Earth's surface. Some of their most notable geologic features are canyons cleaving the continental slopes, mid-ocean mountain ridges, steep trenches, broad, flat abyssal plains, and hydrothermal vents.

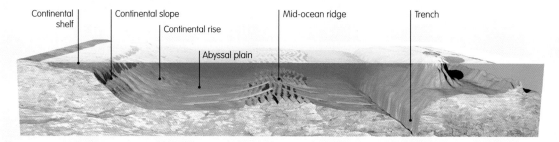

Continental shelf | Continental slope | Continental rise | Abyssal plain | Mid-ocean ridge | Trench

Ocean floor (above)
Features of the ocean floor include trenches, which are the Earth's deepest points. Trenches typically extend at least 2 miles (3.2 km) below the level of the surrounding ocean floor.

Mariana Trench

The highest point on Earth, the summit of Mount Everest, was first reached by climbers in May 1953. Seven years later, in 1960, the bathyscaphe *Trieste*, a specially built diving vessel capable of withstanding the tremendous pressure in the Mariana Trench, came close to the deepest point on Earth, reaching 35,797 feet (10,911 m). To the surprise of the occupants, they saw shrimp and fish, even at such great depth.

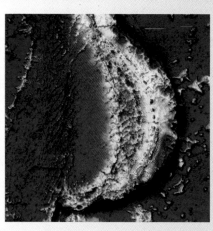

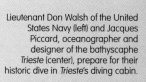

The sickle-shaped Mariana Trench (left) in the western Pacific, slices 35,826 feet (10,920 m) into Earth's crust. Due in part to the lack of food at that depth, life there is scarce.

Lieutenant Don Walsh of the United States Navy (left) and Jacques Piccard, oceanographer and designer of the bathyscaphe *Trieste* (center), prepare for their historic dive in *Trieste*'s diving cabin.

Exploring the deep

Submarines must be built to withstand the crushing pressure of the water around them— a pressure that grows steadily with depth. Research submersibles are smaller than military submarines and can go much deeper.

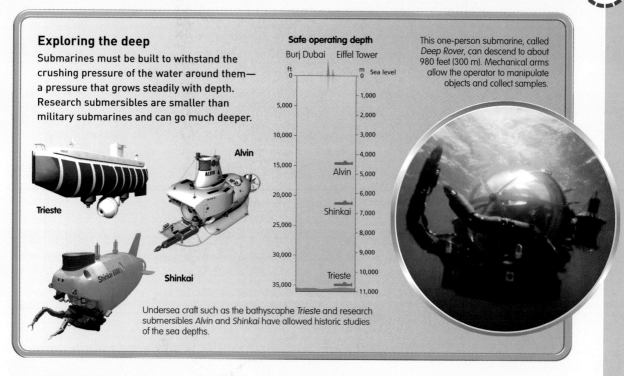

Trieste

Alvin

Shinkai

Safe operating depth

Burj Dubai   Eiffel Tower

ft		m
0		0 Sea level
		1,000
5,000		2,000
10,000		3,000
		4,000
15,000	Alvin	5,000
20,000		6,000
	Shinkai	7,000
25,000		8,000
30,000		9,000
		10,000
35,000	Trieste	11,000

This one-person submarine, called *Deep Rover*, can descend to about 980 feet (300 m). Mechanical arms allow the operator to manipulate objects and collect samples.

Undersea craft such as the bathyscaphe *Trieste* and research submersibles *Alvin* and *Shinkai* have allowed historic studies of the sea depths.

Deep-sea vent (below center)

Hydrothermal vents may develop along crustal cracks where seafloor spreading is occurring. Dozens are known, all spewing a scalding blend of water and chemicals that may exceed 600°F (350°C). Some vents build into "smokers" that spout water chemically tinted gray or black. These towering structures have been known to rise 15 stories before collapsing. Vent communities include some of the strangest of all marine animals.

Black smoker
Black smokers are the hottest vents. This one is at a hydrothermal spring in the mid-ocean ridge of the Atlantic.

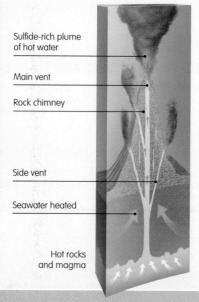

Sulfide-rich plume of hot water

Main vent

Rock chimney

Side vent

Seawater heated

Hot rocks and magma

Mussels
Pale, oversized mussels (*Bathymodiolus sp.*) blanket an area near a hydrothermal spring in the Pacific.

Spiny crab
This 2-inch (5-cm) spiny crab (species unknown) scuttles through a vent community hunting for live food, sometimes including other crabs.

Rock chimney
Minerals in vent plumes harden into whitish chimneys that can be over 63 feet (19 m) high. This small example is 3.3 feet (1 m) across.

HOT SPOTS

The vast majority of volcanoes, including more than 450 in the famous Pacific Ring of Fire, result from collisions between crustal plates. Geologists estimate that there may be as many 10,000 hidden from view under the sea, most situated along mid-ocean ridges. Volcanoes also develop at hot spots, where heat from a site in the mantle erupts at the surface of the crust above it. The resulting volcano remains active until plate movements shift it away from the hot spot. A new volcano then arises in crust that has moved into place above it.

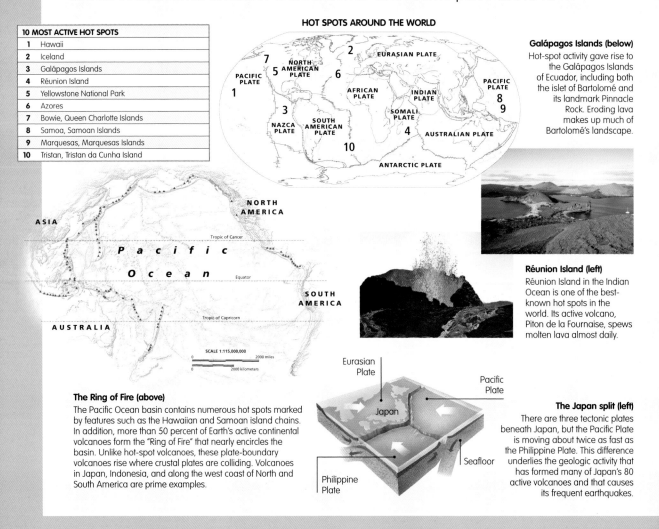

10 MOST ACTIVE HOT SPOTS	
1	Hawaii
2	Iceland
3	Galápagos Islands
4	Réunion Island
5	Yellowstone National Park
6	Azores
7	Bowie, Queen Charlotte Islands
8	Samoa, Samoan Islands
9	Marquesas, Marquesas Islands
10	Tristan, Tristan da Cunha Island

HOT SPOTS AROUND THE WORLD

Galápagos Islands (below)
Hot-spot activity gave rise to the Galápagos Islands of Ecuador, including both the islet of Bartolomé and its landmark Pinnacle Rock. Eroding lava makes up much of Bartolomé's landscape.

Réunion Island (left)
Réunion Island in the Indian Ocean is one of the best-known hot spots in the world. Its active volcano, Piton de la Fournaise, spews molten lava almost daily.

The Ring of Fire (above)
The Pacific Ocean basin contains numerous hot spots marked by features such as the Hawaiian and Samoan island chains. In addition, more than 50 percent of Earth's active continental volcanoes form the "Ring of Fire" that nearly encircles the basin. Unlike hot-spot volcanoes, these plate-boundary volcanoes rise where crustal plates are colliding. Volcanoes in Japan, Indonesia, and along the west coast of North and South America are prime examples.

The Japan split (left)
There are three tectonic plates beneath Japan, but the Pacific Plate is moving about twice as fast as the Philippine Plate. This difference underlies the geologic activity that has formed many of Japan's 80 active volcanoes and that causes its frequent earthquakes.

Unique Hawaiian species

Hawaii's isolated location in the Pacific Ocean has triggered the evolution of a striking mix of endemic plants and animals. Uniquely Hawaiian marine species include marine mammals, seabirds, fish, and crustaceans. Endemic species may be unusually vulnerable to extinction if they face introduced predators or diseases against which they have few or no natural defenses.

This banded spiny lobster (*Panulirus marginatus*) is a relatively common denizen of nearshore waters. Its distant cousins include spiny lobsters of the Caribbean and other tropical seas.

⊘ The endemic Hawaiian monk seal (*Monachus schauinslandi*), Hawaii's state mammal, has become critically endangered due to hunting and other pressures. It is estimated only 1,200 individuals remain.

Formation of an island chain (below)

Hawaii is a prime example of how hot spots may create marine island chains. The site of a hot spot's magma plume remains fixed while an oceanic plate slowly travels over it. Discharged magma gradually builds a volcano that breaks the surface as an island. As the plate moves over millions of years, a series of volcanic islands form, move away from the hot spot, become extinct, and erode.

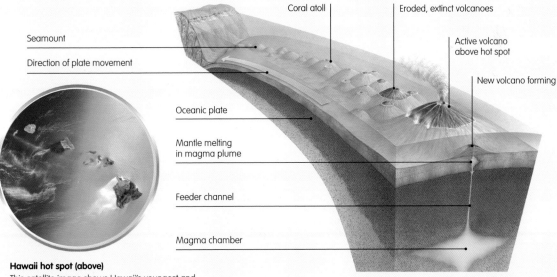

Coral atoll

Eroded, extinct volcanoes

Seamount

Active volcano above hot spot

Direction of plate movement

New volcano forming

Oceanic plate

Mantle melting in magma plume

Feeder channel

Magma chamber

Hawaii hot spot (above)

This satellite image shows Hawaii's youngest and largest island—Hawaii—in the lower right corner.

COASTLINES

A geologically young, emergent coast occurs where tectonic movements are pushing up the edge of a continent. Conversely, older coasts may gradually subside partly because of the weight of accumulating sediments. Sea level changes also submerge or expose coastal land as ice caps and glaciers form or melt, crustal plates shift, and the seafloor expands at mid-ocean ridges. Erosion by wave action, tides, and river flows mold the contours of the shore, forming beaches where the substrate is soft material such as sandstone. Along high-energy coastlines, where wave action is intense, erosion may sculpt dramatic features such as cliffs, caves, and arches.

Tectonically uplifted cliffs (below)

The pale color of the famous cliffs along England's Dover coast comes from their main constituent, calcium carbonate, remains of ancient marine zooplankton. The highest cliff rises 350 feet (106 m) above the sea.

Glacial coast (below)

An ice-age glacier sculpted the rolling headlands typical of Orkney, an archipelago of more than 70 islands in northern Scotland. Erosion of underlying sandstone and volcanic granite produced the dark rock-strewn beach.

Lava flow coast (above)

The Hawaiian island of Maui formed relatively recently as a hot-spot volcano and much of its coastline consists of lava rock. Over time, grinding wave action may produce beaches of coarse black lava bits.

Barrier island (right)

Barrier islands form from sand deposited between two tidal inlets.

Coastal landforms (right)

Vigorous waves and tides cut into rocky coasts, producing cliffs, terraces, blowholes, and other landforms. The sea deposits the eroded material elsewhere, building sandbars and spits, and extending beaches.

Beach

Old marsh

Dune ridge

Barrier flat

Salt marsh

Open ocean

Rocks and sand set down at a river mouth, the beginnings of a delta

The Twelve Apostles (right)

A set of 12 distinct sea stacks off the southern coast of Australia was named the Twelve Apostles in the 1950s. Since then, ongoing erosion has toppled four of the original stacks—a fate that will eventually claim them all.

Coastal erosion (below)

Coastal cliffs form when waves erode hills along the shore. As this process continues, the cliffs retreat inland. Erosion due to wave action and weathering continues to play a major role in shaping subsequent coastal features, such as sea stacks, arches, and caves.

Cave

When coastal currents erode softer rocks from the face of a headland, a sea cave is hollowed out.

Stack

The top of the arch thins and collapses, leaving a sea stack separated from the shore.

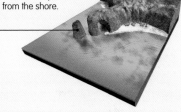

Arch

Wave action continues to widen the cave and eventually wears through the headland, producing an arch.

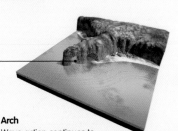

Tombolo, formed from sand deposited where the sea flows over a seafloor ridge

Lagoon, a bay partially enclosed behind a sandbar

Spit, created by deposition of sand where the sea current slows down

Terrace in the cliff, cut by wave action

Blowhole, where the roof of a cave has collapsed

Stack, created by wave erosion at the end of a headland

Sand dunes built from accumulated windblown sand

Rocks at the foot of a cliff, where the cliff face is moving inland due to erosion

Beach, formed from sand set down by waves and tides

Caves hollowed out by wave action

Arch, where wave action has cut right through the headland

BEACHES AND DUNES

Beaches develop where coastal topography encourages the build-up of sediments. Depending on the location and other characteristics of a coast, beach material may be deposited by river or lava flows, nearshore currents and waves, by the wind or glacial action, or another source. Worldwide, sand beaches are the most common, often backed by dunes in places where strong onshore winds push beach sand landward.

Beach makeup

Geologically a beach is a blanket of loose sediment particles deposited along the shore. Grinding wave action and erosion by wind and water produce these deposits from bedrock, coral, or lava, creating beaches of cobbles, pebbles, or sand. Many dazzling white tropical beaches consist of coral sand, while the dramatic black beaches of Iceland and some Hawaiian islands are the remains of lava flows.

Copacabana (above)
The 2.5-mile (4-km) Copacabana Beach in Rio de Janeiro, Brazil, is one of the most famous beaches in the world.

Lava sand beach
This black beach at Vík í Mýrdal is one of numerous Icelandic beaches formed when basalt lava flowed into the sea.

Coral sand beach
Bora Bora, part of the South Pacific nation of French Polynesia, is renowned for its sparkling white, often secluded, coral sand beaches.

Shingle beach
Large pebbles mark a shingle beach at Brighton, England. Shingle beaches are composites of pebbles and sand.

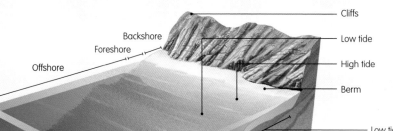

Cliffs

Low tide

High tide

Berm

Backshore

Foreshore

Offshore

Low tide terrace runs down to the low tide mark

Longshore trough created by longshore currents and wave action

Longshore bar

Beach shape (left)
Most beaches have the cross-section shown on the left. The berm marks the limit of sediment deposited by wave action, and its crest is often the highest point on the beach. Wave action at the base of the berm creates a scarp that marks the top of the foreshore and the start of the low tide terrace.

Dune systems

Coastal sand dune systems form where onshore winds pick up and redeposit sand from drier parts of a beach. The largest coastal dunes may grow to more than 330 feet (100 m). A combination of factors determines dune size. The available supply of sand, grain size, and the strength of prevailing winds all contribute. Strong winds and abundant sand may sculpt dunes hundreds of feet high. Similarly, powerful storms may shift their location.

WIND-SHAPED DUNES

Transverse
Where sand is abundant, dune ridges develop at right angles to the wind.

Barchan dunes
Crescent dunes, with tips pointing downwind, form where wind direction is constant but sand supply is limited.

Star
Where winds come from three or more opposing directions, star dunes form.

Parabolic
The tips of these U-shaped dunes point upwind. They form when wind direction is more or less constant.

Longitudinal
Linear dunes form parallel to the average wind direction where sand is plentiful and wind direction is slightly variable.

Towering dunes (left)
The world's tallest dunes occur in the Namib Desert of western Africa. A narrow beach separates them from the Atlantic Ocean.

Rip currents

A rip current, or undertow, is a small, strong current that flows out to sea. The current develops when a series of approaching waves causes water to accumulate in the surf zone faster than circulation patterns can disperse it. Some of this water then rushes back out to sea, possibly carrying a swimmer along with it.

Bondi Beach in Sydney, Australia, is known for its soft pale sand, vibrant social scene, and dangerous rip currents.

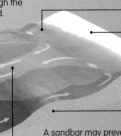

Gap in sandbar
Eventually accumulating water breaks through the normal wave line and flows rapidly seaward.

Surf zone

Beach

Spreading rip current

Weakened rip
The currrent weakens and slows. Some distance from shore it finally disappears.

Rip current

Underwater sandbar
A sandbar may prevent water from dispersing along the shore.

CONTINENTAL MARGINS

A continent's dry land stops at the shore but the continent itself extends below the waves, its edge forming a gently sloping, submerged continental shelf that has "land" features such as hills and canyons blanketed with sediments. At plate boundaries, as off western South America, continental shelves are narrow, but in parts of the Arctic Ocean the shelf is more than 750 miles (1,200 km) wide. Shallow shelf waters are the most accessible areas of the sea where marine resources are most abundant. They are the prime focus for fisheries and undersea mining.

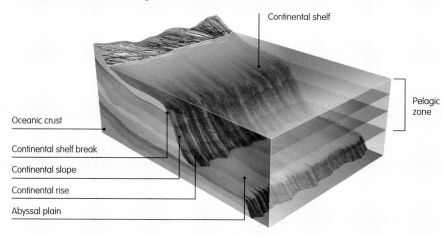

Continental shelf

Pelagic zone

Oceanic crust

Continental shelf break

Continental slope

Continental rise

Abyssal plain

Shallow shelf waters (left)
The outer edge of a shelf forms a feature called a continental slope. Beyond this steeply tilting area is the continental rise, where the continent ends. Where there is little or no tectonic activity, deep-sea sediments accumulate at continental rises. The sediment layer can be as thick as 6 miles (10 km) in some oceans. Shelf waters encompass only the epipelagic zone, the upper 660 feet (200 m) of the sea where light and life are abundant.

Continental shelf off eastern North America

Off eastern North America, the continental shelf overall is broad with a shallow incline. The northern portion of the shelf (illustrated on the right) also clearly shows the effects of the last ice age, when the sea level was much lower and the shelf was exposed to erosion. The shelf's submerged canyons, deep channels, and fanlike deltas were all carved by ancient river flows and similar events.

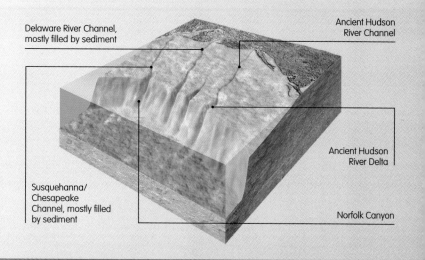

Delaware River Channel, mostly filled by sediment

Ancient Hudson River Channel

Ancient Hudson River Delta

Susquehanna/ Chesapeake Channel, mostly filled by sediment

Norfolk Canyon

Shelf variations (below)

On mountainous coastlines, shelf zones are narrow, rough, and steep. By contrast, they are smooth and gently sloping where plains meet the sea. Everywhere the shelf ends at a steep drop-off called the shelf break.

Broad and gentle

A broad gentle shelf with offshore ridges and sandbars often occurs at the boundary of the continent and an abutting oceanic plate with limited recent tectonic activity.

Barrier reefs

In shallow, tropical shelf areas, the long-term activity of coral communities may produce a barrier reef landscape both below and above the sea surface.

Cliff edge

Strong coastal currents, sometimes in combination with other factors, may scour out sediments and other material from the seaward edge of a continental shelf.

Ice age erosion

During the last ice age, so much seawater was locked in ice caps that previously submerged continental shelves were exposed. Ice streams and rivers carried exposed sediments seaward.

Geologic faulting

Where a continental plate and the adjoining oceanic plate are actively shifting, cracks or faults between plates may also alter the contours of the continental shelf.

Canyons and gorges

Erosion by moving water and sediment, often river flows or ancient flowing glaciers, creates steep-walled V-shaped submarine canyons and gorges cut deeply into the shelf and slope.

A banded butterflyfish (*Chaetodon striatus*) is a denizen of a coral reef in the Caribbean Sea.

The dusky shark (*Carcharhinus obscurus*) frequents the shelf waters of temperate seas. Once abundant, the species is now threatened or endangered in many areas.

This photograph shows eggs that have been deposited by a waved whelk (*Buccinum undatum*), a North Atlantic snail. The species is a bottom dweller of the continental shelf.

CORAL REEFS AND ATOLLS

Coral reefs occur mostly in warm, shallow seas. Home to diverse communities of corals, fish, sponges, and other species, coral reefs are the work of coral polyps. Algae living within a polyp's tissues manufacture most of its food by photosynthesis. Reef-building corals secrete a hard, protective limestone casing over their soft bodies, and over centuries, polyps of different species may produce vast reef systems. A barrier reef is higher than the adjacent land, while fringing reefs form in the shallows around volcanic islands.

Coral life cycle (right)
Most coral species have a multi-step life cycle. Eggs and sperm are released into the sea and unite. Colonies also expand as polyps reproduce asexually, by budding from the parent.

Atolls

An atoll is a shallow lagoon surrounded by a coral reef. Atolls usually occur in groups, most of them in the central and southern Pacific. Pacific atolls have generally developed as fringing reefs around a subsiding volcano. Elsewhere they may be atop subsided blocks of continental or oceanic crust.

This atoll (below) in the Maldives is still developing. As the coral heads grow together they will eventually encircle a shallow lagoon.

ATOLL FORMATION

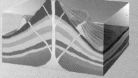

1. Emerging volcano

2. Fringing reef

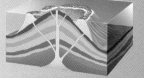

3. Volcano subsides

Atoll formation (above)
Where volcanoes emerge from the sea, fringing reefs may form around the sides. As the volcano subsides or erodes, growing corals encircle a central lagoon.

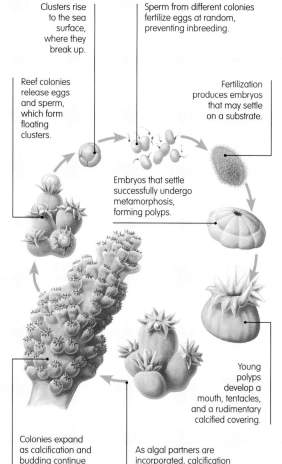

Clusters rise to the sea surface, where they break up.

Sperm from different colonies fertilize eggs at random, preventing inbreeding.

Reef colonies release eggs and sperm, which form floating clusters.

Fertilization produces embryos that may settle on a substrate.

Embryos that settle successfully undergo metamorphosis, forming polyps.

Young polyps develop a mouth, tentacles, and a rudimentary calcified covering.

Colonies expand as calcification and budding continue over time.

As algal partners are incorporated, calcification increases and budding begins.

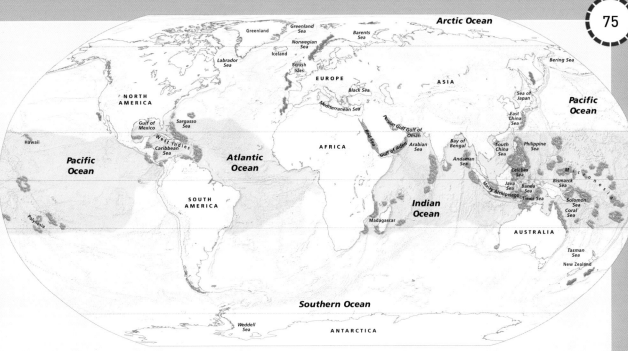

Corals around the globe (above)
Coral reefs occur in every ocean region except the Arctic and South Atlantic. Tropical reefs range in age from 6,000 to 9,000 years. Researchers are just beginning to identify aggregations of cold-water soft corals, some of which occur at great depths.

☐ Warm ocean
☐ Cold ocean
▨ Warm-water coral reefs
▧ Deep cold-water coral reefs

Brain coral (left)
A giant brain coral (*Colpophyllia natans*) flourishes off the coast of Honduras. Under ideal conditions, brain corals can live for an estimated 200 years, growing slowly to a maximum height of 7 feet (2 m).

Cold-water coral community (right)
A sunstar rests among a species of soft coral commonly called dead man's fingers (*Alcyonium digitatum*), in the cold waters off the coast of Scotland.

Harlequin shrimp

Reef animals often specialize in their diet, a natural mechanism for allotting resources in a highly competitive environment. The harlequin shrimp (*Hymenocera picta*), found in the Indo-Pacific, preys mainly on sea stars, often grazing on the echinoderm's tube feet. With a maximum size of only about 2 inches (5 cm), harlequin shrimps may devour their much larger but less mobile prey over a period of days.

SEA AND ICE

Surface waters freeze into sea ice for much of the year in the Arctic. In the Antarctic, most sea ice melts during the southern hemisphere summer. Off Antarctica, Canada, and Greenland, ice shelves as thick as 3,300 feet (1,000 m) extend from the land and float on the sea surface. Antarctica's huge Ross Ice Shelf covers about 188,000 square miles (487,000 km^2). Species in and around icy seas include fish with blood containing natural antifreeze, giant squids, whales, seals, Antarctic penguins, and Arctic polar bears.

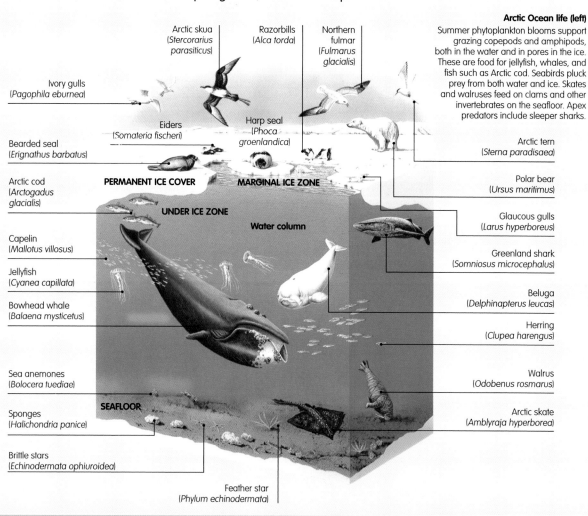

Arctic Ocean life (left)
Summer phytoplankton blooms support grazing copepods and amphipods, both in the water and in pores in the ice. These are food for jellyfish, whales, and fish such as Arctic cod. Seabirds pluck prey from both water and ice. Skates and walruses feed on clams and other invertebrates on the seafloor. Apex predators include sleeper sharks.

Arctic skua
(*Stercorarius parasiticus*)

Razorbills
(*Alca torda*)

Northern fulmar
(*Fulmarus glacialis*)

Ivory gulls
(*Pagophila eburnea*)

Eiders
(*Somateria fischeri*)

Harp seal
(*Phoca groenlandica*)

Arctic tern
(*Sterna paradisaea*)

Bearded seal
(*Erignathus barbatus*)

PERMANENT ICE COVER

MARGINAL ICE ZONE

Polar bear
(*Ursus maritimus*)

Arctic cod
(*Arctogadus glacialis*)

UNDER ICE ZONE

Water column

Glaucous gulls
(*Larus hyperboreus*)

Capelin
(*Mallotus villosus*)

Greenland shark
(*Somniosus microcephalus*)

Jellyfish
(*Cyanea capillata*)

Beluga
(*Delphinapterus leucas*)

Bowhead whale
(*Balaena mysticetus*)

Herring
(*Clupea harengus*)

Sea anemones
(*Bolocera tuediae*)

Walrus
(*Odobenus rosmarus*)

SEAFLOOR

Sponges
(*Halichondria panice*)

Arctic skate
(*Amblyraja hyperborea*)

Brittle stars
(*Echinodermata ophiuroidea*)

Feather star
(*Phylum echinodermata*)

Forms of sea ice (below)

Sea ice comes in various types. Frazil ice is a thin, loose coating of ice crystals. In calm waters, crystals may freeze into a thin layer called nilas ice. Other physical processes produce pancake ice and pack ice.

Frazil ice

Soft ice forms on water that is too turbulent for the ice to freeze solid. It is also the first stage in the formation of sea ice.

Nilas ice

Recently formed nilas ice is thin enough to be transparent. As it thickens from the bottom up it eventually turns white.

Pancake ice

Flat plates of pancake ice form as swells and waves consolidate freezing slush that has formed on the sea surface.

Pack ice

Over time, sea ice may be compressed into large, thick sheets called pack ice. Arctic pack ice is thickest, up to 9 feet (3 m).

Icebergs (above)

Icebergs are chunks of ice that have broken off an ice sheet or glacier. This process, called calving, occurs when wave action, currents, or other forces produce enough physical stress to cut the berg away. To qualify as a berg, the floating ice chunk must be at least 98 feet (30 m) wide at its visible base and rise a minimum of 16 feet (5 m) above the sea surface. Most of its bulk, however, lies unseen underwater. Huge icebergs that break off Antarctic ice sheets may exist for three years or longer before melting away.

Arctic sea ice (above)

More or less permanent ice once covered up to 5.6 million square miles (14.6 million km^2) of the Arctic Ocean. Historically, only the outer portions of this frozen salt water melted in warmer months. Since the early 1950s, however, the maximum extent of Arctic sea ice has been steadily shrinking due to global warming.

- Ice caps
- Permanent ice shelves
- Permanent pack ice
- Pack ice extent in summer
- Pack ice extent in winter

Sea ice in the Antarctic (below)

In the Antarctic, sea ice covers about 7.7 million square miles (20 million km^2) in the depths of winter. It shrinks to about 1.5 million square miles (4 million km^2) by summer's end. In contrast to the Arctic, the extent of Antarctic sea ice has remained relatively stable. Even so, the ice cap is melting more rapidly than models predicted.

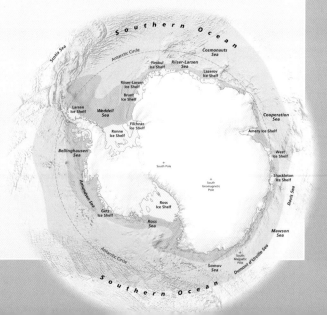

ESTUARIES

An estuary is a partially enclosed body of water in which seawater mingles with fresh water from rivers and streams. Some estuaries are glacier-carved fjords. Others are lagoons protected by islands or sandbars, and coastal plain estuaries such as Chesapeake Bay in the United States. California's San Francisco Bay is a tectonic estuary formed when seawater flooded an area that was sinking due to movements of crustal plates. Conditions in estuaries constantly change. Salinity shifts with tidal fluxes and variations in rainfall and runoff. Water temperature variations may also be extreme. Even so, estuaries support abundant wildlife.

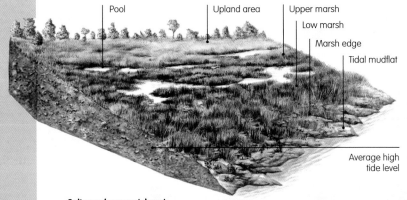

Pool   Upland area   Upper marsh

Low marsh

Marsh edge

Tidal mudflat

Average high tide level

Salt marsh zones (above)
A salt marsh has two zones that place differing demands on plant and animal life. Organisms in the low marsh must cope with daily flooding at high tide. Flooding is intermittent or rare in the drier upper marsh.

Salt marsh (above)
Salt marshes occur worldwide except in polar areas. This example is near Cole Harbour, Nova Scotia, Canada, where North Atlantic high tides flood its lower zone with brackish water twice daily.

Osmoregulation

Estuarine fish and other aquatic wildlife have physiological means of osmoregulation—maintaining the slightly salty chemistry of their body fluids. In freshwater environments these mechanisms remove excess water that enters from outside. In the sea, osmoregulation removes excess salts. Australian barramundi (*Lates calcarifer*; shown below) live mostly in rivers. Once a year, adults move into brackish estuary waters to breed.

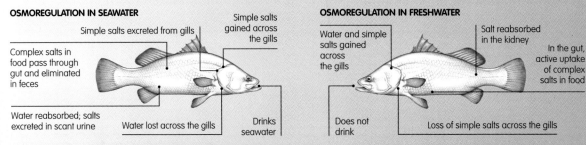

OSMOREGULATION IN SEAWATER

Simple salts excreted from gills

Simple salts gained across the gills

Complex salts in food pass through gut and eliminated in feces

Water reabsorbed; salts excreted in scant urine

Water lost across the gills

Drinks seawater

OSMOREGULATION IN FRESHWATER

Water and simple salts gained across the gills

Salt reabsorbed in the kidney

In the gut, active uptake of complex salts in food

Does not drink

Loss of simple salts across the gills

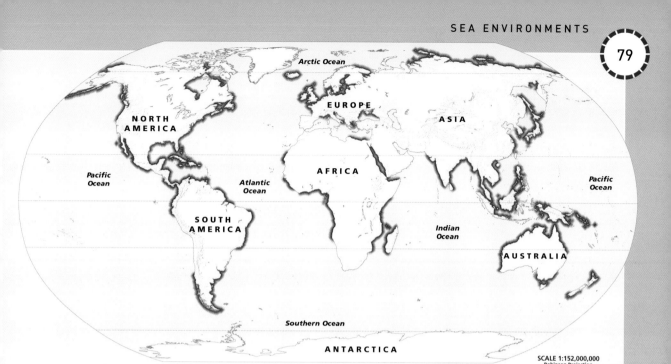

NORTH AMERICA

EUROPE

ASIA

Arctic Ocean

Pacific Ocean

Atlantic Ocean

AFRICA

Pacific Ocean

SOUTH AMERICA

Indian Ocean

AUSTRALIA

Southern Ocean

ANTARCTICA

SCALE 1:152,000,000
Robinson Projection

Estuary habitats (above)

Estuaries are common features along the coastlines of every continent except Antarctica. Estuaries contain specialized and diverse communities of plants and animals adapted to cope with the ever-changing conditions. In temperate regions, grassy salt marshes fringe estuaries. In the tropics and subtropics, mangroves are the dominant plant life.

Salt marshes
Mangrove forests

Estuaries (below)

Various geological processes of formation, such as erosion and sedimentation, are used as part of a scheme to classify estuaries. The four main types are drowned river valleys, fjords, bar-built estuaries, and tectonic estuaries.

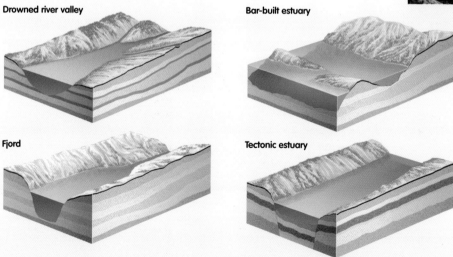

Drowned river valley

Bar-built estuary

Fjord

Tectonic estuary

Roaming otter (above)

In addition to living in totally freshwater habitats, North American river otters (*Lontra canadensis*) may also thrive in estuaries and along rocky seacoasts.

MANGROVE FORESTS

In tropical and some subtropical locales, mangrove forests line the fringes of estuaries and shallow coastal areas. The term "mangroves" may refer to the mangrove family of plants, or to all the plants in these saline woodland habitats. Mangroves are a family of shrubby tree species that are tolerant of salt and adapted to harsh coastal conditions. They are common in the intertidal zone where waters are warm, shallow, and calm. Mangrove forests are a perfect nursery and feeding ground for many small aquatic creatures.

Mangrove pitta (below)

The mangrove pitta (*Pitta megarhyncha*) is found from India to Malaysia and Indonesia, in mangrove and nipa palm forests. It feeds on insects, crustaceans, and mollusks.

Submerged aquatic grasses

Submerged grasses and other aquatic vegetation flourish in the shallows of La Jolla Cove in California. Like mangrove habitats, such brackish coastal waters are vitally important nurseries for the young of many fish species. They also attract diverse wetlands birds, such as rails and herons. Clams and other small invertebrates live on or in the muddy bottom.

Floating through (right)

The upside down jellyfish (*Cassiopeia xamachana*) inhabits a variety of tropical waters, including mangroves.

Scarlet ibis (above)
The scarlet ibis (*Eudocimus ruber*), of northern South America, roams between coastal mangroves and marshes and interior wetlands—a behavior common to many birds that visit estuaries.

Red mangroves (above)
Red mangroves, photographed here in Florida, USA, are the dominant vegetation in saltier tropical estuaries. Black mangroves and white mangroves inhabit less saline estuarine environments.

Striated heron
(*Ardeola striata*)

Calm waters
Mangrove habitats occur particularly in tropical coastal areas having shallow, calm waters.

Archerfish
(*Toxotes chatareus*)

Gobies
(*Gobiidae*)

Targeting its prey
Unerring aim with a forceful jet of water shot from its mouth allows the archerfish to knock insects from overhanging foliage.

Fiddler crabs
(*Uca sp.*)

Mangrove menagerie
Stilt-like mangrove roots support a diverse community of animal life. Gobies and other small fish find food and shelter there, while fiddler crabs inhabit mud burrows below.

Stilt roots

INLAND SEAS

Inland seas are branches of ancient oceans that are now enclosed by land. The Caspian Sea, between southern Russia and northern Iran, is the largest of these lakelike bodies of water, covering some 143,000 square miles (370,000 km²). Famous for its caviar-producing sturgeon, the Caspian is also home to abundant birdlife and other animals. The Caspian and the neighboring Black and Aral Seas were cut off from the prehistoric Tethys Sea as plate movements raised the Himalaya and surrounding lands. The world's saltiest inland sea is the Dead Sea, once a branch of the Mediterranean Sea. Like many other inland seas, the Dead Sea has no outlets.

Ancient inland sea (left)
Some 300 million years ago, an inland sea spread across the site of Arches National Park in Utah, USA. Slowly over time, the sea evaporated and a thick layer of sandstone developed atop the salt bed left behind. Geologic upheavals and erosion produced the park's famous arches and other striking rock formations.

Dead Sea (above)
The Dead Sea is a hypersaline lake in a basin created by the separation of crustal plates underlying the continents of Asia and Africa. Fed by rivers such as the Jordan, the Dead Sea has steadily been shrinking—and becoming saltier—as nearby countries divert river flows for agriculture and other uses. It is relatively easy to float in salt water because it is denser than the human body. The Dead Sea is roughly nine times saltier than any ocean.

Evaporite deposits

Evaporite deposits are sediments laid down by the evaporation of salty water. During geologic time, multiple cycles of evaporation and replenishment of Dead Sea waters have created thick layers of evaporite salts, including halite—the rock salt from which table salt (sodium chloride) is refined. Chemical conditions near the bottom cause crystals of these salts to precipitate out on the lake floor. They also wash up on the shore.

Rock salt

Dead Sea salt deposits are the raw material of valuable commercial operations. Some consumers believe that salt-laden mud in the lake bottom also has health benefits.

Dying Aral Sea

The Aral Sea was a vast lake that has been shrinking due to the loss of the river flows that once replenished it. Since the early 1960s, upstream damming and diversions for agriculture have dramatically reduced the lake's size, which can be seen in the photographs here. Today, only a few hypersaline ponds remain and the Aral Sea is rapidly becoming only a memory.

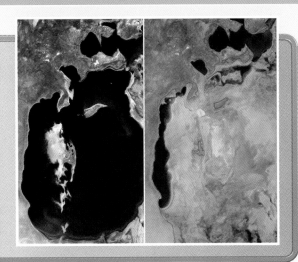

The Aral Sea in 1989 and 2014 (right)
NASA satellite photographs taken in 1989 and 2014 reveal the dramatic shrinking of the Aral Sea. Today, the eastern basin is called the Aralkum Desert.

Caspian Sea (left)
The Caspian Sea is Earth's largest inland sea. Although some 130 rivers deliver fresh water to it, none flows out. Intensive fisheries, river-borne industrial pollution, and development along the shore have all taken a toll on the Caspian's ecological health. The discovery of significant oil and gas deposits under the Caspian is increasing pressure on the Caspian's natural systems and wildlife, including the sevruga sturgeon, seals, and birdlife.

Caspian tern (right)
The outsized Caspian tern (*Hydroprogne caspia*) has a maximum wingspan of about 4 feet (1.2 m). Caspian terns use freshwater and saltwater habitats around the globe.

⚡ Sevruga sturgeon

The Caspian Sea's sevruga sturgeon (*Acipenser stellatus*) is endangered because of overharvesting of its eggs for sevruga caviar, pollution, and disruption of its spawning areas.

CHAPTER FIVE

SEA LIFE

⚡ Hawksbill turtle

Hawksbill (*Eretmochelys imbricata*) populations have been depleted by human consumption of its eggs and use of its shell for ornaments. It is critically endangered. The hawksbill has a wide distribution, but is found primarily in coral reefs of the Indian, Pacific, and Atlantic Oceans. It is often seen resting in caves and ledges.

CLIMATE ZONES

Water temperature establishes four overall marine regions: polar waters, the coldest; cold temperate seas; warm temperate seas; and the warmest, tropical seas. In all four regions, sunlight profoundly affects the abundance of marine life, with most species living within the sunlight zone that extends down to about 660 feet (200 m). Most marine animals, including familiar sharks, whales, and finfish, inhabit this top layer in temperate and tropical seas. Regardless of exactly where a species occurs, however, its biological design allows it to meet the constant challenges of living, finding food, reproducing, and evading predators in the undersea world.

Polar adaptations

Marine creatures have a number of adaptations that allow them to survive in the freezing waters of the Southern and Arctic Oceans. Some Antarctic species of fish accumulate sodium, potassium, chloride ions, or urea, which lowers the freezing point of their bodies. Seals and whales have a thick layer of blubber for insulation, and round bodies with a small surface to volume ratio, which minimizes heat loss.

Antarctic icefish (left)
Antarctic icefish (*Notothenioidei sp.*) live in waters as cold as 28°F (-2°C), lower than the freezing point of freshwater because of the dissolved salts. Many icefish species are able to survive at these temperatures because of the presence of an antifreeze glycoprotein in their blood and body fluids.

Chinstrap penguin (right)
The chinstrap penguin (*Pygoscelis antarctica*) breeds on Antarctica and subantarctic islands, as well as the southern tips of Argentina and Chile. It is able to withstand swimming in freezing waters due to its thick blubber and waterproof coat of tightly packed feathers. Blood vessels in its flippers and legs have evolved intricate structures that also preserve heat.

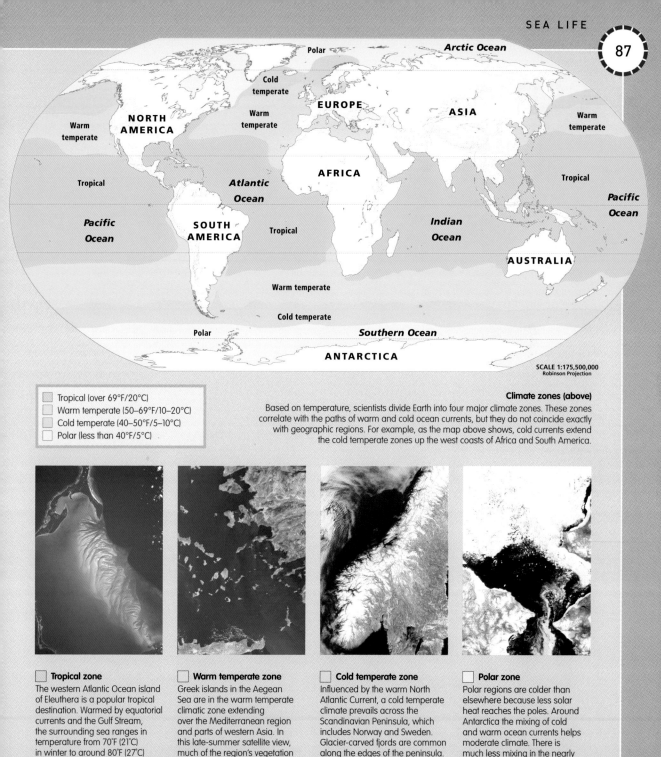

Tropical (over 69°F/20°C)
Warm temperate (50–69°F/10–20°C)
Cold temperate (40–50°F/5–10°C)
Polar (less than 40°F/5°C)

Climate zones (above)
Based on temperature, scientists divide Earth into four major climate zones. These zones correlate with the paths of warm and cold ocean currents, but they do not coincide exactly with geographic regions. For example, as the map above shows, cold currents extend the cold temperate zones up the west coasts of Africa and South America.

SCALE 1:175,500,000
Robinson Projection

Tropical zone
The western Atlantic Ocean island of Eleuthera is a popular tropical destination. Warmed by equatorial currents and the Gulf Stream, the surrounding sea ranges in temperature from 70°F (21°C) in winter to around 80°F (27°C) in summer.

Warm temperate zone
Greek islands in the Aegean Sea are in the warm temperate climatic zone extending over the Mediterranean region and parts of western Asia. In this late-summer satellite view, much of the region's vegetation is brown.

Cold temperate zone
Influenced by the warm North Atlantic Current, a cold temperate climate prevails across the Scandinavian Peninsula, which includes Norway and Sweden. Glacier-carved fjords are common along the edges of the peninsula. Finland lies to the northeast.

Polar zone
Polar regions are colder than elsewhere because less solar heat reaches the poles. Around Antarctica the mixing of cold and warm ocean currents helps moderate climate. There is much less mixing in the nearly landlocked Arctic Sea.

OCEANIC ZONES

At least several hundred thousand species of animals, plants, and other organisms inhabit the sea's varied environments. Roughly 98 percent of these marine organisms live in, on, or just over the seafloor that extends from the shore downward to the deepest abyss. The rest, from floating phytoplankton to sleek swimmers such as tunas, inhabit open waters—the pelagic realm.

Oceanic zones (below)

Living space in the sea is divided into two major realms: pelagic, up in the water column; and benthic, on the seafloor. The majority of marine creatures are benthic. Sunlight, temperature, pressure, and animal life change dramatically with depth, and the ocean can be divided into three main vertical layers: the narrow upper band of the sunlight zone, the dim middle layer of the twilight zone, and the inky depths of the midnight zone below.

OCEANIC ZONES		
ZONE		**DESCRIPTION**
1	Sunlight zone Surface to 660 feet (200 m)	With enough light for plants to perform photosynthesis, this zone contains most of the ocean's life.
2	Twilight zone 660–3,300 feet (200–1,000 m)	Some sunlight filters down into the twilight zone, but not enough to sustain plants.
3	Midnight zone 3,300 feet (1,000 m) to bottom	Apart from bioluminescence produced by deep-sea species, this deep zone is pitch black.

Benthos
Marine bottom dwellers include creepers such as crabs, and immobile mollusks such as mussels.

Nekton
Nekton are species that actively swim. Examples include sharks and other fish as well as marine mammals.

Plankton Floating or drifting species are made up of zooplankton (animals such as krill) and phytoplankton (such as algae).

Snipe eel
The snipe eel (*Nemichthys scolopaceus*) grows to 5 feet (1.5 m). It uses its long beaklike mouth to entangle the antennae of shrimp.

Striped marlin
The striped marlin (*Tetrapturus audax*), a fast-swimming fish, lives near the surface, where it uses its upper jaw to strike tunas and other prey.

Vampire squid The vampire squid (*Vampyroteuthis infernalis*) occurs in deep tropical and temperate seas. It has webbed legs, a pinkish-gray body, and red-purple eyes.

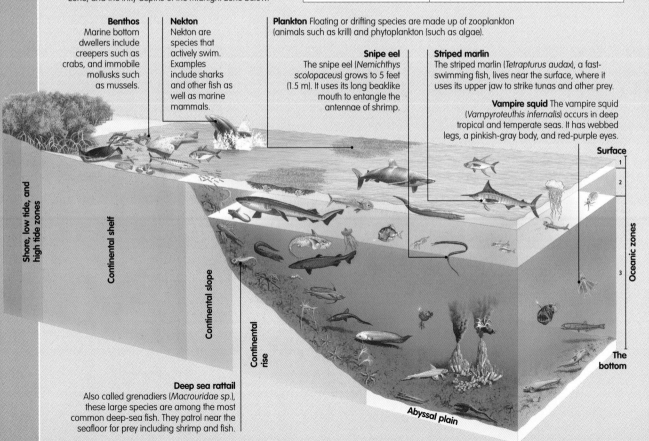

Shore, low tide, and high tide zones

Continental shelf

Continental slope

Continental rise

Deep sea rattail
Also called grenadiers (*Macrouridae sp.*), these large species are among the most common deep-sea fish. They patrol near the seafloor for prey including shrimp and fish.

Abyssal plain

Surface

1

2

3

Oceanic zones

The bottom

Phytoplankton

The marine food web starts with phytoplankton, which survive by using photosynthesis to make their own food. As shown in the images at right, satellite instruments can be used to monitor light reflected from the sea surface to reveal how well or poorly this process occurs. The instruments measure chlorophyll, a pigment used in photosynthesis. Less photosynthesis occurs and food-web nutrients are scarcest in dark blue areas, but more plentiful in red and green areas.

North/South America

Asia/Australia

Africa

Pacific

Phytoplankton bloom

Phaeocystis is a genus of widespread marine phytoplankton species. They are able to form a floating colony of hundreds of cells in a gel matrix. Colonies can increase massively in size during blooms, forming smelly foams on beaches. A bloom is a rapid increase in the population of algae in a water system, caused by an increase in nutrients.

Bioluminescent dinoflagellates

There are at least 1,500 marine species of dinoflagellates. Many dinoflagellates can use bioluminescence as a defense, startling their predators. The bioluminescence pictured here is caused by *Noctiluca scintillans*, commonly known as sea sparkle. A bloom of some dinoflagellate species can cause discoloration of the water, known as red tide.

Diatoms

Diatoms are the most common type of phytoplankton. These tiny examples, seen here under a microscope, are encased within a silicate cell wall. They were found between crystals of sea ice in McMurdo Sound, Antarctica.

SURVIVAL STRATEGIES

All ocean species have body features and behaviors that help them survive in their habitats and produce young. These adaptations range from gills that enable fish to acquire oxygen from seawater to the hydrodynamic body shape of fast swimmers such as mako sharks. Many adaptations are for defense. Camouflage, poisonous venom, and the ability to burrow into seafloor sediments all help protect the species from predation.

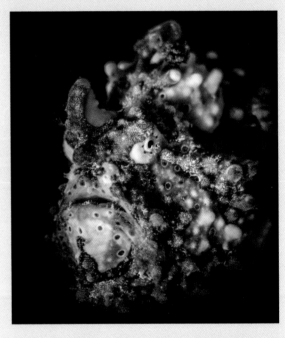

Wide-eyed flounder (above)
This flounder (*Bothus podas*) is a member of the lefteye flounder family, Bothidae. They are called "lefteye flounders" because most species lie on the sea floor on their right side, with both eyes on the left side of their head. Hatchlings have one eye on each side of their head, but one eye migrates to the other side as it grows. Adults are well camouflaged on the sea floor, protecting them from predators.

Warty frogfish (above)
The warty frogfish (*Antennarius maculatus*) lives among rocky and coral reefs, and is perfectly camouflaged to pass unnoticed by both prey and predators. Frogfish are colored to match their environment: from white, pink, and cream to black, yellow, and red, often with dark patches. They can change coloration in just a few weeks: during coral bleaching events, they turn white. Their body is also covered with wart-like bumps, resembling the texture of coral or sponges. The frogfish's large mouth allows it to consume prey as large as itself.

Pygmy seahorse (left)
The coloration pattern of a pygmy seahorse (*Hippocampus bargibanti*) enables it to almost disappear against a gorgonian coral. This species is always found on gorgonian corals of the genus Muricella. It spends its whole adult life on a single coral. *Hippocampus bargibanti* is the largest pygmy seahorse, at just over 1 inch (2.5 cm) long.

Flying fish (left)

Equipped with unusually long pectoral fins, flying fish (*Exocoetidae sp.*) glide through the air to escape predators. Flying fish are found in the surface waters of tropical and subtropical oceans. About 64 species exist. Flying fish can leap out of the water into air, where their wing-like fins enable gliding flight for up to 45 seconds.

Bobtail squid (right)

During the day, bobtail squid (*Euprymna sp.*) bury themselves beneath the substrate. In order to hunt prey at night, these squid have a symbiotic relationship with bioluminescent bacteria (*Aliivibrio fischeri*), which live in a light organ in the squid's mantle. The bacteria hide the squid's silhouette when viewed from below by matching the light hitting the top of the mantle.

Blue-ringed octopus (left)

The blue-ringed octopuses (*Hapalochlaena sp.*) live in tidal pools and coral reefs in the Pacific and Indian Oceans. They hide in tiny crevices, even piling up rocks outside the entrance for extra protection. However, when these octopuses are agitated, they change color: iridescent blue rings appear and pulsate. This is a warning display. If the threat continues and the octopus cannot flee, it will inflict a venomous bite. Blue-ringed octopuses are among the most venomous marine animals as their venom contains a powerful neurotoxin, tetrodotoxin.

ROCKY COASTS

The sea begins where tides ebb and flow—the intertidal or littoral zone. Whether this narrow ribbon consists of rocks, sand, or mud, it is populated by communities of organisms equipped to survive its challenges. Buffeted by waves, high-energy rocky shores are home to organisms that attach to the hard substrate, such as barnacles, limpets, sea stars, and kelps and other seaweeds. Shorebirds are a feature of every littoral community.

Threats to the shore

Intertidal habitats are increasingly threatened by coastal development, sewage, and accumulating trash. Globally, tens of millions of tons of garbage—an estimated 80 percent of it plastic—pile up along the shore, entangling or poisoning wildlife and degrading the seaside's natural beauty.

Croatian coast (left)
The beautiful rocky coastline of Dubrovnik, Croatia, draws millions of tourists every year. National parks and conservation measures help to protect the environment.

Blue-banded goby (left)
The blue-banded goby (*Lythrypnus dalli*) darts through shallow waters with rocky substrates in which there are crevices to hide in. It is up to 2.5 inches (6.4 cm) long and an aggressive predator.

⚡ Southern sea otter

Southern sea otters (*Enhydra lutris nereis*) are marine mammals native to rocky coasts of the northeastern Pacific. They feed on urchins, shellfish, and small fish. This mother has rare twin pups.

Rock attachers (left)

All attached to the same rock are: rustic limpets (*Patella rustica*), at the top; two lined top shells (*Phorcus lineatus*), which are top snails, named for their spinning-top shaped shells; blue mussels (*Mytilus edulis*), at bottom right; and acorn barnacles (*Semibalanus balanoides*), at top right.

Coastal cruiser (right)

Purple sea urchins (*Strongylocentrotus purpuratus*) are common inhabitants of rocky coastal areas of western North America. They feed on kelps and other algae.

Rocky shore life (below)

Complex communities of marine organisms survive along rocky shores. Most of those living in the intertidal zone have shells or other adaptations that help protect them from wave action and the drying effects of air. Mussels, oysters, limpets, sea stars, chitons, and snails attach to the hard substrate. Small fish and creatures such as sea urchins are found only underwater, in the subtidal zone.

Gooseneck barnacle (right)

Chunky gooseneck barnacles (*Pollicipes polymerus*) may attach to intertidal rocks or to floating debris such as driftwood.

Rock louse
(*Ligia occidentalis*)

Periwinkle
(*Littorina littorea*)

Limpet
(*Patellacea*)

Highest high tide

Gooseneck barnacle
(*Pollicipes polymerus*)

White acorn barnacles
(*Balanus glandula*)

Chiton
(*Chitonidae*)

Blue mussels
(*Mytilus edulis*)

High tide

Mussels
(*Mytilus californianus*)

Purple sea urchin
(*Strongylocentrotus purpuratus*)

Hermit crab
(*Ceonobita sp.*)

Sea anemone
(*Urticina crassicornis*)

Low tide

Algae or seaweed
(*Enteromorpha sp.*)

Ochre sea star
(*Pisaster sp.*)

SEDIMENT LIFE

Sandy and mud beaches are extremely challenging environments. The Sun's heat, salt water, salt-laden winds, and constant wave action are all potential threats to survival. As a result, many species in the intertidal zone spend much or all of their time burrowed beneath the surface or in the shelter of driftwood and washed-up seaweeds and shells. Microscopic animals thrive in the spaces between sand grains or sediment particles.

Sea cucumber (left)
Sea cucumbers occur in rocky or sandy shallows as well as on the deep seafloor. This specimen is a chocolate chip sea cucumber (*Isostichopus badionotus*), common in the shallow waters of the western Atlantic Ocean.

Disco clam (below)
Disco clams (*Ctenoides ales*) burrow into the soft substrate and filter bits of food from seawater. This species is named because it flashes like a disco ball, caused not by bioluminescence but by sunlight flashing off the highly reflective edge to its mantle. It is widespread in the tropical Indo-Pacific.

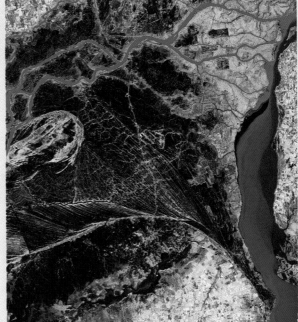

River-borne sediments (above)
Rivers transport sediments to coastal areas, sometimes creating sprawling, fertile deltas. The forested and densely vegetated Parana River Delta shown here is northeast of Buenos Aires, Argentina.

Mud communities (right)

Muddy sediments conceal a thriving community of grazers, burrowers, and other life. In this illustrated community, mud snails graze along the surface, and moon snails and dog whelks hunt prey. Below the surface are buried worms, shrimps, and clams. These species extract food deposited on the surface or suspended in the water above it.

Dog whelk (*Nucella lapillus*)

Soft-shelled clam (*Mya arenaria*)

Burrowing shrimp (*Callianassa subterranea*)

Mud snail (*Hydrobiidae sp.*)

Moon snail (*Polinices sp.*)

Cockle (*Cardiidae sp.*)

Sand worm (*Nereis virens*)

Peanut worm (*Sipuncula sp.*)

Hard-shelled clam (*Mercenaria mercenaria*)

Telltale cast (right)

A lugworm takes in sand and digests microscopic organisms living between the grains. It expels the unwanted sand to the surface, leaving a cast.

Lugworm (*Arenicola marina*)

Lugworm "dimples" (left)

This pocked sand surface indicates a lugworm below. They can grow to 9 inches (23 cm) and anglers use them as bait.

Sand communities (below)

Sandy beaches are a hallmark of depositional coasts, where rivers or wave action deposit sediment particles. Sandy shores are suited to burrowers such as clams, worms, and shrimplike amphipods.

Isopod (right)

Isopods (*Cyathura sp.*) are crustaceans with pairs of leg-like appendages and a flattened tail called a telson.

Beach flea (right)

Beach fleas (*Orchestia sp.*) belong to the crustacean group called amphipods. Like fleas, they move by hopping.

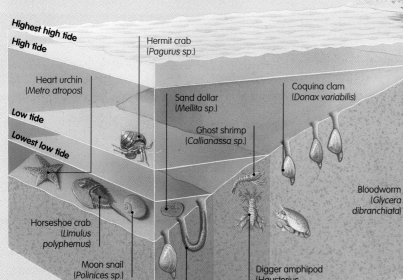

Highest high tide

High tide

Low tide

Lowest low tide

Heart urchin (*Metro atropos*)

Hermit crab (*Pagurus sp.*)

Sand dollar (*Mellita sp.*)

Ghost shrimp (*Callianassa sp.*)

Coquina clam (*Donax variabilis*)

Clam worm (*Nereis sp.*)

Bloodworm (*Glycera dibranchiata*)

Ghost crab (*Ocypode quadrata*)

Mole crab (*Emerita sp.*)

Horseshoe crab (*Limulus polyphemus*)

Moon snail (*Polinices sp.*)

Lugworm (*Arenicola marina*)

Digger amphipod (*Haustorius canadensis*)

LIFE IN SHALLOW SEAS

Shallow, sunlit seas extend from the shore to the outer margins of continental shelves. This realm harbors the greatest numbers of marine animals, plants, and other organisms. There are approximately 230,000 documented marine species, including thousands of bony fish, sharks and their relatives, marine mammals and sea turtles, and invertebrates such as squids, shrimps, and the tiny floating animals collectively called zooplankton. Many more, yet undiscovered, species are thought to exist, and some researchers estimate that the true tally may approach 1 million. Sea grasses and an estimated 9,000 species of seaweeds live in coastal areas.

SEA GRASS SPECIFICS		
Type of sea grass	Ocean climatic zone	Interesting fact
Eelgrass	Temperate	Like other seagrasses, has tiny flowers at base of leaves
Widgeon grass	Temperate	Favorite food of wild ducks
Turtle grass	Subtropical Florida and Caribbean	Favored food of sea turtles and parrotfish
Shoal grass	Tropical, subtropical	Short, narrow blades only 0.08–0.1 inch wide (2–3 mm)
Posidonia	Temperate	May form colonies tens of thousands of years old
Johnson's seagrass	Subtropical Florida	Occurs only in Indian River Lagoon, Florida

Shallow-water corals (above)
Coral reefs in shallow, warm waters, like this strikingly colorful one in the Red Sea, are extraordinarily diverse marine habitats. Many species may coexist in a small area.

Food from sunlight (below)
Photosynthesis is the process by which green plants capture solar energy and use it to form sugars. These compounds fuel the plant's own growth and are also stored in plant tissues animals use as food. Specialized plant pigment molecules, mainly chlorophylls, initially trap sunlight. Its energy then drives chemical reactions that convert water and carbon dioxide into sugar. The reactions simultaneously release oxygen.

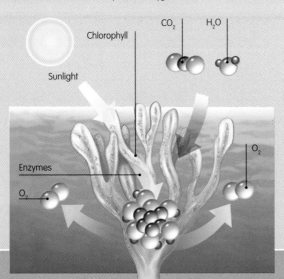

Chlorophyll

CO_2 H_2O

Sunlight

Enzymes

O_2

O_2

Bat ray (right)
The California bat ray (*Myliobatis californica*) is found around estuaries and bays, kelp beds, and rocky-bottomed shoreline in the eastern Pacific Ocean, between Oregon and the Gulf of California. It can grow to have a wingspan of up to 6 feet (1.8 m).

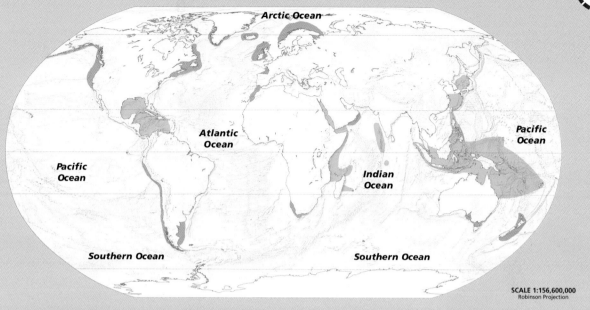

SCALE 1:156,600,000
Robinson Projection

Arctic Ocean

Atlantic
Ocean

Pacific
Ocean

Pacific
Ocean

Indian
Ocean

Southern Ocean

Southern Ocean

Coastal pastures (above)

In tropical and temperate waters, sea grasses and the large seaweeds called kelp are crucial parts of many coastal marine communities. Growing in the nearshore shallows, this submerged vegetation provides small fish and other marine creatures with both food and shelter from predators. Sea grasses are common along sandy shores. Kelps form lush forests along some rocky coasts.

- Sea grass beds
- Kelp forest

Day octopus (right)

A day octopus (*Octopus cyaneus*) moves through a sea grass meadow. Rooted in the soft bottom, sea grasses and algae growing on them provide food for grazing snails and small crustaceans. These densely vegetated beds also serve as cover for crabs and juvenile fish.

Bottlenose dolphin (right)

Bottlenose dolphins (*Tursiops truncatus*) occur in shallow waters of tropical and temperate regions of the global ocean. These sociable animals often travel in groups in search of fish.

Giant clam (right)

The tropical Pacific is home to giant clams (*Tridacna gigas*). This vulnerable species can grow, over many years, up to 4 feet (1.2 m) wide and can weigh 440 pounds (220 kg).

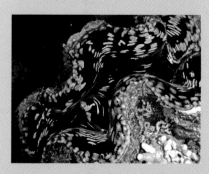

Goldspotted snake eel (right)

The goldspotted snake eel (*Myrichthys ocellatus*) hunts after dark for crabs in sandy sea grass beds of tropical seas. It also burrows into the bottom with its hard, pointy tail.

HUNTING ON THE WING

Keen-eyed seabirds have evolved a variety of methods for finding food. Some simply scavenge dead material floating at the sea surface. Others actively dive to snare fish or other prey near the surface. Still other seabirds excel at underwater hunting and are able to stay submerged for extended periods. Scientists have observed some penguins diving for 8 minutes or longer without surfacing to breathe.

Laysan albatross (left)
The Laysan albatross (*Phoebastria immutabilis*) is one of the most common of Hawaiian seabirds. Although they range widely over the North Pacific, the birds return to Hawaii to breed.

Black skimmer (right)
Black skimmers (*Rynchops niger*) usually feed in flocks, flying low over the ocean surface with the lower mandible skimming the water, scooping up small fish, insects, crustaceans, and mollusks.

Skua
(*Stercorarius sp.*)

Dive-bombers
Gannets and brown pelicans target a fish on their downward swoop and snatch it up as they return to the surface.

Food thieves
Skuas often harass other seabirds until they part with their catch.

Gannet
(*Morus sp.*)

Frigatebird
(*Fregata sp.*)

Plankton eaters
Storm petrels feed largely on plankton at or just below the surface.

Storm petrel
(*Hydrobatidae sp.*)

Food on the fly
Frigatebirds divide their hunting efforts between snatching flying fish and pirating the catches of other birds.

Cape pigeon
(*Daption capense*)

Black-footed albatross
(*Phoebastria nigripes*)

Powerful paddling
Cormorants hunt underwater, but use their muscular legs and paddle-like feet for propulsion.

Auk
(*Alca sp.*)

Cormorant
(*Phalacrocorax sp.*)

Flocking together (right)
Bird Rock at Cape St. Mary's Seabird Sanctuary, Newfoundland, is a coastal nesting ground for thousands of northern gannets.

Razorbill auk (left)
The razorbill (*Alca torda*) comes to land only to breed. It chooses one partner for life, nesting along coastal cliffs. Razorbills dive up to 390 feet (120 m) below the sea surface when hunting for prey, using their wings and their streamlined bodies to propel themselves.

Brown pelican
(*Pelicanus sp.*)

Surface action
Noddies and gulls snatch fish and small squid swimming just below the sea surface.

Tern
(*Sterna sp.*)

Gull
(*Larus sp.*)

Skimmer
(*Rhynchops sp.*)

Noddy
(*Anous sp.*)

Giant petrel
(*Macronectes sp.*)

Tropicbird
(*Phaethon sp.*)

Food scavengers
Giant petrels make a living by scavenging floating carrion.

Wing-propelled
Shearwaters pursue fish by using their wings like oars to propel themselves through the water.

Shearwater
(*Puffinus sp.*)

Eider
(*Somateria sp.*)

BEYOND THE SHELF

The open ocean begins where continental shelves end and ocean basins slope downward to the deepest seafloor. Sunlit and relatively warm near the surface, these waters become dimmer as the depth increases, and their temperature drops sharply. At about 3,300 feet (1,000 m), sunlight no longer penetrates and the temperature averages roughly 39°F (4°C). Warmer surface waters teem with uncountable billions of floating phytoplankton, tiny plantlike organisms that are the foundation of the marine food web.

Speedy tuna

From its bullet-like body to its crescent-shaped tail, a bluefin tuna's (*Thunnus thynnus*) adaptations make it a powerful high seas predator. Its cruising speed is about 1.3 miles per hour (2 km/h), fast for a fish. When chasing prey, however, a tuna can accelerate in a burst of speed, reaching 12–18 miles per hour (20–30 km/h) in less than 10 seconds.

A predator's large eyes

Dorsal fin

Crescent-shaped tail
The bluefin tuna has a narrow, stiff tail fin shaped like a crescent moon. This shape, and the "keels" on the sides of the tail, reduce turbulence or "drag" that can slow the tuna.

Warm muscles
A network of blood vessels called a rete mirabile, or "wonderful net," keeps warm blood flowing to a tuna's muscles. This allows tunas to swim fast in cold waters.

Gills

Powerful swimming muscles
The bluefin tuna is globally endangered largely because its strong muscles are the "meat" that so many people prize as food.

Countershading
The back of a bluefin tuna is dark blue, while its underside and flanks are silvery. This countershading makes it harder for both predators and prey to see a bluefin in the water.

Chambered nautilus (right)
The chambered nautilus (*Nautilus pompilius*), related to the octopus and squid, retracts its tentacled body into a multichambered shell.

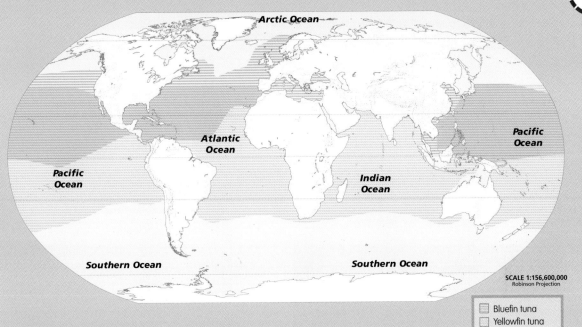

Arctic Ocean

Atlantic
Ocean

Pacific
Ocean

Pacific
Ocean

Indian
Ocean

Southern Ocean

Southern Ocean

SCALE 1:156,600,000
Robinson Projection

Bluefin tuna
Yellowfin tuna

Tuna geographic range (above)

Two of the best-known tunas are the bluefin (*Thunnus thynnus*) and yellowfin (*Thunnus albacares*). Both are somewhat "warm-blooded," with dense arrays of blood vessels that are warmed by the swimming muscles. This mechanism is most efficient in bluefin tunas, which spawn in tropical and subtropical regions but range in summer well up into cold temperate seas. Yellowfin tunas are restricted to tropical and subtropical waters year-round.

TUNA VITAL STATISTICS		
Common name	Bluefin tuna	Yellowfin tuna
Scientific name	*Thunnus thynnus*	*Thunnus albacares*
Average length	6.6 feet (2 m)	4.6 feet (1.4 m)
Maximum length	10 feet (3 m)	9 feet (2.8 m)
Maximum weight	1,500 pounds (680 kg)	880 pounds (400 kg)
Top speed	62 miles per hour (100 km/h)	50 miles per hour (80 km/h)
Maximum depth	3,000 feet (914 m)	820 feet (250 m)
Average life span	15 years	9 years

High seas shark (below)

The oceanic white tip (*Carcharinus longimanus*), seen here with pilot fish (*Naucrates ductor*), is one of the open ocean's large predators, growing up to 13 feet (4 m) long. Its sizable fins make this shark a target for fishers who slice off the fins and throw the doomed fish overboard. Pilot fish cluster around sharks and sea turtles, eating parasites on the shark itself, as well as its leftover food.

Humpback whale (above)

Humpback whales (*Megaptera novaeangliae*) are known for their acrobatic breaching. Humpbacks occur around the globe, migrating seasonally between polar and temperate seas. They feed on fish and krill.

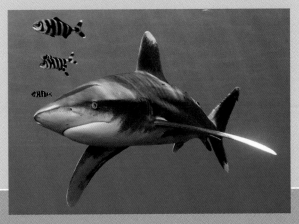

DEEP DWELLERS

Although the deep ocean contains more than 75 percent of the sea's total volume, relatively few species survive there. The sea becomes increasingly inhospitable to life with depth. In the deep abyss, the water temperature stabilizes at a frigid 30°F (-1°C). Lack of sunlight means that, in the dim twilight zone and the dark waters beneath, species with light-producing organs are common. Casting an eerie glow are many species of squids, red shrimps, and fish whose eyes are 100 times more sensitive to light than those of humans.

Viperfish and lanternfish (below)
A viperfish (*Chauliodus sp.*) attacks a lanternfish (*Diaphus sp.*). Both fish spend the day away from surface predators, but migrate upward at night to feed in the dark. A viperfish attacks prey after luring it with light-producing organs, called photophores, along the sides of its body, and with a prominent photophore in the dorsal fin.

Atlantic longarm octopus (above)
The delicate-looking Atlantic longarm octopus (*Octopus defilippi*) is named for elongated arms that stretch about five times the length of its body. It lives on or near the seafloor.

Humpback anglerfish (left)

Humpback anglerfish (*Melanacetus johnsoni*) have a luminous fin spine on the head that attracts prey and potential mates. Several species live as deep as 6,600 feet (2,000 m).

Giant tubeworms (above)

Giant tubeworms (*Riftia pachyptila*) live below 2,000 feet (1,600 m), and sometimes far deeper, on the floor of the Pacific Ocean near black smoker hydrothermal vents. They can tolerate extremely high hydrogen sulfide levels and water temperatures ranging from 35 to 86°F (2–30°C). These worms can reach 7 feet 10 inches (2.4 m) long.

Adaptations

In the eerie realm of the deep sea, many species, including fish, brittle stars, and squids, are bioluminescent. Below about 3,300 feet (1,000 m) fish and other creatures have soft bodies that require little food to sustain, and the fish species are small with large mouths. Some have large eyes; others are blind. Food is relatively scarce in this environment. Some predators have light organs that lure prey while others hunt using keen senses of smell and touch.

Normal fish eye (below)

Eyes of upper and mid-water fish are rounded, with a moderate-sized lens and retina. This design works reasonably well for gathering ambient light.

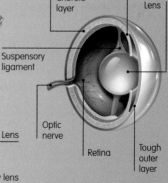

Choroid layer

Iris

Lens

Suspensory ligament

Optic nerve

Retina

Tough outer layer

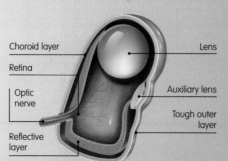

Choroid layer

Retina

Optic nerve

Reflective layer

Lens

Auxiliary lens

Tough outer layer

Scaly dragonfish (above)

The scaly dragonfish (*Stomias boa boa*) inhabits waters deeper than 3,300 feet (1,000 m) in the daytime, but migrates upward to feed at night. It sports a long chin barbell that may attract both prey and potential mates. This species has large light-producing photophores scattered across its body. Special organs near the eyes detect the level of light so the fish can adjust the light emitted by its photophores, thus masking its silhouette. The bioluminescence can also be turned on and off to confuse potential predators.

Tubular eye (left)

Some deep-sea fish have tubular eyes. The large lens and specialized, multi-layered retina help maximize the detection of available light in the depths.

MIGRATIONS

Migration is a basic survival strategy for many marine creatures. Species ranging from fish and jellyfish to squids and plankton move vertically between the surface and deeper, darker waters in a daily rhythm that affords a balance between finding food and being less visible to predators. Sea turtles, whales, salmon, some sharks, and many seabirds migrate long distances to find mates, food, or to avoid harmful environmental shifts as seasons change. Cues from the sun, odors, sounds, or Earth's magnetic field are thought to guide these remarkable journeys.

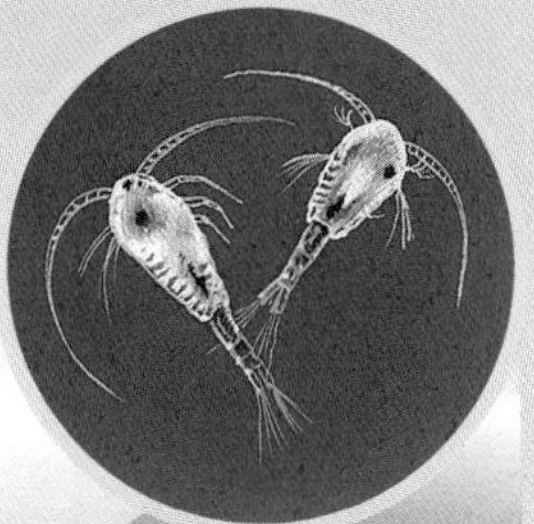

Copepods (right) Marine plankton includes countless billions of copepods, tiny crustaceans with long, bristly antennae, and nearly transparent bodies.

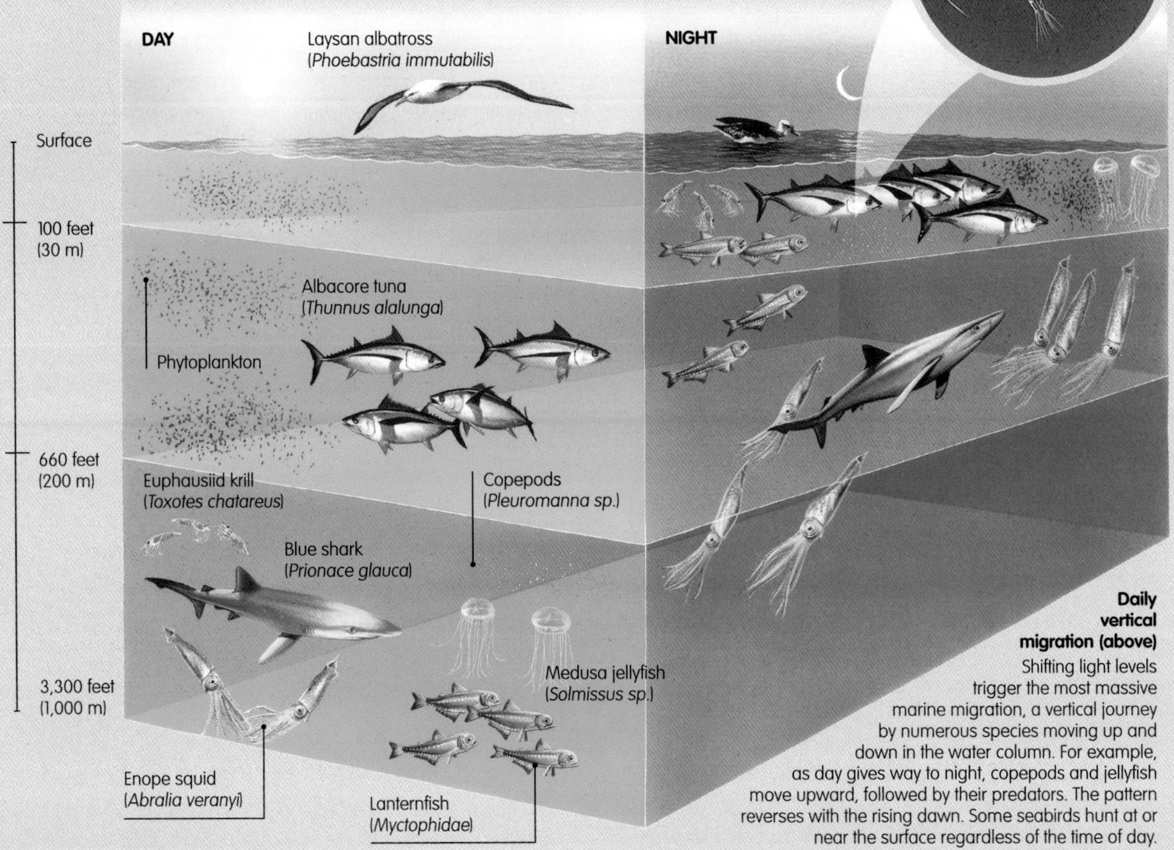

DAY

NIGHT

Laysan albatross
(*Phoebastria immutabilis*)

Surface

100 feet
(30 m)

Albacore tuna
(*Thunnus alalunga*)

Phytoplankton

660 feet
(200 m)

Euphausiid krill
(*Toxotes chatareus*)

Copepods
(*Pleuromanna sp.*)

Blue shark
(*Prionace glauca*)

3,300 feet
(1,000 m)

Medusa jellyfish
(*Solmissus sp.*)

Enope squid
(*Abralia veranyi*)

Lanternfish
(*Myctophidae*)

Daily vertical migration (above)
Shifting light levels trigger the most massive marine migration, a vertical journey by numerous species moving up and down in the water column. For example, as day gives way to night, copepods and jellyfish move upward, followed by their predators. The pattern reverses with the rising dawn. Some seabirds hunt at or near the surface regardless of the time of day.

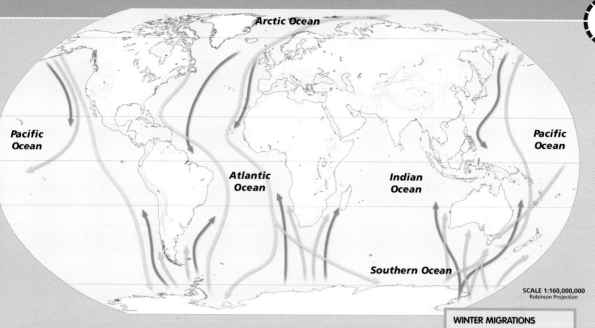

Arctic Ocean

Pacific
Ocean

Pacific
Ocean

Atlantic
Ocean

Indian
Ocean

Southern Ocean

SCALE 1:160,000,000
Robinson Projection

WINTER MIGRATIONS
- Humpback whale
- Arctic tern
- Short-tailed shearwater
- Southern right whale

Migration paths (above)

Most migrating marine animals remain in their home hemisphere, even though they may travel long distances. Birds have no such limits, however, and may migrate from pole to pole. Whales migrate from polar regions where they feed in summer to the tropics where they mate and have their young. Seals migrate to bear their young on islands or other coasts in subpolar latitudes.

Short-tailed shearwater (left)

Short-tailed shearwaters (*Puffinus tenuirostris*) migrate about 20,000 miles (32,000 km) around the Pacific. They return to Australia to breed.

Humpback whales (above)

Humpback whales (*Megaptera novaeangliae*) feed in the Arctic in summer (pictured here off the coast of Juneau, Alaska), but they do not eat while at their warmer winter breeding sites. Humpback whales hold the record for a migrating marine mammal: they travel as much as 5,600 miles (9,000 km) between feeding and breeding grounds.

Arctic terns (left)

The Arctic tern (*Sterna paradisaea*) migrates between Antarctica and breeding grounds in the Arctic and subarctic regions. It traverses as much as 22,000 miles (35,400 km) in its annual migratory journey— the longest animal migration known.

Southern right whale

The southern right whale (*Eubalaena australis*) spends summer just off Antarctica and migrates northward to winter breeding grounds.

GULF STREAM TRAVELERS

Loggerhead sea turtles and eels are among a variety of marine migrators that take advantage of the powerful Gulf Stream traveling up the east coast of North America. The Gulf Stream is the fastest-moving ocean current. It moves at about 5.6 miles per hour (9 km/h). The Gulf Stream is part of a clockwise-rotating system of currents in the North Atlantic.

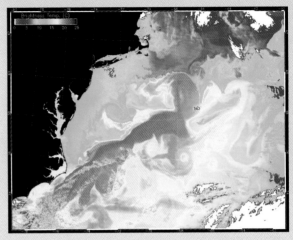

Gulf Stream (above)
The Gulf Stream, shown in this satellite image in red, off the eastern coast of North America, is known as "the river in the ocean."

Loggerhead sea turtles

Loggerhead sea turtles (*Caretta caretta*) can detect and use Earth's magnetic field to navigate. Using different types of tracking devices, scientists have been able to monitor both the turtles' routes and the length of time they remain in the Gulf Stream.

Migration routes (above)
Loggerhead turtles hatched on Florida beaches navigate into the Gulf Stream, which carries them northeast, then south around the North Atlantic. Six to 12 years later the turtles are carried to the US as large juveniles.

Satellite-tagged female
Satellite tags have revealed crucial information about loggerhead migration. The tags, on the turtle's shell, are bulky but harmless. The simpler "living tag" is a pale plug from the turtle's plastron transplanted to its dark carapace. Living tags are used to mark wild turtles under study.

Hatchlings
Hatchlings dig their way out of their nest, which lies above the high-tide line. They make for the waves lower down the beach. The loggerhead's sex is dictated by the temperature of its underground nest. Females return to nest on a beach near where they were born.

Nesting sites
Nests are at risk from sunbathers and their umbrellas on the beach at Gerakas, on Zakynthos, Greece.

The mysterious lives of eels

The European eel (*Anguilla anguilla*) and the American eel (*Anguilla rostrata*), delicacies in Europe and America, spawn in the Sargasso Sea. The sea is at the center of the North Atlantic Gyre, a group of clockwise currents. The sea is characterized by floating masses of sargassum seaweed. The juvenile eels then migrate into the rivers of North America and Europe.

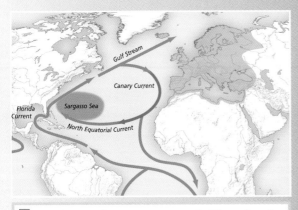

Gulf Stream

Canary Current

Florida Current

Sargasso Sea

North Equatorial Current

◼ Spawning grounds
◻ Range of European eel

➡ Cool Canary Current
➡ Warm water Currents

Captured American eel (below)

A great blue heron (*Ardea herodias*) captures an American eel. This wading bird lives in a range of wetland habitats in North and Central America, from saltwater marshes and mangroves to lake edges.

Parallel lives (below left)
The lifecycle of the European eel and its relative, the American eel, takes decades and up to 7,000 miles (11,250 km) to complete.

1. The journey starts
European eels spawn in the Sargasso Sea. The leaflike larvae drift on Gulf Stream currents for up to three years.

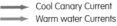

2. See-through change
Larvae metamorphose into juveniles, known as glass eels, when they arrive on European coasts, then mature into yellow eels.

4. Mature migration
Adult eels make their way downriver to the Atlantic Ocean to return to their birthplace. They spawn once and die.

3. Long lives
Yellow eels spend 6–20 years in fresh water. At maturity they become silver eels.

GATHERING TOGETHER

When individuals of a marine species periodically gather in one location, the behavior is no accident. In particular, pre-migration gatherings, or those for mating, spawning, or protecting young, involve complex gene-based mechanisms for coordinating the activity of dozens, hundreds, or thousands of individuals. Such strategies improve chances that the members of a species, and the species as a whole, will survive. Some sea gatherings are scientific puzzles. Scalloped hammerhead sharks are normally solitary hunters, but for unknown reasons they converge during the winter at sites such as the Straits of Florida, only to disperse again over the continental shelf in summer.

Ray roundup (above)
In early fall, a million or more Atlantic cownose rays (*Rhinoptera bonasus*) gather at the mouth of Chesapeake Bay, then migrate together to warmer Florida waters. Pregnant females carry unborn pups until the following spring, when they are born upon the rays' return.

Gathering arthropods

Horseshoe crabs (*Limulus sp.*) occur in areas as distant as the Atlantic coast of North America and the Sea of Japan. At spawning season, males move close to shore. Females arrive some days later. Males attach to the egg-bearing females, which then drag the males along as they creep onto the shore. The males fertilize clusters of eggs the females deposit in a series of hollows scooped into the sand.

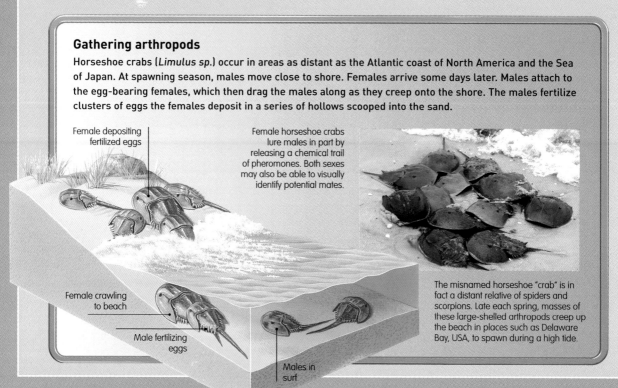

Female depositing fertilized eggs

Female horseshoe crabs lure males in part by releasing a chemical trail of pheromones. Both sexes may also be able to visually identify potential mates.

Female crawling to beach

Male fertilizing eggs

Males in surf

The misnamed horseshoe "crab" is in fact a distant relative of spiders and scorpions. Late each spring, masses of these large-shelled arthropods creep up the beach in places such as Delaware Bay, USA, to spawn during a high tide.

King penguins (left)
King penguins (*Aptenodytes patagonicus*) range far and wide in their usual foraging activities, but they gather into large breeding colonies.

California grunion (right)
California grunions (*Leuresthes tenuis*) go ashore in large numbers to spawn on spring and summer nights. At very high tides, the females dig their tails into the sand to lay their eggs. The male wraps himself around the female to deposit his sperm. After two weeks, waves carry the young out to sea.

Seal mating groups (above)
Northern elephant seals (*Mirounga angustirostris*)—named for the dangling snout of the males—gather at mid-winter at several points along the central California coast; there pregnant females give birth. The cycle begins anew as adults mate before leaving the area.

Hungry sharks (above)
Attracted by the presence of a rich food trove, blacktip sharks (*Carcharhinus limbatus*) converge to feed.

Red knot rendezvous

Red knots (*Calidris canutus*) gather by the thousands to feed heavily before a long spring migration. A major stopover is Delaware Bay on the US Atlantic coast, where the birds' arrival tracks the spawning of horseshoe crabs. For countless generations of red knots, horseshoe crab eggs have been the key food resource fueling their migration. As human harvesting of horseshoe crabs has increased, red knot populations have been decreasing. Red knots migrate between subpolar regions of Eurasia and Canada and destinations in southern Europe, West Africa, South America, and Australia.

These red knots are but a few of the thousands that must build up their energy reserves before continuing their migratory journey.

RED KNOT MIGRATORY PATH

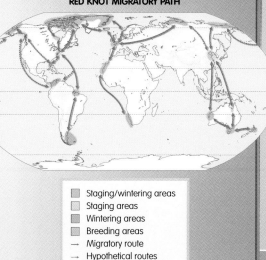

- ▨ Staging/wintering areas
- ▨ Staging areas
- ▨ Wintering areas
- ▨ Breeding areas
- → Migratory route
- → Hypothetical routes

RESOURCES AND CONSERVATION

Manatee

Manatees (*Trichechus sp.*) are classified (with dugongs) as sirenians. Genetic studies suggest that elephants are the group's closest living relatives. Two of the three recognized species—the West Indian manatee (pictured here) and the West African manatee—spend time in salt water. All manatee populations are small and under threat from habitat destruction and collisions with boats.

MINERALS

Salt works, where impounded seawater slowly evaporates and leaves behind salt crystals, produce more than 30 percent of the world's table salt. Magnesium is also extracted from seawater for use in manufacturing precision metal parts. Other sought-after industrial minerals include manganese, copper, and iron in seafloor fields of fist-sized nodules at depths of 13,000–20,000 feet (4,000–6,000 m). Beaches, dunes, and ocean bottom are heavily mined for sand used in construction, industrial processes, and beach replenishment. Intensive sand mining now threatens numerous coastal habitats. Sand and many other minerals enter the sea when wind and rain erode them from land-based deposits.

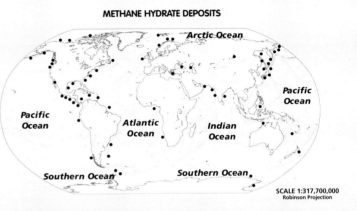

METHANE HYDRATE DEPOSITS

SCALE 1:317,700,000
Robinson Projection

Methane hydrates (above)
Methane is the main component of natural gas. Methane hydrates basically consist of methane trapped in slushy ice. Large deposits have been found under several continental shelves, and geologists estimate that the amount of methane they hold totals more than twice the world's reserves of other fossil fuels. Because the hydrates are located undersea, however, recovering them and safely extracting methane may prove both difficult and costly, particularly due to methane's status as a greenhouse gas that stokes global warming.

Phosphate from the sea
Earth's crust contains phosphates, which contain the mineral phosphorus used in fertilizers and other industrial chemicals. Phosphates are most accessible in land deposits. Despite this, one rich marine source is the accumulation of droppings of certain seabirds. This guano is collected and processed commercially, or used by local farmers who apply it directly to the soil—a centuries-old practice.

The Islas Ballestas (left) off the coast of Peru are favored nesting sites for seabirds, making the rocky isles a major guano "mine." Scaffolding allows workers to collect the guano, which is then processed to extract phosphates.

TOP TEN PHOSPHATE PRODUCERS	
1 USA	6 South Africa
2 Russia	7 Egypt
3 China	8 Israel
4 Brazil	9 Morocco
5 Australia	10 Tunisia

Manganese-phosphorite rock

●	Iron	◆	Gold
●	Tin	✳	Sand and gravel
●	Chrome	✱	Shell sands
●	Copper	⬤	Coal
●	Titanium	▲	Sulfur
■	Monazite		Phosphorite
■	Zircon	→	Derivation
◆	Diamond		of placer

SCALE 1:178,000,000
Robinson Projection

Targeting undersea minerals (above)
A variety of potentially valuable mineral deposits exist in deeper offshore waters in various locations around the globe. Of these, oil and gas deposits in continental shelves in locales such as the North Sea and Gulf of Mexico currently have the most commercial appeal. As land-based sources diminish, it may become economically viable to pursue other deepwater mineral resources, including phosphates and manganese nodules.

Desalination (below)
Fresh water moves into salt water if a semi-permeable membrane separates them. Applying pressure to the salt water stops this osmosis. Increasing the pressure causes reverse osmosis: pure water flows out of the salt water.

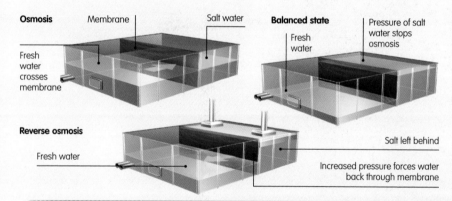

Osmosis   Membrane   Salt water

Fresh water crosses membrane

Balanced state   Pressure of salt water stops osmosis

Fresh water

Reverse osmosis

Fresh water

Salt left behind

Increased pressure forces water back through membrane

Salt supplies (above)
Piles of sea salt—the mineral compound sodium chloride—are extracted in evaporation ponds, as shown here in Sicily. Windmills have been used to power the pumping of brackish water into the ponds since medieval times.

Manganese nodules

Lumpy nodules of manganese were first observed in the 1870s by the Challenger deep-sea expedition. The nodules lie scattered across the deep-sea floor of the world's oceans. Although not yet commercially viable because of the depths where they are located, manganese nodules are a potentially valuable source of nickel, copper, and manganese. Nodules enlarge as minerals accumulate, giving them an intricate interior structure.

Cross-section

External view

Researchers are developing methods to retrieve manganese nodules from as deep as 19,500 feet (6,000 m) below the sea. By current estimates, the supply of key ores in the richest Pacific Ocean nodule fields could meet human needs for 20 centuries.

OIL AND GAS

At dozens of sites around the globe, the seabed conceals major fields of oil and natural gas. Both these fossil fuels formed over millions of years as buried, carbon-rich remains of animals and plants were compressed under accumulating rock layers. They gradually seep upward through porous rock strata until becoming trapped in pressurized pools under a hard, impermeable layer called caprock. Drilling at depths ranging from a few hundred feet to more than 34,000 feet (10,360 m) taps these pools and allows crude oil and natural gas to be piped to the surface. Due to the time span required for fossil fuels to form, they are finite resources.

Remains accumulate
Dead organisms drop to the ocean floor and are quickly covered by mud and silt.

Controlled decay
As rock layers accumulate, organic remains trapped within them are subjected to moderate heat and increasing pressure. These conditions favor the formation of oil and gas.

Rise of fossil fuels
Oil and gas percolate upward through the overlying layers of rock. Both seep through porous sandstone, but stop rising and pool when they reach higher, nonporous rock such as shale.

Transporting oil (above)
Fleets of supertankers move crude oil from its sources to refineries around the globe. Smaller vessels carry refined petroleum products to the market. The largest crude oil tankers transport 550,000 dead-weight tons (500,000 t) of oil, roughly 6 million barrels.

Formation of a reservoir
The oil and gas collect in reservoir rock that is porous. The nonporous caprock prevents the pooled fossil fuels from leaking away.

Sediment layers

Settling remains

Accumulating rock layers

Porous rock

Trapped organic material

Impermeable rock

Oil and gas formation (above right)
Oil and natural gas form from the buried remains of marine life that have been compressed over millions of years between rock layers. These layers form as sediments are compacted in low-oxygen conditions, which preserve carbon compounds in decaying tissues. The modern-day inland location of many oil and gas deposits is due to tectonic movements and changing sea levels during Earth's geological past.

Rising oil and gas

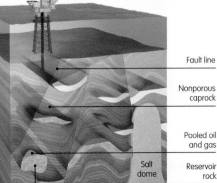

Fault line

Nonporous caprock

Pooled oil and gas

Salt dome

Reservoir rock

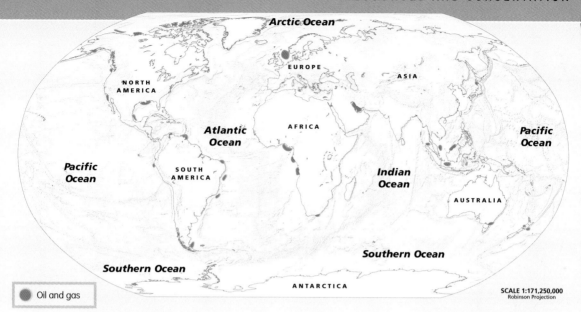

Oil and gas

SCALE 1:171,250,000
Robinson Projection

Oil and gas production (above)
This map shows the most important areas of offshore oil and gas production. The multibillion-dollar oil and gas industry employs hundreds of thousands of workers. More than 60 percent of the world's oil reserves lie in the territory of five Middle Eastern countries.

Drilling support (right)
Oil platforms are built on steel or concrete supports that must withstand the force of waves, currents, and in some areas ice. Some rigs float while others rest atop pillars sunk into the seafloor.

Oil platform (below)
Oil platforms pump out millions of barrels of oil per day. Most stay operational for about 25 years. Large platforms may have living quarters for as many as 300 workers and derricks supporting multiple drills.

Helipad

Derrick

Office and living space

Reinforced support pillars

Life around the rig (left)
The submerged portions of oil platforms lure large numbers of marine organisms, especially where the seafloor lacks rocky surfaces that attract species requiring a hard substrate. In such places, hard platform supports may become home to thriving communities including corals and arrays of other invertebrates and fish. Platforms in warm and temperate seas have the most diverse marine life.

SEA POLLUTION

Pollution is a serious threat to the seas, in part because roughly 40 percent of the world's population lives within 65 miles (104 km) of an ocean. Agricultural and urban runoff contaminate coastal waters with minimally processed sewage, trash, pesticides, and fertilizers that cause unnatural algal blooms. Industrial discharges to the air and waterways add toxins such as polychlorinated biphenyls (PCBs) and polycyclic aromatic hydrocarbons (PAHs) that accumulate in the tissues of marine organisms and become magnified through the food web. Although international regulations prohibit the once-common practices of ocean dumping of radioactive and industrial wastes, garbage, and sewage sludge, enforcement is difficult.

OCEAN POLLUTION SOURCES	
Type	**Source**
Land-based	• Runoff—nitrogen and phosphorus from farming fertilizers and pesticides • River-borne industrial chemicals • Dumping of waste at sea • Sewage, gray water, and waste water • Radioactive waste dumping • Improper garbage disposal
Airborne	• Pollutants such as wind-borne nitrogen and sulfur compounds deposited at sea • Acid rain
Maritime transportation	• Oil pollution from tanker spills • Waste and vessel sewage from tankers, naval ships, cruise liners, and recreational boats • Oil and gas platform waste

Agricultural inputs (left)
In Chesapeake Bay, runoff from farmland contains large quantities of fertilizers, which fuels overgrowth of phytoplankton, creating large "dead zones" in bay waters. Virginia is one of several US states bordering the bay. Many farmers there are experimenting with methods that can help reduce the use of agricultural chemicals.

Animals in trouble

Floating garbage, noxious chemicals, and other pollution all harm marine wildlife. One of the worst offenders is plastic, in the form of discarded fishing lines and nets, trash bags, bottle holders, and other debris. Oil slicks that coat seabirds or other large wildlife also take a toll. Small organisms along oil-fouled coastlines may take a double hit, because they can be killed by some kinds of clean-up efforts.

When oil fouls the plumage of seabirds like this duck caught in the *Exxon Valdez* spill, they lose body heat and cannot fly. Hundreds of thousands of affected seabirds died, as did sea otters, whales, and millions of fish.

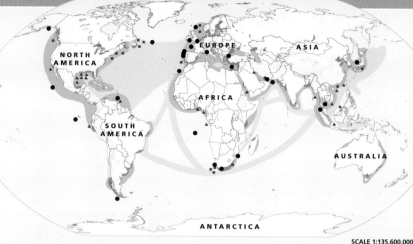

Severely polluted sea areas

Less polluted sea areas

Areas of frequent oil pollution by shipping

● Sites of major oil tanker spills

▲ Major oil rig blow-outs

■ Offshore dump sites for industrial and municipal waste

SCALE 1:135,600,000
Robinson Projection

A sea of contamination (left)

Much coastal pollution is due to the combined effects of coastal development and marine ship traffic to and from ports. Fortunately, improvements to oil tanker design and operation have gradually reduced marine oil spills.

Blooming algae

Surplus nutrients in runoff can fuel algal blooms that deplete oxygen and kill life in the water.

Most polluted Mediterranean

Industrial and agricultural wastes make up the majority of contaminants in the heavily polluted Mediterranean Sea.

Mumbai rubbish

Debris covering this beach in Mumbai, India, provides a mother pig and her piglets with food scraps, and they leave their droppings behind.

Exxon Valdez disaster (left)

When the supertanker *Exxon Valdez* went aground in Prince William Sound, Alaska, in 1989, about one-fifth of the ship's cargo leaked from its damaged hull.

Spill and clean-up (below)

The *Exxon Valdez* oil spill had a severe impact on Alaska's Prince William Sound. About 11,000 tons (10,000 t) of the spilled oil came ashore, affecting wildlife and fisheries along more than 300 miles (480 km) of coastline. Clean-up efforts took years, cost billions, and were only partially effective.

Shore effects

Oiled rocks and sand were blasted with hot, pressurized water. Later studies revealed the hot blasts killed many small animals.

Aerial attack

Helicopters sprayed a strong detergent on the spreading slick. The spray only helped disperse about 5 percent of the oil.

Oil slick

About 30 percent of the spilled oil formed a slick on the water's surface. Currents and wave action drove most of this oil ashore.

Detergent spray

Containment

Containment booms enclose areas of oil above and below the surface. Much of the oil evaporates, some is burned off, and some is pumped out by skimmer ships.

COMMERCIAL FISHING

Early fishermen used nets, spears, traps, hook-and-line, and their hands. Such low-impact practices sustained generations of coastal peoples. Today, millions of vessels using electronic gear, trawl, longline, or set massive nets along the continental shelves and on the high seas. This industrial fishery earns annual revenues of US $400 billion. Millions of tons of non-target "bycatch" species are discarded. Around half of marine fish populations are harvested to the maximum sustainable limit, while another quarter are overharvested.

Fishing methods (right)
Commercial fishing operations use longlines set with baited hooks, bottom trawls, purse-like seine nets, gill nets, pots, and other strategies to capture fish. Huge factory ships are equipped to process catches at sea.

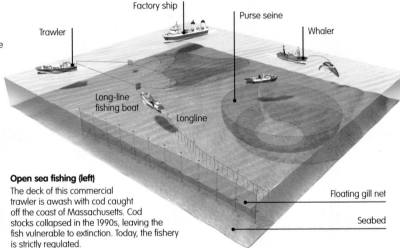

Factory ship

Trawler

Purse seine

Whaler

Long-line fishing boat

Longline

Floating gill net

Seabed

Open sea fishing (left)
The deck of this commercial trawler is awash with cod caught off the coast of Massachusetts. Cod stocks collapsed in the 1990s, leaving the fish vulnerable to extinction. Today, the fishery is strictly regulated.

Arctic fishing tradition
Arctic peoples traditionally traveled in skin-covered kayaks or larger craft called umiaks. They used spears, nets, and hook-and-line methods to catch fish, while seals, walrus, and whales were taken with harpoons. Although some Inuit of Canada and Greenland still use traditional methods, others employ motorized vessels and use a harpoon cannon or rifle to kill large prey.

Traditional Inuit hunting tools are made from bone, animal hide, and walrus ivory.

A fisherman may wait many hours at holes cut in the ice for Arctic char and other coveted fish species.

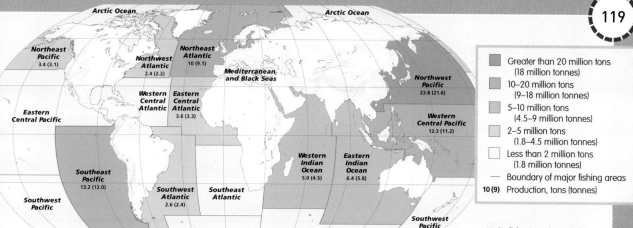

Arctic Ocean
Arctic Ocean

Northeast Pacific 3.4 (3.1)
Northwest Atlantic 2.4 (2.2)
Northeast Atlantic 10 (9.1)
Mediterranean and Black Seas
Northwest Pacific 23.8 (21.6)

Eastern Central Pacific
Western Central Atlantic
Eastern Central Atlantic 3.6 (3.3)
Western Central Pacific 12.3 (11.2)

Southeast Pacific 13.2 (12.0)
Western Indian Ocean 5.0 (4.5)
Eastern Indian Ocean 6.4 (5.8)

Southwest Pacific
Southwest Atlantic 2.6 (2.4)
Southeast Atlantic
Southwest Pacific

Antarctic Pacific
Antarctic Atlantic
Antarctic and Southern Indian Ocean

Greater than 20 million tons (18 million tonnes)
10–20 million tons (9–18 million tonnes)
5–10 million tons (4.5–9 million tonnes)
2–5 million tons (1.8–4.5 million tonnes)
Less than 2 million tons (1.8 million tonnes)
— Boundary of major fishing areas
10 (9) Production, tons (tonnes)

Main fisheries (above left)

Fishing operations annually capture hundreds of millions of metric tons of fish used for human food, animal feed, and fertilizers. Three nations—China, Peru, and the USA—account for nearly one-third of all catches. By weight, the Peruvian anchovy (anchoveta) outstrips all other commercially caught wild fish.

Shrimping (left)

The majority of wild shrimp are caught with specialized trawl nets that rake in millions of tons annually.

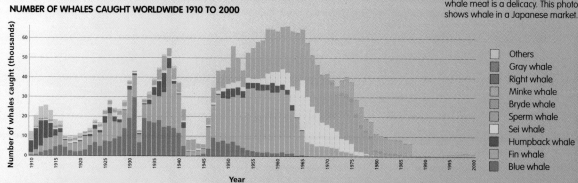

Whaling

In the twentieth century, populations of many whale species fell as whaling fleets used spotter planes to locate animals and processed catches at sea on factory ships. The International Whaling Commission introduced protection for blue, gray, and humpback whales in 1965. In 1985 an international moratorium banned nearly all whaling, although a few nations still conduct "scientific" whaling.

In Japan, Norway, and other countries, whale meat is a delicacy. This photo shows whale in a Japanese market.

くじら Whale
고래 Baleine 鲸鱼

NUMBER OF WHALES CAUGHT WORLDWIDE 1910 TO 2000

Number of whales caught (thousands)
60
50
40
30
20
10
0
1910 1915 1920 1925 1930 1935 1940 1945 1950 1955 1960 1965 1970 1975 1980 1985 1990 1995 2000
Year

Others
Gray whale
Right whale
Minke whale
Bryde whale
Sperm whale
Sei whale
Humpback whale
Fin whale
Blue whale

LIVING ON THE COAST

Coastal areas have always been vulnerable to damage from storm surges as well as day-to-day impacts of wave action and tidal fluxes. Seawalls and structures called groins are common solutions to these ongoing problems. A seawall protects developed coastal areas by deflecting wave energy back toward the ocean. Grouped groins help establish and maintain beaches by preventing the loss of sand or other sediments. Coasts are also places where humankind can harness the power of the wind and waves, giving us a source of renewable energy.

The Thames Barrier is just over 1,700 feet (520 m) long. Each of its 10 submerged gates spans 200 feet (61 m) and can rise 35 feet (10.7 m) above the Thames River's normal water level.

Thames Barrier

In some harbor areas where extreme high tides or storm surge may threaten cities and towns, engineers have created barriers that can be moved into place to block the tidal flow. One of the largest protects areas of London, England, from tidal flooding of the Thames. Its water-filled, crescent-shaped steel gates can be rotated upward to block floodwater, then rotated back underwater when danger is past.

Barrier raised
The Thames Barrier is raised to protect against an impending flood and a remotely controlled gate arm pivots each gate upward.
The gates can also be rotated 180 degrees for maintenance and are put through a monthly test run.

Barrier lowered
The Thames Barrier is lowered when not in use and its curved gates nest in concave concrete foundations sunk into the riverbed. The depth of the channels above allows normal vessel traffic on the river.

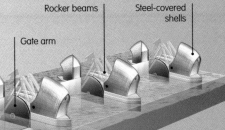

Potential high-water level from flood surge

Gate

Gate arm

Rocker beams

Steel-covered shells

Normal river flow

Seawall
Modern seawalls are often reinforced concrete. This one in Zeeland, Holland, was erected following major storm surge damage in 1953.

Groin
Sets of groins, typically constructed of rocks, wood or concrete, are a common sight in coastal areas where beach erosion is a recurring problem.

Palm Jumeirah
Tourism creates millions of jobs in coastal regions. Palm Jumeirah is an artificial archipelago in Dubai, United Arab Emirates, created by land reclamation. It is one of three planned Palm Islands, which would increase Dubai's shoreline by 325 miles (520 km).

Tsunami warnings (right)
In coastal nations around the world, early-warning systems help civil defense personnel predict when and where a tsunami will strike, and to inform the populace. The systems include sensors that monitor undersea earthquakes and other seismic shifts, and devices mounted on specialized buoys that track unusual shifts in the height of the sea surface.

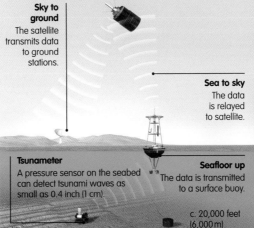

Sky to ground
The satellite transmits data to ground stations.

Sea to sky
The data is relayed to satellite.

Tsunameter
A pressure sensor on the seabed can detect tsunami waves as small as 0.4 inch (1 cm).

Seafloor up
The data is transmitted to a surface buoy.

c. 20,000 feet (6,000 m)

This sign (below) provides tsunami evacuation instructions at the beach on Koh Lipe, Thailand. Similar signs now appear in many beach areas vulnerable to tsunamis.

Hydraulic pump encased in a buoy

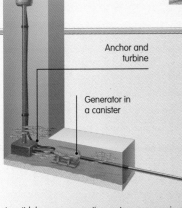

Anchor and turbine

Generator in a canister

In a tidal power-generating system, a pump in a buoy drives seawater through a turbine, which in turn drives a generator connected to the shore.

Wind and wave power
Several coastal nations are exploiting ocean waves and winds as a renewable source of electrical energy that does not contribute to global warming. Technologies already in place include wave-powered generators, underwater turbines, and coastal wind farms that take advantage of steady sea breezes. The ceaseless motion of tides can also be used to produce electricity.

A wind farm is under construction in the North Sea, off the coast of the Netherlands.

CLIMATE CHANGE

Changes to the composition of the atmosphere, especially an increase in greenhouse gases, are warming the atmosphere in ways that have begun to alter global climate. One of the major impacts of global warming is a rise in ocean temperature, resulting in coral bleaching. In addition, rising temperatures are causing the melting of ice sheets and glaciers. This, combined with thermal expansion of the warmed oceans, is causing an increase in sea level that puts ecosystems, island communities, and coastal settlements at risk.

Sea ice changes (below)

Both permanent and annually renewed Arctic sea ice have declined by 38 percent since the mid-1970s. Ice provides crucial habitat for both Arctic seals and polar bears. Although such species have survived previous climate shifts, the numbers of both are likely to decrease and in some areas populations may disappear altogether.

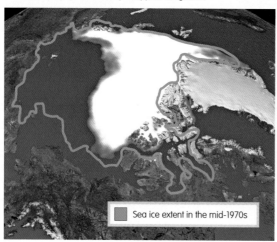

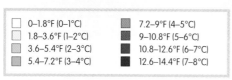

Sea ice extent in the mid-1970s

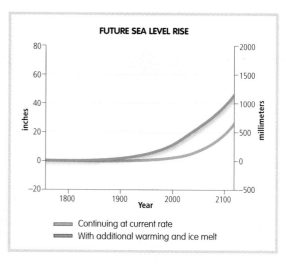

FUTURE SEA LEVEL RISE

Continuing at current rate
With additional warming and ice melt

Estimating sea level rise (above)

At the current rate of sea level rise, sea level will gain 19 inches (480 mm) by 2100 (green line). Additional ice melting in Greenland or Antarctica could boost the increase to 39 inches (1,000 mm) or more (red line).

Temperature rise (right)

Today, the predicted annual surface warming is 5.4°F (3°C) in the tropics and up to 14.4°F (8°C) in polar regions. Some species are already shifting their habitat range to cooler areas; others are becoming extinct. Ice-dependent creatures such as penguins and polar bears are vulnerable.

☐ 0–1.8°F (0–1°C)	7.2–9°F (4–5°C)
1.8–3.6°F (1–2°C)	9–10.8°F (5–6°C)
3.6–5.4°F (2–3°C)	10.8–12.6°F (6–7°C)
5.4–7.2°F (3–4°C)	12.6–14.4°F (7–8°C)

PROJECTED INCREASE IN SURFACE TEMPERATURE BY 2099

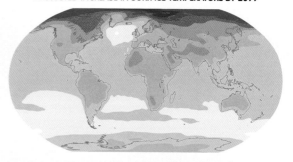

Acidification

Increasing atmospheric carbon dioxide is a major phenomenon in global warming and climate change. As the level of carbon dioxide rises, related chemical reactions may be making the ocean more acidic. This can reduce the amount of calcium carbonate available to form the shells and skeletons of organisms such as corals, mollusks, and crustaceans.

Monitoring calcium carbonate (below)
In these diagrams, red marks ocean depths where too little calcium carbonate is (or will be) available for use by marine invertebrates.

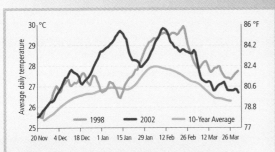

1994

2100

Not modeled

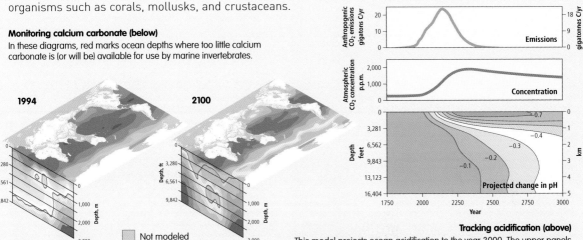

Tracking acidification (above)
This model projects ocean acidification to the year 3000. The upper panels track carbon dioxide produced by human activity and in the atmosphere.

Coral threat

In tropical regions a sea temperature increase of only 2.7–3.6°F (1.5–2°C) can lead to the loss of the symbiotic algae called zooxanthellae that nourish coral polyps. As the polyps become malnourished, they turn white, a phenomenon called coral bleaching. Affected corals can sometimes recover, but only if the bleaching is quickly reversed.

During sustained periods of coral bleaching in 1998 and 2002 (yellow and orange lines), global sea temperatures were much higher than the 10-year average.

Coral polyps secrete a calcium carbonate skeleton that is covered by a layer of living tissue containing zooxanthellae. Warming seawater upsets the symbiosis in which the coral shelters its algal partner, which leads to coral bleaching.

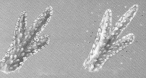

Corals stressed by warming seas may expel their zooxanthellae, or the algae may die. If conditions improve before the starving coral polyps die, they can take up new zooxanthellae.

Healthy coral
1 Zooxanthellae provide sugars and oxygen in exchange for protection.

Bleached coral
2 Polyp tissues no longer contain functioning zooxanthellae.

Dead coral
3 Surface algae blanket the bleached calcium carbonate skeletons.

THREATENED SEA LIFE

Certain ocean areas and species have been hard hit by aggressive fisheries, coastal development, pollution, and environmental changes due to global warming. Pollution, coral bleaching, and fishing with explosives have placed coral reefs in the Caribbean and Indo-Pacific into the critically endangered category. More than 20 percent of mangrove estuaries have been destroyed. Development and oxygen-depleting nutrient pollution seriously threaten many estuaries that are nursery grounds for young fish and shrimp.

MOST ENDANGERED SHARKS	
1	Ganges shark (*Glyphis gangeticus*)
2	Striped smoothhound (*Mustelis fasciatus*)
3	Pondicherry shark (*Carcharhinus hemiodon*)
4	Daggernose shark (*Isogomphodon oxyrhynchus*)
5	Angel shark (*Squatina squatina*)
6	Dumb gulper shark (*Centrophorus harrissoni*)
7	Borneo shark (*Carcharhinus borneensis*)
8	New Guinea river shark (*Glyphis sp.*)
9	Speartooth shark (*Glyphis glyphis*)
10	Narrownose smoothhound (*Mustelis schmitti*)
11	Smoothtooth blacktip (*Carcharhinus leiodon*)
12	Whitefin topeshark (*Hemitriakis leucopeript*)
13	Bizant river shark (*Glyphis sp.*)
14	Smoothback angel shark (*Squatina oculata*)
15	Sawback angel shark (*Squatina aculeata*)

Death by finning (above)
Fisheries for shark fins are destructive and wasteful. The fins are used in a luxury soup consumed in some Asian cultures. Typically, once fins are sliced off, the living shark is thrown back into the sea where it drowns.

⚡ Ghost nets (left)
Caught in an abandoned, drifting "ghost net," this endangered green sea turtle (*Chelonia mydas*) was unable to surface and breathe. Ghost nets probably also kill large numbers of sharks, which must swim unfettered in order to breathe.

Death by dynamite (right)
In some tropical regions, fishermen use the highly destructive practice of dynamiting to "harvest" reef fish. This harmful practice is illegal, but unfortunately common.

On the brink

Scores of marine animals are listed as vulnerable, endangered, or critically endangered by the International Union for the Conservation of Nature (IUCN). Four of the five species pictured here are critically endangered, meaning that their numbers are so few that they may be on the brink of extinction. Human activities, including overharvesting and habitat destruction, have been the key factors placing these species in peril.

⚡ North Atlantic right whale (right)

Heavy whaling from the late 1840s to the mid-1880s decimated populations of the North Atlantic right whale (*Eubalaena glacialis*).

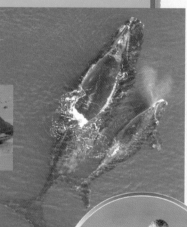

⚡ Kemp's ridley sea turtle (above)

Kemp's ridley (*Lepidochelys kempii*) is the rarest species of sea turtle and is critically endangered, caused by past hunting and continued threats from habitat loss, pollution, and entanglement in shrimping nets. All sea turtle species are endangered.

⚡ Spoonbilled sandpiper (right)

This wading bird (*Calidris pygmaea*) is endangered due to habitat loss in its breeding grounds on the shores of northeast Russia and loss of tidal flats in its migratory and wintering range in Southeast Asia.

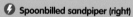

⚡ Giant sea bass (left)

The giant sea bass (*Stereolepis gigas*) is native to the north Pacific Ocean. Due to overfishing, in the 1980s it faced becoming locally extinct off the California coast. Today, it is protected and numbers may be increasing.

⚡ Smalltooth sawfish (right)

Numbers of this tropical ray (*Pristis pectinata*) have perished in nets set for other species. Its habitat has been destroyed by development. It also has a slow rate of population growth.

EXTINCT MARINE ANIMALS

Caribbean monk seal

This small, inquisitive seal (*Monachus tropicalis*), native to the Caribbean and Gulf of Mexico, was sought after for its oil. In 1952 it was declared extinct.

Steller's sea cow

This immense 26-foot (7.9-m) long marine mammal, the steller sea cow (*Hydrodamalis gigas*) was hunted to extinction in less than three decades after it was discovered in 1741.

Great auk

The great auk (*Pinguinus impennis*) was flightless and therefore an easy target for hunters. It was last seen in Newfoundland, Canada, in 1852.

CONSERVATION OF THE SEAS

By the 1970s, overfishing and habitat destruction were global concerns. In 1972, the United Nations Educational, Scientific and Cultural Organization (UNESCO) began its World Heritage program that now includes dozens of undersea sites. Today, government agencies and organizations including the International Union for the Conservation of Nature (IUCN) and World Wildlife Fund work to conserve marine habitats through research, fisheries management, and education.

Pop-up shark tag (left)
This great white shark is wearing a pop-up satellite tag, logging temperature, depth, and location. After a time, the tag releases from the fish, floats to the surface, and uploads its data via satellite. Such tags allows researchers to keep track of the movements of vulnerable shark populations.

Turtle excluders (left)
When shrimp trawl nets are equipped with turtle excluder devices (TEDs) like those shown here, sea turtles (such as this loggerhead) caught in the nets are shunted back out.

Monitoring reef health (above)
Scientists celebrate the set-up of a Coral Reef Early Warning System (CREWS) station in the Caribbean Sea. These sites gather meteorological and oceanographic data at sensitive areas, then transmit via satellite. The data is used to create forecasts of coral bleaching and upwelling.

⚡ Leatherback sea turtles

Leatherbacks (*Dermochelys coriacea*) have a thick, leathery skin instead of hard scutes and grow to about 7 feet (2 m). They range through much of the global sea, with nesting beaches concentrated in the tropics and subtropics. The largest of living marine reptiles, leatherbacks are critically endangered due mainly to intensive human consumption of their eggs and meat. Conservation efforts focus on halting and possibly reversing the decline. Satellite tracking allows researchers to monitor a leatherback's diving behavior and travel patterns. The tag, attached to a harness, feeds information to a satellite.

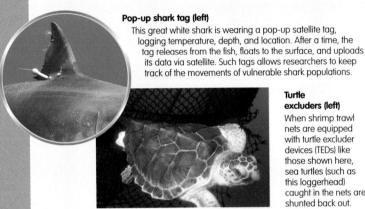

DECLINE OF LEATHERBACKS

Nesters: 3,000 / 2,000 / 1,000 / 0

Year: 1965 1970 1975 1980 1985 1990 1995 2000

— Leatherback turtle populations
···· Missing data

Numbering (above)
Numbers painted onto a sea turtle's back allow scientists to identify it after it is released back into the wild.

Marine Heritage sites

UNESCO designates protected Marine Heritage sites in coastal areas around the globe. The more than 40 sites are selected for their outstanding natural and/or cultural significance. Site personnel receive training and support for state-of-the-science management methods to counter damage to the world's marine environments. For a complete list of sites, turn to page 259.

Ogasawara Islands (above)
Japan's remote Ogasawara Islands were designated a Marine Heritage site in 2011. These 30 or so tropical and subtropical islands lie around 600 miles (1,000 km) south of Tokyo. Many species on the islands have undergone unique evolutionary processes, earning the islands the nickname "Galápagos of the Orient."

Great Barrier Reef
The Great Barrier Reef of Australia is the world's largest coral reef system. It consists of hundreds of islands and nearly 3,000 separate reefs. It has been designated a Marine Heritage site since 1981.

Giant's Causeway
A Marine Heritage site since 1986, the Giant's Causeway, located on the coast of Northern Ireland, consists of more than 4,000 basalt blocks formed by volcanic activity.

Ha Long Bay
The shimmering seawaters of Ha Long Bay in Vietnam encompass several thousand intriguingly shaped limestone islands. It has been a Marine Heritage site since 1984.

Cocos Island
The coral reef of Cocos Island, Costa Rica, is renowned for its sea life including whale sharks and hammerhead sharks, and fish such as these snapper. Its biodiversity led to its going on the Marine Heritage list in 1997.

CHAPTER SEVEN

ARCTIC OCEAN

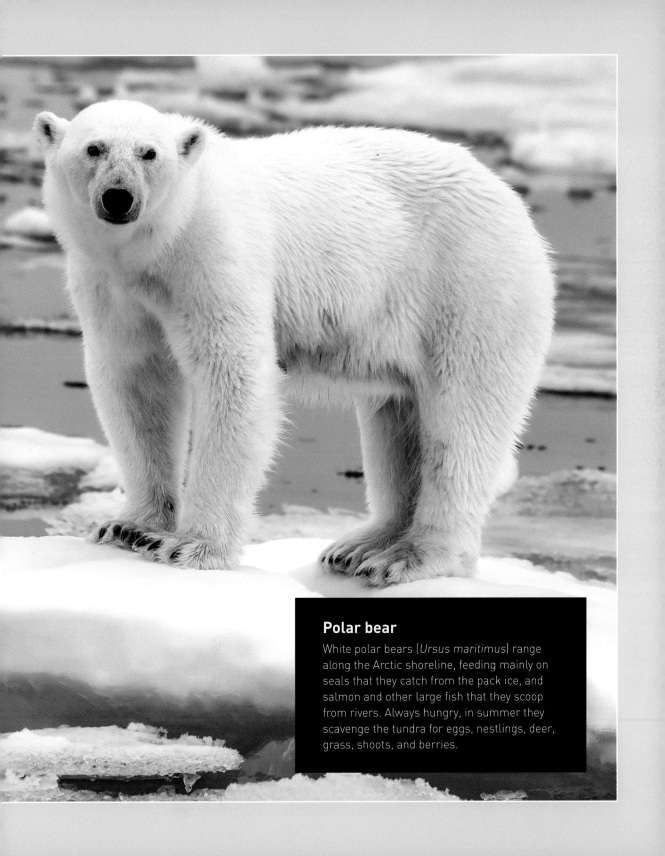

Polar bear

White polar bears (*Ursus maritimus*) range along the Arctic shoreline, feeding mainly on seals that they catch from the pack ice, and salmon and other large fish that they scoop from rivers. Always hungry, in summer they scavenge the tundra for eggs, nestlings, deer, grass, shoots, and berries.

ARCTIC OCEAN

In the sixteenth and seventeenth centuries, ship-borne explorers heading north from Europe on early spring voyages soon found themselves among dangerous sea ice. Was there an Arctic Ocean, and could it be crossed to reach the wealth of China and the Indies? Penetrating the fringe seas east and west of Greenland, early Dutch and British explorers brought home tales of hardship. Those that headed northeast toward Russia, favored by warm currents from the north Atlantic Ocean, became the first Europeans to enter the Arctic Ocean. The "Northeast Passage" to China evaded them. The ocean was first crossed by Nansen's ship *Fram* in 1893–96.

THE FACTS	
Area	5.4 million square miles (14.1 million km²)
Average depth	4,690 feet (1,430 m)
Maximum depth	18,455 feet (5,625 m)
Maximum width	2,000 miles (3,200 km)
Maximum length	3,100 miles (5,000 km)

OCEAN SHARE

All other oceans

Arctic Ocean
5.4 million sq miles
(14.1 million km²)
4%

- ⤙ Fishing
- ⤙ Shellfish
- ✕ Mining
- 🛢 Oil production
- ♂ Gas production

BATHYMETRIC DEPTHS

Feet	Meters
Sea level	Sea level
656	200
1640	500
3281	1000
6562	2000
9842	3000
13,123	4000
16,404	5000
19,685	6000
26,246	8000

NATURAL RESOURCES (above)
There are rich fisheries in the Barents, Greenland, and Bering Seas. Seals are still hunted commercially throughout the Arctic; whales are hunted off Norway; and Inuit communities take small numbers of whales and seals locally. Northern Siberia and Alaska have huge reserves of oil, coal, and gas.

Walrus herd (below)
Walrus (*Odobenus rosmarus*) feed mainly on clams, which they seek in the mud of the nearshore seabed, using their whiskers as sensors and their tusks as rakes. Many thousands of walruses have been killed commercially for the solid ivory in their tusks, and for their tough leather hides.

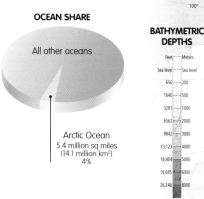

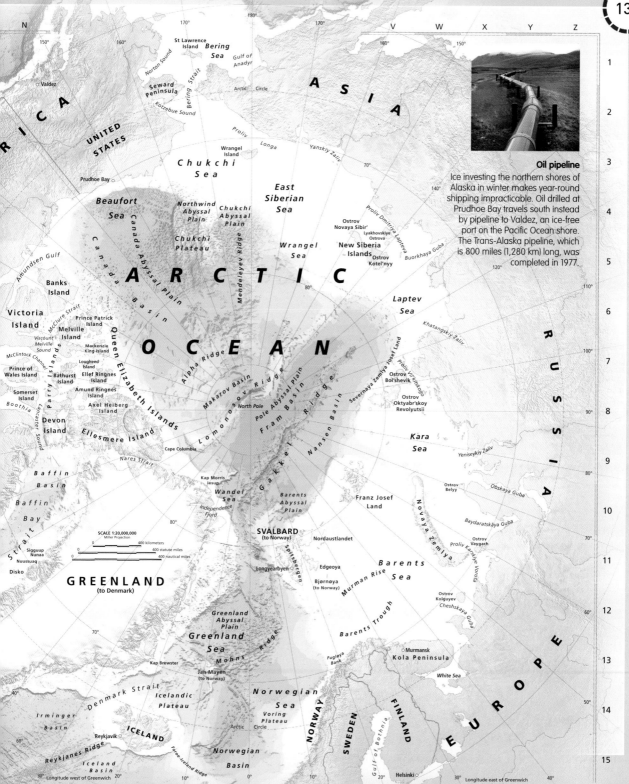

N

ARCTIC OCEAN

ASIA

St Lawrence Island
Bering Sea
Gulf of Anadyr
Norton Sound
Seward Peninsula
Bering Strait
Arctic Circle
Kotzebue Sound
Valdez

UNITED STATES

Prudhoe Bay

Chukchi Sea

Proliv Longa
Wrangel Island
Yanskiy Zaliv

East Siberian Sea

Beaufort Sea
Northwind Abyssal Plain
Chukchi Abyssal Plain
Chukchi Plateau

Canada Abyssal Plain
Canada Basin

Wrangel Sea

Ostrov Novaya Sibir'
Lyakhovskiye Ostrova
Proliv Dmitriya Lapteva
New Siberia Islands
Ostrov Kotel'nyy
Buorkhaya Guba

ARCTIC

Amundsen Gulf
Banks Island
Victoria Island
Prince Patrick Island
Melville Island
McClure Strait
Viscount Melville Sound
Mackenzie King Island
Lougheed Island
Ellef Ringnes Island
Amund Ringnes Island
Axel Heiberg Island
Queen Elizabeth Islands
Prince of Wales Island
Bathurst Island
Somerset Island
Boothia
Lancaster Sound
McClintock Channel
Parry Islands
Devon Island
Ellesmere Island

Mendeleyev Ridge

OCEAN

Alpha Ridge
North Pole
Makarov Basin
Lomonosov Ridge
Pole Abyssal Plain
Fram Basin
Gakkel Ridge
Nansen Basin

Laptev Sea

Khatangskiy Zaliv
Ostrov Bol'shevik
Proliv Vil'kitskogo
Severnaya Zemlya
Ostrov Oktyabr'skoy Revolyutsii

Kara Sea

Yeniseyskiy Zaliv
Obskaya Guba
Ostrov Belyy

RUSSIA

Cape Columbia
Nares Strait
Kap Morris Jesup
Wandel Sea
Independence Fjord
Barents Abyssal Plain
Franz Josef Land

Baffin Basin
Baffin Bay
Strait
Sigguup Nunaa
Disko

Greenland Abyssal Plain
Greenland Sea

SVALBARD (to Norway)
Nordaustlandet
Spitsbergen
Longyearbyen
Edgeoya
Bjørnøya (to Norway)
Murman Rise

Novaya Zemlya
Proliv Karskiye Vorota
Baydaratskaya Guba
Ostrov Vaygach

Barents Sea
Barents Trough
Ostrov Kolguyev
Cheshskaya Guba

GREENLAND
(to Denmark)

Kap Brewster
Mohns Ridge
Jan Mayen (to Norway)

Fugloya Bank
Murmansk
Kola Peninsula
White Sea

Denmark Strait
Icelandic Plateau
Kap Brewster

Norwegian Sea
Voring Plateau

EUROPE

Irminger Basin
Reykjavik
Reykjanes Ridge
ICELAND
Iceland Basin
Faroe-Iceland Ridge

Arctic Circle

Norwegian Basin

NORWAY
SWEDEN
FINLAND
Gulf of Bothnia
Helsinki

SCALE 1:20,000,000
Miller Projection
0   400 kilometers
0   400 statute miles
0   400 nautical miles

80° 70° 60° 50° 40°
30° Longitude west of Greenwich 20° 10° 0° 10° 20° 30° Longitude east of Greenwich 40°

Oil pipeline
Ice investing the northern shores of Alaska in winter makes year-round shipping impracticable. Oil drilled at Prudhoe Bay travels south instead by pipeline to Valdez, an ice-free port on the Pacific Ocean shore. The Trans-Alaska pipeline, which is 800 miles (1,280 km) long, was completed in 1977.

V W X Y Z
1 2 3 4 5 6 7 8 9 10 11 12 13 14 15

EAST OF GREENLAND

The seas and coasts east of Greenland are warmed by surface waters of the North Atlantic Drift—the northernmost branch of the Gulf Stream—which extends far into the Kara Sea. Without the North Atlantic Drift, Britain, Iceland, and Norway would be as cold in winter as Labrador and Newfoundland. The admixture of cold and warm currents brings fertility to the surface waters. Deep-sea fishing for cod and prawns brings prosperity to most neighboring countries. Seabed gas and oil command continuing interest.

Hammerfest, Norway (above)
Since the sixteenth century, North Europeans have exploited the huge stocks of cod, herring, and other fish of cold North Atlantic and Arctic fringe waters. Today commercial fishing boats continue to hunt for reduced stocks, working within scientifically managed limits.

Kittiwakes (above)
Crags and cliffs of hundreds of rocky islands provide breeding space, and the cold oceans provide rich feeding grounds, for these kittiwakes (*Rissa sp.*) and many other species of seabirds. This group has been foraging among the broken ice and open water in front of an active glacier.

SURFACE CURRENTS (right)
Strong surface currents leave the polar basin, carrying streams of old sea ice and icebergs southward between Greenland, Svalbard, and the Siberian islands, and blocking and chilling harbors along the coasts. Warm currents from the North Atlantic keep the shores of Iceland and Norway relatively ice-free.

→ East Greenland Current
→ East Spitsbergen Current
→ Irminger Current
→ Norwegian Atlantic Current

GREENLAND

Narsarsuaq
Ammassalik
Kap Farvel
Ittoqqortoormiit
Kap Brewster
Daneborg

Irminger Basin
Denmark Strait
Greenland–Iceland Rise
Spar Fracture Zone
Jan Mayen Fracture Zone
Mohn
Kolbeinsey Ridge
Jan Mayen
Icelandic Plateau
Jan Mayen Ridge
Reykjanes Ridge
REYKJAVÍK
ICELAND
Vík
Arctic Circle
Aegir Ridge
Faroe–Iceland Ridge
Norwegian Sea
Vøring
Faroe–Shetland Trough
Faroe Islands
Shetland Islands
Ålesund
Bergen
North Sea

D E F G H I J K L M

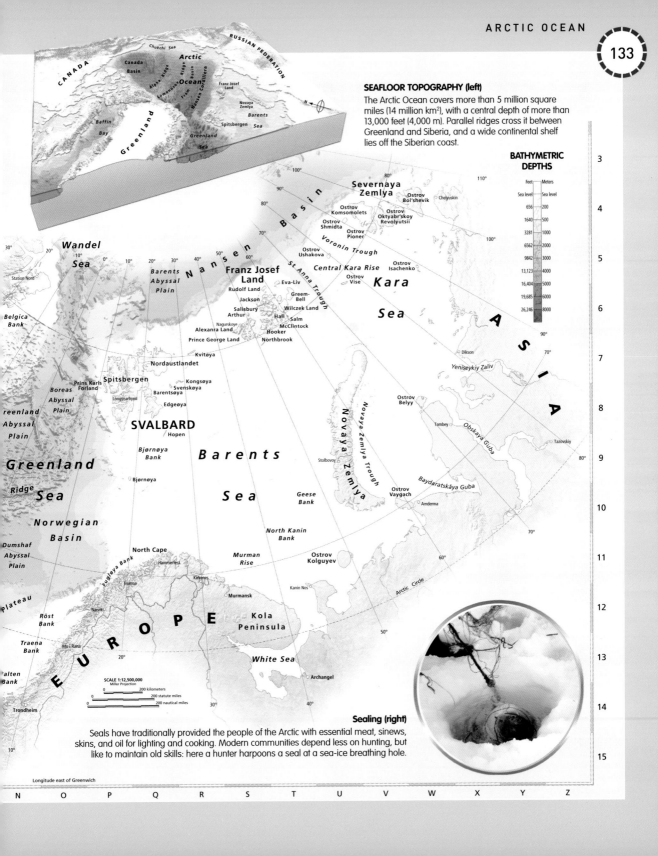

SEAFLOOR TOPOGRAPHY (left)
The Arctic Ocean covers more than 5 million square miles (14 million km²), with a central depth of more than 13,000 feet (4,000 m). Parallel ridges cross it between Greenland and Siberia, and a wide continental shelf lies off the Siberian coast.

BATHYMETRIC DEPTHS

Feet	Meters
Sea level	Sea level
656	200
1640	500
3281	1000
6562	2000
9842	3000
13,123	4000
16,404	5000
19,685	6000
26,246	8000

Seafloor topography inset labels: CANADA, Chukchi Sea, Arctic Ocean, RUSSIAN FEDERATION, Canada Basin, Alpha Ridge, Lomonosov Ridge, Nansen Cordillera, Fram Basin, Franz Josef Land, Novaya Zemlya, Baffin Bay, Greenland, Spitsbergen, Barents Sea, Greenland Sea, N

Main map labels:
Wandel Sea, Station Nord, Belgica Bank, Greenland Abyssal Plain, Boreas Abyssal Plain, Greenland Sea, Greenland Ridge, Norwegian Basin, Dumshaf Abyssal Plain, plateau, Röst Bank, Traena Bank, alten Bank, Trondheim, EUROPE, Mo i Rana, Narvik, Tromsø, Fugløya Bank, North Cape, Hammerfest, Kirkenes, Murmansk, Kola Peninsula, White Sea, Archangel, Kanin Nos, Murman Rise, North Kanin Bank, Geese Bank, North Cape, Barents Sea, Bjørnøya Bank, Bjørnøya, Hopen, SVALBARD, Prins Karls Forland, Spitsbergen, Longyearbyen, Nordaustlandet, Kvitøya, Kongsøya, Svenskøya, Barentsøya, Edgeøya, Prince George Land, Alexanra Land, Nagurskoye, Northbrook, Hooker, Salm, McClintock, Hall, Salisbury, Arthur, Wilczek Land, Jackson, Greem-Bell, Eva-Liv, Rudolf Land, Franz Josef Land, Barents Abyssal Plain, Nansen Basin, St Anna Trough, Central Kara Rise, Voronin Trough, Ostrov Ushakova, Ostrov Vise, Ostrov Isachenko, Ostrov Pioner, Ostrov Shmidta, Ostrov Komsomolets, Ostrov Oktyabr'skoy Revolyutsii, Ostrov Bol'shevik, Chelyuskin, Severnaya Zemlya, Kara Sea, Ostrov Belyy, Dikson, Yeniseykiy Zaliv, ASIA, Tambey, Obskaya Guba, Tazovskiy, Novaya Zemlya Trough, Novaya Zemlya, Stolbovoy, Ostrov Vaygach, Baydaratskaya Guba, Ostrov Kolguyev, Ostrov Belyy, Amderma, Arctic Circle

Longitude east of Greenwich

SCALE 1:12,500,000
Miller Projection
200 kilometers
200 statute miles
200 nautical miles

Sealing (right)
Seals have traditionally provided the people of the Arctic with essential meat, sinews, skins, and oil for lighting and cooking. Modern communities depend less on hunting, but like to maintain old skills: here a hunter harpoons a seal at a sea-ice breathing hole.

NORTHWEST PASSAGES

When geographers thought it likely that an ocean surrounded the North Pole, the search for the shortest sea route to China and the Indies began. Explorers sailing north from Europe found concentrated ice off Svalbard. Sailing northeast brought them little farther than Russia's Kola Peninsula. Exploration to the northwest was more promising: voyages by Davis, Baffin, and Hudson in the late sixteenth and early seventeenth centuries took them as far as Baffin Bay. Not until the early twentieth century was the passage to the Bering Sea completed in a single voyage, by the Norwegian explorer Roald Amundsen.

SURFACE CURRENTS (left)

Cold surface currents carry icebergs and sea ice northward along the west Greenland coast toward Baffin Bay, to be joined by colder, ice-filled water from the polar basin. Baffin Bay and central Davis Strait contain year-round ice that drifts south with the Baffin Island and Labrador Currents.

→ Baffin Island Current
→ Labrador Current
→ West Greenland Current

Drifting icebergs (below)

Icebergs and pack ice drift south constantly from the Arctic. Remnants like these may reach shipping lanes, where they can become a danger to shipping. In 1912, the *Titanic* was lost to an iceberg from Davis Strait. Satellite monitoring now reduces the risk considerably.

Whaling (above)

North European ships, particularly German, Dutch, and British, hunted Arctic whales from the seventeenth to the twentieth century, bringing home blubber for oil and baleen ("whalebone") for corset stays. Harpooning a 40-foot (12-m) whale from an open boat was a hazardous business.

BATHYMETRIC DEPTHS

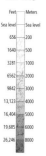

Feet	Meters
Sea level	Sea level
656	200
1640	500
3281	1000
6562	2000
9842	3000
13,123	4000
16,404	5000
19,685	6000
26,246	8000

Beaufort Sea
Queen
Prince Patrick Island
Lands End
Mackenzie King Island
Eglinton Island
Hazen
Cape Prince Alfred
Parry
McClure Strait
Melville Island
Cape Bathurst
Ikaahuk
Banks Island
Thesiger Bay
Passage Point
Viscount Melville Sound
Amundsen Gulf
Prince of Wales Strait
Prince Albert Peninsula
Stefansson Island
Paulatuk
Uluqsaqtuuq
Storkerson Peninsula
McClintock Channel
Prince Albert Sound
Victoria Island
Wollaston Peninsula
Kugluktuk
Collinson Peninsula
Coronation Gulf
Cambridge Bay
Umingmaktok
Queen Maud Gulf
C
A
N
Bathurst Inlet

G   H   I   J   K   L   M

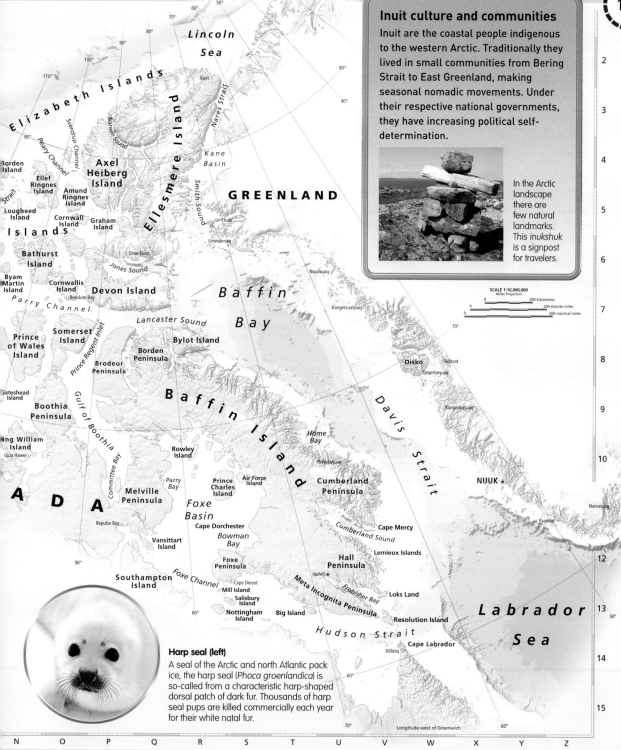

Inuit culture and communities

Inuit are the coastal people indigenous to the western Arctic. Traditionally they lived in small communities from Bering Strait to East Greenland, making seasonal nomadic movements. Under their respective national governments, they have increasing political self-determination.

In the Arctic landscape there are few natural landmarks. This *inukshuk* is a signpost for travelers.

SCALE 1:10,000,000
Miller Projection

0   200 kilometers
0   200 statute miles
0   200 nautical miles

Lincoln Sea

Elizabeth Islands

Alert

Nares Strait

Ellesmere Island

Axel Heiberg Island

Mansen Sound

Sverdrup Channel

Peary Channel

Borden Island

Ellef Ringnes Island

Amund Ringnes Island

Cornwall Island

Graham Island

Lougheed Island

Strait

Islands

Kane Basin

Smith Sound

GREENLAND

Thule

Ummannaq

Grise Fiord

Bathurst Island

Byam Martin Island

Cornwallis Island

Devon Island

Resolute Bay

Jones Sound

Nuussuaq

Parry Channel

Baffin Bay

Kangersuatsiaq

Lancaster Sound

Prince of Wales Island

Somerset Island

Bylot Island

Borden Peninsula

Bylot Island

Brodeur Peninsula

Disko
Ilulissat
Qeqertarsuaq

Gateshead Island

Baffin Island

Kangerlussuaq

Boothia Peninsula

Gulf of Boothia

ing William Island

Gjoa Haven

Rowley Island

Home Bay

Qikiqtarjuaq

Davis Strait

Committee Bay

Melville Peninsula

Parry Bay

Prince Charles Island

Air Force Island

Cumberland Peninsula

NUUK

Narsasuaq

A

D

A

Repulse Bay

Foxe Basin

Cape Dorchester

Bowman Bay

Cumberland Sound

Cape Mercy

Lemieux Islands

Paamiut

Vansittart Island

Foxe Peninsula

Hall Peninsula

Southampton Island

Foxe Channel

Cape Dorset

Mill Island

Iqaluit

Frobisher Bay

Meta Incognita Peninsula

Loks Land

Labrador Sea

Salisbury Island

Nottingham Island

Big Island

Resolution Island

Hudson Strait

Cape Labrador

Killiniq

Harp seal (left)

A seal of the Arctic and north Atlantic pack ice, the harp seal (*Phoca groenlandica*) is so-called from a characteristic harp-shaped dorsal patch of dark fur. Thousands of harp seal pups are killed commercially each year for their white natal fur.

Longitude west of Greenwich

N   O   P   Q   R   S   T   U   V   W   X   Y   Z

CHAPTER EIGHT

SOUTHERN OCEAN

Penguins

Penguins relax on a wave-sculpted iceberg of the Southern Ocean. Ice covers both polar oceans in winter, melting and breaking up in spring to release nutrients and surface food. On this annual bonanza depend the fish, seals, whales, and seabirds abundant in polar oceans both north and south. Icebergs provide sanctuary away from land for penguins and other seabirds.

SOUTHERN OCEAN

Some call it the Antarctic Ocean, but Captain James Cook, RN, the explorer who defined it in the 1770s, called it the Southern Ocean. Its northern oceanographic limit is the Antarctic Convergence or Polar Front, where cold waters spreading north from Antarctica pass beneath warmer subtropical waters. Its southern limit is Antarctica itself. Of the total area, a high proportion is frozen over every winter, pack ice sometimes extending as far north as the Antarctic Convergence. In summer, pack ice persists in coastal areas.

Map labels: Falkland, 50°, North, Falkland Islands, 60°, SOUTH AMERICA, ARGENTINA, Tierra del Fuego, Punta Arenas, 70°, CHILE, Drake Passage, Mornington Abyssal Plain, 80°, Southeast, 90°, 100°, 110°

THE FACTS

Area	7.8 million square miles (20.3 million km²)
Average depth	14,750 feet (4,500 m)
Maximum depth	24,032 feet (7,325 m)
Maximum width	1,700 miles (2,700 km)
Maximum length	13,400 miles (21,500 km)

OCEAN SHARE

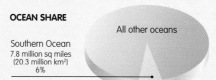

All other oceans

Southern Ocean
7.8 million sq miles
(20.3 million km²)
6%

Polynyas: ice-free pockets

In both polar oceans, areas called polynas remain ice-free even in mid-winter. They may be formed by strong winds blowing freshly formed ice away, or by water at temperatures above freezing upwelling from below. They are important to wildlife, allowing whales and seals to breathe and birds to feed throughout the year.

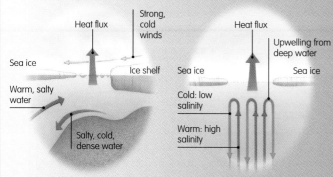

Left diagram labels: Heat flux, Strong, cold winds, Sea ice, Ice shelf, Warm, salty water, Salty, cold, dense water

Right diagram labels: Heat flux, Upwelling from deep water, Sea ice, Cold: low salinity, Warm: high salinity, Sea ice

Wind-formed polynyas
These occur where strong downslope winds from land keep thin, newly formed sea ice moving.

Upwelling polynyas
These occur on the open sea or channels where relatively warm vertical currents erode sea ice as fast as it forms.

Crabeater seals (below)
Crabeater seals (*Lobodon carcinophagus*) breed on Antarctic pack ice. They feed on shoals of tiny shrimps that swarm in Antarctic waters in summer, filtering them through their trilobed teeth.

NATURAL RESOURCES

The Southern Ocean has no exploited seabed minerals, and mineral prospecting and development are prohibited within the area of the Antarctic Treaty (south of 60°S). Past industries have been based on a wealth of fur seals and whales. Currently the region's resources support deep-sea fishing and tourism.

Fishing
Tourism

J K L M

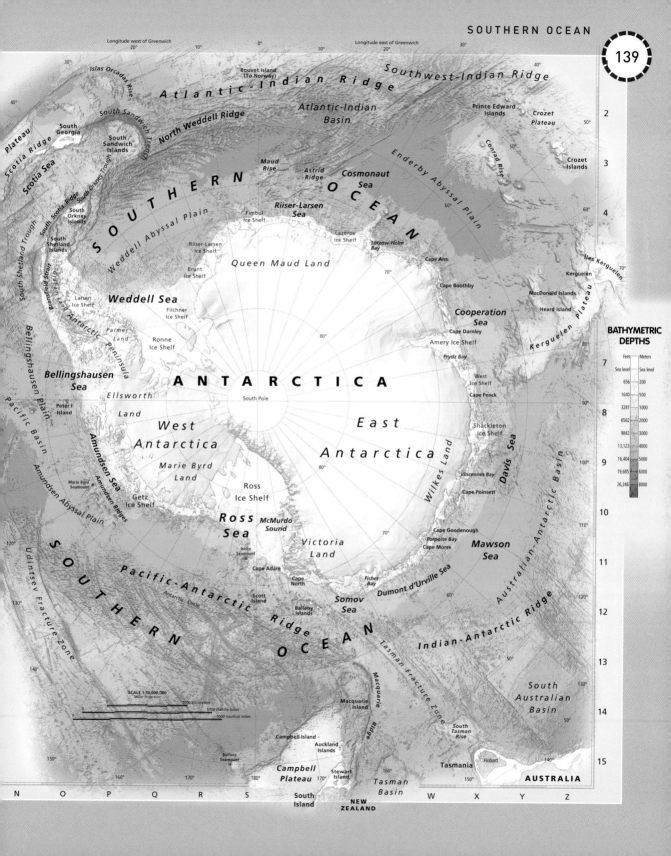

Longitude west of Greenwich
Longitude east of Greenwich

Islas Orcadas Rise
Bouvet Island (To Norway)
Southwest-Indian Ridge
Atlantic-Indian Ridge
Prince Edward Islands
Crozet Plateau

Plateau
South Georgia
Scotia Ridge
South Sandwich Trench
South Sandwich Islands
North Weddell Ridge
Atlantic-Indian Basin
Conrad Rise
Crozet Islands

Scotia Sea
South Scotia Ridge
South Orkney Trough
South Orkney Islands
Maud Rise
Astrid Ridge
Cosmonaut Sea
Enderby Abyssal Plain

South Shetland Trough
South Shetland Islands
Weddell Abyssal Plain
Riiser-Larsen Sea
Fimbul Ice Shelf
Lazerov Ice Shelf
Lützow-Holm Bay
Cape Ann
Iles Kerguelen
Kerguelen

SOUTHERN OCEAN

Bransfield Strait
Graham Land
Riiser-Larsen Ice Shelf
Queen Maud Land
Cape Boothby
MacDonald Islands
Heard Island

Larsen Ice Shelf
Weddell Sea
Brunt Ice Shelf
Cape Darnley
Cooperation Sea
Kerguelen Plateau

Palmer Land
Antarctic Peninsula
Filchner Ice Shelf
Ronne Ice Shelf
Amery Ice Shelf
Prydz Bay

Bellingshausen Plain
Ellsworth Land
ANTARCTICA
South Pole
West Ice Shelf
Cape Penck

Peter I Island
West Antarctica
East Antarctica
Shackleton Ice Shelf

Pacific Basin
Bellingshausen Sea
Marie Byrd Land
Wilkes Land
Davis Sea
Australian-Antarctic Basin

Amundsen Ridges
Marie Byrd Seamount
Amundsen Sea
Ross Ice Shelf
Vincennes Bay
Cape Poinsett

Getz Ice Shelf
Ross Sea
McMurdo Sound
Cape Goodenough
Porpoise Bay
Cape Morse
Mawson Sea

Amundsen Abyssal Plain
Iselin Seamount
Victoria Land
Dumont d'Urville Sea

Udintsev Fracture Zone
SOUTHERN OCEAN
Pacific-Antarctic Ridge
Cape Adare
Scott Island
Cape North
Balleny Islands
Somov Sea
Fisher Bay
Indian-Antarctic Ridge

Antarctic Circle
Tasman Fracture Zone
South Australian Basin

Macquarie Ridge
Macquarie Island

SCALE 1:30,000,000
Miller Projection
1000 kilometers
1000 statute miles
1000 nautical miles

South Tasman Rise
Campbell Island
Auckland Islands
Tasmania
Hobart
AUSTRALIA

Bollons Seamount
Campbell Plateau
Stewart Island
Tasman Basin
South Island
NEW ZEALAND

BATHYMETRIC DEPTHS

Feet	Meters
Sea level	Sea level
656	200
1640	500
3281	1000
6562	2000
9842	3000
13,123	4000
16,404	5000
19,685	6000
26,246	8000

N O P Q R S W X Y Z

ANTARCTIC PENINSULA

The Antarctic Peninsula and the islands of the Scotia Arc form stepping stones between South America and West Antarctica—a path first traced by early nineteenth-century sealers, and now followed each summer by thousands of cruise ship tourists. Geologically the peninsula is a southern extension of the Andes. It is much warmer year-round than continental Antarctica and has richer vegetation. The Weddell Sea, east of the peninsula, is renowned for its circulating pack ice that destroyed Shackleton's expedition ship *Endurance*.

Peninsula scenery (left)

While more than 95 percent of Antarctica's coastal scenery is ice cliffs, with no mountains visible, the west coast of the Antarctic Peninsula features spectacular mountains, islands, and channels, which in recent years have made it a major tourist attraction. Piedmont ice cliffs and glaciers line the shores.

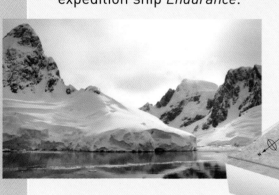

SEAFLOOR TOPOGRAPHY (left)

This image shows the Antarctic Peninsula, with the off-lying chain of South Shetland Islands to the right. The Weddell Sea (left) is lined with ice shelves ending in ice cliffs.

SURFACE CURRENTS (below)

The predominantly westward-flowing Antarctic Coastal Current, encountering the eastern shore of the peninsula, fills the Weddell Sea with a massive, persistent gyre of multi-year sea ice. This rotates southward along the Coats Land coast, and packs northward-moving masses of ice tightly against the peninsula flank.

⟶ Antarctic Circumpolar Current
⟶ Antarctic Coastal Current
⟶ Weddell Sea Gyre

Cruise ships (above)

Smaller tourist cruise ships like this one land their passengers at penguin colonies and other points of interest. Bigger ships carrying more than 500 passengers cruise the scenic waterways but make no landings.

Farwell Island
Thurston Island
Sherman Island
King Peninsula
Pine Island Bay
Abbot Ice Shelf
Eights Coast
Walgreen Coast
90°
100°
110°

I   J   K   L   M

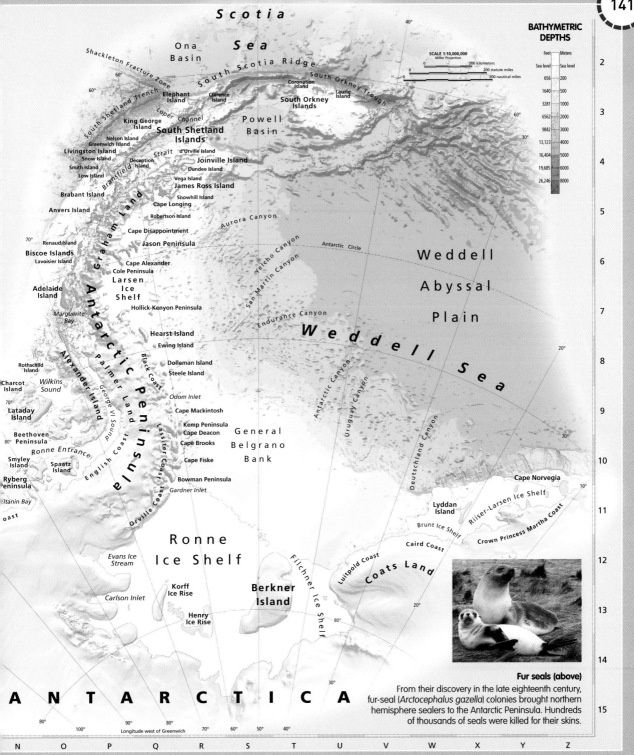

Scotia Sea

Ona Basin

Shackleton Fracture Zone

South Scotia Ridge

South Orkney Trough

Coronation Island

Elephant Island

Clarence Island

South Orkney Islands

Laurie Island

South Shetland Trench

Loper Channel

King George Island

South Shetland Islands

Powell Basin

Nelson Island

Greenwich Island

Livingston Island

Snow Island

Smith Island

Low Island

d'Urville Island

Strait

Deception Island

Joinville Island

Dundee Island

Vega Island

James Ross Island

Bransfield

Brabant Island

Snowhill Island

Cape Longing

Anvers Island

Robertson Island

Cape Disappointment

Aurora Canyon

Antarctic Circle

Weddell

Renaud Island

Jason Peninsula

Biscoe Islands

Cape Alexander

Lavoisier Island

Cole Peninsula

Larsen Ice Shelf

Abyssal

Yelcho Canyon

San Martin Canyon

Plain

Adelaide Island

Hollick-Kenyon Peninsula

Marguerite Bay

Endurance Canyon

Weddell Sea

Hearst Island

Ewing Island

Rothschild Island

Dolleman Island

Charcot Island

Wilkins Sound

Steele Island

Antarctic Canyon

Uruguay Canyon

Lataday Island

Odom Inlet

Cape Mackintosh

General Belgrano Bank

Deutschland Canyon

Beethoven Peninsula

Kemp Peninsula

Cape Deacon

Ronne Entrance

Cape Brooks

Smyley Island

Spaatz Island

Cape Fiske

Cape Norvegia

Ryberg Peninsula

Bowman Peninsula

Gardner Inlet

Lyddan Island

Riiser-Larsen Ice Shelf

Eltanin Bay

Brunt Ice Shelf

Crown Princess Martha Coast

Coast

Ronne Ice Shelf

Caird Coast

Coats Land

Evans Ice Stream

Luitpold Coast

Korff Ice Rise

Berkner Island

Filchner Ice Shelf

Carlson Inlet

Henry Ice Rise

ANTARCTICA

Graham Land

Antarctic Peninsula

Palmer Land

Alexander Island

George VI Sound

Black Coast

Lassiter Coast

English Coast

Orville Coast

BATHYMETRIC DEPTHS

Feet	Meters
Sea level	Sea level
656	200
1640	500
3281	1000
6562	2000
9842	3000
13,123	4000
16,404	5000
19,685	6000
26,246	8000

SCALE 1:10,000,000
Miller Projection

Fur seals (above)
From their discovery in the late eighteenth century, fur-seal (*Arctocephalus gazella*) colonies brought northern hemisphere sealers to the Antarctic Peninsula. Hundreds of thousands of seals were killed for their skins.

Longitude west of Greenwich

ROSS SEA

One of two great embayments in the flanks of Antarctica, the Ross Sea was discovered by Captain James Clark Ross, RN, on a Royal Navy expedition of 1841. Despite its high latitude, circulation of pack ice within the sea allows ships of minimal icebreaking capacity to reach 78°S, making it a gateway for land expeditions, such as those led by Scott, Shackleton, Amundsen, Borchgrevink, and Byrd. The southern limit of the sea is the Ross Ice Shelf, a floating sheet of glacier ice that descends from the high plateau of central Antarctica and terminates in a continuous ice cliff 500 miles (800 km) long.

Shackleton's team (below)
Ernest Shackleton (center left) and three companions in 1908–09 discovered a route from McMurdo Sound, in the southwestern Ross Sea, via Beardmore Glacier to the South Pole. The route is today used by US tractor trains to replenish Amundsen-Scott, the permanent US South Pole station.

Emperor penguins (right)
Largest of all living penguins, emperor penguins (*Aptenodytes forsteri*) live in Antarctic coastal colonies as far south as Cape Crozier, Ross Island, incubating their single eggs on the sea ice in winter, and rearing their chicks through early spring. Fewer than 50 colonies are known around the continent.

McMurdo Station

McMurdo Station was established by the United States in 1955 as the logistical base from which Amundsen-Scott (South Pole) and other Antarctic stations and camps could be established and re-supplied. With some 90 buildings, it is a township with laboratories, workshops, garaging, fuel stores, airstrips, shops, and accommodation for more than 1,000 support staff and scientists.

Ice cliffs (below)
On the southern flank of Ross Island, Windless Bight's heavily glaciated cliffs face the Ross Ice Shelf. It was named by a party from Scott's Terra Nova expedition of 1910–13, who found it an oasis of calm on their otherwise storm-ridden journey to Cape Crozier.

Erected in 1902, this hut was an emergency depot for Scott's expedition ship *Discovery*, which lay frozen in close by. It stands on the edge of McMurdo Station, Antarctica's largest community.

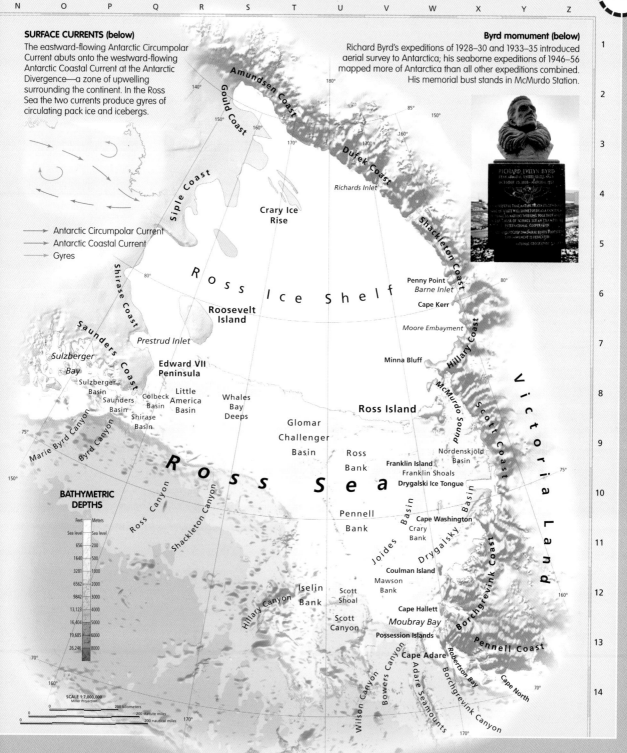

SURFACE CURRENTS (below)
The eastward-flowing Antarctic Circumpolar Current abuts onto the westward-flowing Antarctic Coastal Current at the Antarctic Divergence—a zone of upwelling surrounding the continent. In the Ross Sea the two currents produce gyres of circulating pack ice and icebergs.

→ Antarctic Circumpolar Current
→ Antarctic Coastal Current
→ Gyres

Byrd momument (below)
Richard Byrd's expeditions of 1928–30 and 1933–35 introduced aerial survey to Antarctica; his seaborne expeditions of 1946–56 mapped more of Antarctica than all other expeditions combined. His memorial bust stands in McMurdo Station.

RICHARD EVELYN BYRD
REAR ADMIRAL UNITED STATES NAVY
OCTOBER 25 1888 - MARCH 11 1957

Amundsen Coast
Gould Coast
Dufek Coast
Richards Inlet
Shackleton Coast
Siple Coast
Crary Ice Rise
140°
150°
160°
170°
180°
170°
85°
150°
160°

Ross Ice Shelf
Penny Point
Barne Inlet
Cape Kerr
80°
80°
Shirase Coast
Roosevelt Island
Moore Embayment
Saunders Coast
Prestrud Inlet
Minna Bluff
Hillary Coast
Sulzberger Bay
Edward VII Peninsula
Sulzberger Basin
Little America Basin
Whales Bay Deeps
Saunders Basin
Colbeck Basin
Ross Island
McMurdo Sound
Victoria Land
Shirase Basin
Glomar Challenger Basin
75°
Nordenskjöld Basin
Scott Coast
Marie Byrd Canyon
Byrd Canyon
Ross Bank
Franklin Island
Franklin Shoals
Drygalski Ice Tongue
75°
150°

Ross Sea
Pennell Bank
Cape Washington
Crary Bank

BATHYMETRIC DEPTHS

Feet	Meters
Sea level	Sea level
656	200
1640	500
3281	1000
6562	2000
9842	3000
13,123	4000
16,404	5000
19,685	6000
26,246	8000

Ross Canyon
Shackleton Canyon
Joides Basin
Drygalski Basin
160°
Coulman Island
Mawson Bank
Borchgrevink Coast
Iselin Bank
Scott Shoal
Cape Hallett
Moubray Bay
Hillary Canyon
Scott Canyon
Possession Islands
Pennell Coast
Cape Adare
Robertson Bay
Cape North
70°
70°
Wilson Canyon
Bowers Canyon
Adare Seamounts
Borchgrevink Canyon
Cape North

SCALE 1:7,000,000
Miller Projection
160°
200 kilometers
200 statute miles
200 nautical miles
170°

Longitude west of Greenwich   180°   Longitude east of Greenwich

ATLANTIC OCEAN

Great cormorant

The great cormorant (*Phalacrocorax carbo*) is found throughout the world, with a sub-species that inhabits estuaries around the North Atlantic. In North America the only breeding colonies are found in the Canadian maritime provinces, with most found around the shores of the Gulf of St. Lawrence. Great cormorants are excellent swimmers and divers, with dives in deep water lasting up to a minute or more.

ATLANTIC OCEAN

The Atlantic Ocean covers approximately one-fifth of Earth's surface. It is a relatively young ocean, having been formed about 150 million years ago, and it is still growing. Seafloor spreading from the mid-Atlantic ridge widens it around 1 inch (25 mm) each year. The broad, stable continental shelves around its margins have been a source of wealth for centuries, sustaining fisheries (though many have collapsed) and, more recently, yielding oil and gas.

THE FACTS	
Area	29.7 million square miles (76.8 million km²)
Average depth	11,827 feet (3,605 m)
Maximum depth	28,231 feet (8,605 m)
Maximum width	4,900 miles (7,900 km)
Maximum length	8,770 miles (14,120 km)
Coastline length	69,510 miles (11,866 km)

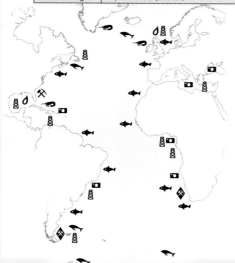

NATURAL RESOURCES (left)

Atlantic fish stocks are supported by nutrient-rich water on the continental shelves, although overfishing has resulted in many species being depleted. Large deposits of oil and gas are being exploited in coastal waters. Sand, gravels, and precious minerals are mined on many Atlantic shores.

- 🐟 Fishing
- 🐋 Whales
- 🦐 Shellfish
- ◆ Metallic minerals
- ⛏ Mining
- 🛢 Oil production
- 🛢 Gas production
- 📷 Tourism

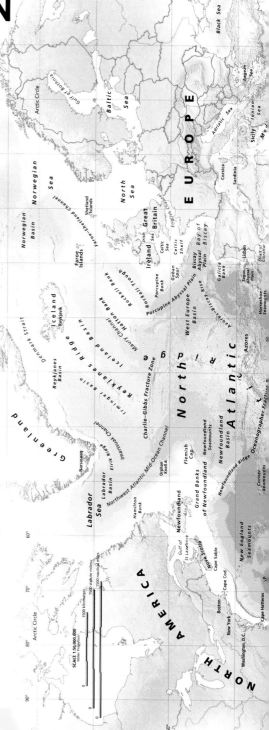

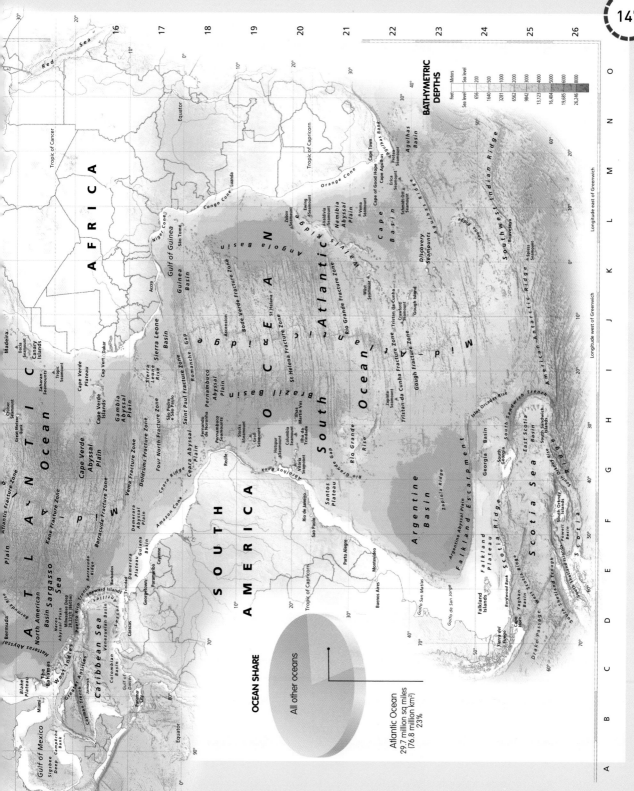

BATHYMETRIC DEPTHS

Feet	Meters
Sea level	Sea level
656	200
1640	500
3281	1000
6562	2000
9842	3000
13,123	4000
16,404	5000
19,685	6000
26,246	8000

OCEAN SHARE

Atlantic Ocean
29.7 million sq miles
(76.8 million km²)
23%

All other oceans

NORTHERN ATLANTIC OCEAN

Warm water from the Gulf of Mexico and Caribbean is carried north along the east coast of North America as the Gulf Stream. It meets the cold waters of the Labrador Current off Newfoundland, giving rise to the fogs of the Grand Banks. Some of the warmer water continues east as the North Atlantic Drift, creating the relatively warm and wet climate of northwest Europe.

Hermit crab (left)
Hermit crabs are found from the shoreline to the depths. Unlike other crustaceans, they have a soft abdomen, which they protect by living in discarded shells. They move to larger shells as they grow.

NATURAL RESOURCES

- Fishing
- Whales
- Shellfish
- Mining
- Oil production
- Gas production
- Tourism

SURFACE CURRENTS (below)

The surface current systems in the North Atlantic form a clockwise gyre comprising the well-defined and fast moving northward Gulf Stream, the more diffuse eastward North Atlantic Drift, the cold southward Canary Current, and the westward North Equatorial Current, which completes the loop.

- Gulf Stream
- North Atlantic Drift
- Norwegian Current
- Labrador Current
- East & West Greenland Current
- Portugal Current
- Canaries Current
- North Equatorial Current
- South Equatorial Current
- Antilles Current

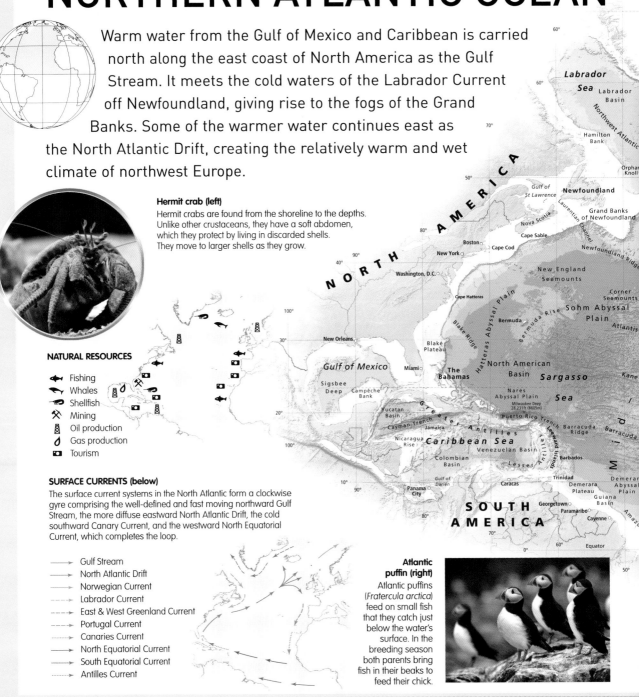

Atlantic puffin (right)
Atlantic puffins (*Fratercula arctica*) feed on small fish that they catch just below the water's surface. In the breeding season both parents bring fish in their beaks to feed their chick.

Labrador Sea · Labrador Basin · Northwest Atlantic · Hamilton Bank · Orphan Knoll · Gulf of St Lawrence · Newfoundland · Nova Scotia · Laurentian Channel · Grand Banks of Newfoundland · Cape Sable · Newfoundland Ridge · Boston · Cape Cod · New York · Washington, D.C. · Cape Hatteras · New England Seamounts · Corner Seamounts · Bermuda · Bermuda Rise · Sohm Abyssal Plain · Atlantis · Blake Ridge · Hatteras Abyssal Plain · New Orleans · Blake Plateau · Gulf of Mexico · Miami · The Bahamas · North American Basin · Sargasso Sea · Kane · Sigsbee Deep · Campêche Bank · Nares Abyssal Plain · Milwaukee Deep 28,231ft (8605m) · Puerto Rico Trench · Barracuda Ridge · Barracuda · Yucatan Basin · Cayman Trench · Jamaica · Greater Antilles · Leeward Islands · Nicaragua Rise · Caribbean Sea · Venezuelan Basin · Barbados · Colombian Basin · Lesser Antilles · Gulf of Darién · Panama City · Caracas · Trinidad · Demerara Plateau · Demerara Abyssal Plain · Guiana Basin · Georgetown · Paramaribo · Amazon · Cayenne · Panama · NORTH AMERICA · SOUTH AMERICA · Equator

F G H I J K L M

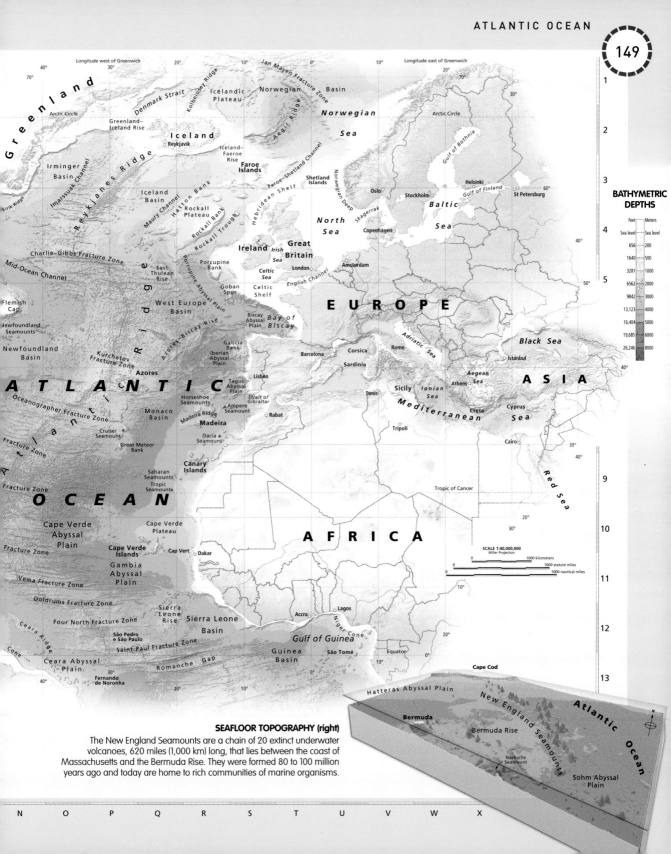

BATHYMETRIC DEPTHS

Feet	Meters
Sea level	Sea level
656	200
1640	500
3281	1000
6562	2000
9842	3000
13,123	4000
16,404	5000
19,685	6000
26,246	8000

Greenland

Longitude west of Greenwich

40° 30° 20° 10°

Jan Mayen Fracture Zone

70°

Arctic Circle

Denmark Strait

Kolbeinsey Ridge

Icelandic Plateau

Norwegian Basin

Longitude east of Greenwich

0° 10°

70°

Arctic Circle

Greenland–Iceland Rise

Iceland

Reykjavik

Icelandic-Faeroe Rise

Norwegian

Sea

Irminger Basin

Imarssuak Channel

Reykjanes Ridge

Faroe Islands

Iceland-Faeroe Rise

Gulf of Bothnia

Eirik Ridge

Iceland Basin

Maury Channel

Hatton Bank

Rockall Plateau

Faroe-Shetland Channel

Hebridean Shelf

Shetland Islands

Norwegian Deep

Oslo

Stockholm

Helsinki

Gulf of Finland

St Petersburg

60°

Charlie-Gibbs Fracture Zone

Rockall Bank

Rockall Trough

Skagerrak

Baltic

Sea

Copenhagen

ASIA

Mid-Ocean Channel

East Thulean Rise

Porcupine Abyssal Plain

Ireland

Irish Sea

Great Britain

North Sea

London

Amsterdam

40°

Flemish Cap

Porcupine Bank

Celtic Sea

English Channel

50°

Newfoundland Seamounts

Goban Spur

Celtic Shelf

EUROPE

Newfoundland Basin

West Europe Basin

Azores-Biscay Rise

Biscay Abyssal Plain

Bay of Biscay

Black Sea

İstanbul

40°

Kurchatov Fracture Zone

Galicia Bank

Barcelona

Corsica

Rome

Adriatic Sea

Athens

Aegean Sea

Cyprus

ATLANTIC

Azores

Iberian Abyssal Plain

Lisbon

Sardinia

Ionian Sea

Crete

30°

Oceanographer Fracture Zone

Mid-Atlantic Ridge

Tagus Abyssal Plain

Horseshoe Seamounts

Strait of Gibraltar

Ampere Seamount

Rabat

Tunis

Sicily

Mediterranean

Tripoli

Cairo

Red Sea

Fracture Zone

Cruiser Seamount

Monaco Basin

Madeira Ridge

Madeira

40°

OCEAN

Great Meteor Bank

Dacia ▲ Seamount

30°

Fracture Zone

Canary Islands

Tropic of Cancer

20°

9

Saharan Seamounts

Tropic Seamount

Cape Verde Plateau

AFRICA

30°

10

Cape Verde Abyssal Plain

Cap Vert

Dakar

Cape Verde Islands

SCALE 1:40,000,000

Miller Projection

Fracture Zone

Gambia Abyssal Plain

0

1000 kilometers

1000 statute miles

1000 nautical miles

11

Vema Fracture Zone

10°

Doldrums Fracture Zone

Sierra Leone Rise

Sierra Leone Basin

Accra

Lagos

Niger Cone

Four North Fracture Zone

20°

12

Ceara Ridge

São Pedro e São Paulo

Saint Paul Fracture Zone

Gulf of Guinea

Guinea Basin

São Tomé

Equator

0°

Cone

Ceara Abyssal Plain

Romanche Gap

30°

Fernando de Noronha

40° 20° 10°

13

SEAFLOOR TOPOGRAPHY (right)

The New England Seamounts are a chain of 20 extinct underwater
volcanoes, 620 miles (1,000 km) long, that lies between the coast of
Massachusetts and the Bermuda Rise. They were formed 80 to 100 million
years ago and today are home to rich communities of marine organisms.

Cape Cod

Hatteras Abyssal Plain

New England Seamounts

Bermuda

Bermuda Rise

Atlantic Ocean

Nashville Seamount

Sohm Abyssal Plain

N O P Q R S T U V W X

NORTH SEA

The North Sea is a semi-enclosed arm of the North Atlantic, with most ocean water flowing in through the northwestern opening between Scotland and Norway, and smaller volumes through the English Channel and the Strait of Dover. There are also substantial freshwater inputs from rivers such as the Rhine. The margins of the North Sea comprise one of the most diverse coastal regions in the world: fjords, estuaries, deltas, banks, beaches, sandbanks and mudflats, marshes, rocks, and islands. Its once abundant fish stocks, particularly cod and herring, have been seriously overfished.

THE FACTS	
Area	222,100 square miles (570,200 km²)
Average depth	308 feet (94 m)
Maximum depth	2,165 feet (660 m)
Maximum width	373 miles (600 km)
Maximum length	621 miles (100 km)

Coastal flooding (right)
The low-lying coasts of the Netherlands and the east coast of England are vulnerable to flooding. In winter the funneling effect of the North Sea from north to south, high spring tides, and strong northerly winds heap up the water in the southern North Sea.

Hamburg Harbor (left)
For centuries Hamburg has been the hub of sea-borne trade between central Europe and the rest of the world, first as one of the main Hanseatic League ports, in the nineteenth century as a major trans-Atlantic port, and now as a container port.

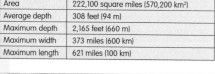

Oil drilling

The broad continental shelf of the North Atlantic that includes the North Sea contains large reserves of oil and gas. The first offshore wells were drilled in 1964 and commercial extraction began in the 1970s, but intense storms in the region make it a difficult working environment. The peak of production has now passed and many rigs are being decommissioned.

The worldwide outcry against the proposed deep-water dumping of a decommissioned North Sea rig in the 1990s forced oil companies to scrap all old rigs on land.

SURFACE CURRENTS (left)
The main surface currents in the North Sea move counterclockwise, generally following the coastlines of the surrounding land with oceanic inputs to the north and south. There are also smaller surface currents that carry less dense low-salinity coastal water offshore and saltier water inshore.

⟶ Inflow from Baltic Sea
⟶ Oceanic inflow
⤏ Wind- and tide-driven circulation

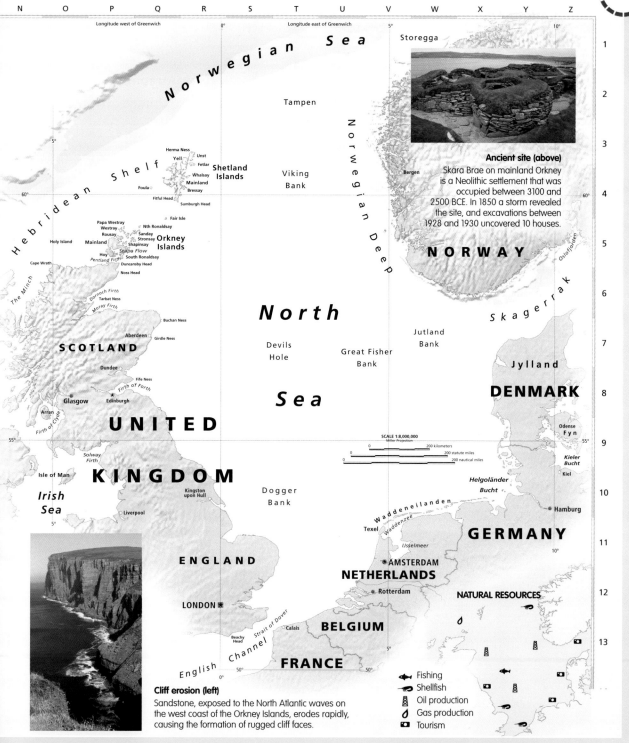

Longitude west of Greenwich   0°   Longitude east of Greenwich   5°   10°

Norwegian Sea

Storegga

Tampen

Norwegian Deep

Viking Bank

Herma Ness
Yell   Unst
Fetlar
Whalsay   Shetland Islands
Mainland
Bressay
Foula

Fitful Head
Sumburgh Head

Bergen

NORWAY

Ancient site (above)
Skara Brae on mainland Orkney is a Neolithic settlement that was occupied between 3100 and 2500 BCE. In 1850 a storm revealed the site, and excavations between 1928 and 1930 uncovered 10 houses.

Fair Isle

Papa Westray
Westray   Nth Ronaldsay
Rousay
Sanday
Stronsay   **Orkney Islands**
Holy Island   Mainland   Shapinsay
Hoy   *Scapa Flow*
Pentland Firth   South Ronaldsay
Duncansby Head
Cape Wrath   Noss Head

The Minch

Dornoch Firth
Tarbat Ness
Moray Firth

Buchan Ness

Aberdeen   Girdle Ness

SCOTLAND

Dundee

Fife Ness
Firth of Forth

Glasgow   Edinburgh

Arran
Firth of Clyde

North

Devils Hole

Great Fisher Bank

Jutland Bank

Skagerrak

Jylland

DENMARK

Oslofjorden

Sea

SCALE 1:8,000,000
Miller Projection

0   200 kilometers
0   200 statute miles
0   200 nautical miles

55°   55°

Odense
Fyn

Kieler Bucht

Kiel

Helgoländer Bucht

Solway Firth

KINGDOM

Isle of Man

Irish Sea

Kingston upon Hull

Dogger Bank

Liverpool

UNITED

Waddeneilanden
Texel   *Waddenzee*

IJsselmeer

GERMANY

Hamburg

10°

ENGLAND

NETHERLANDS

AMSTERDAM

Rotterdam

NATURAL RESOURCES

LONDON

BELGIUM

Beachy Head   Calais
Strait of Dover

English Channel

FRANCE

🐟 Fishing
🦐 Shellfish
Oil production
Gas production
Tourism

Cliff erosion (left)
Sandstone, exposed to the North Atlantic waves on the west coast of the Orkney Islands, erodes rapidly, causing the formation of rugged cliff faces.

1
2
3
4
5
6
7
8
9
10
11
12
13

60°
60°
5°
5°
10°
50°
0°

BALTIC SEA

The Baltic is the world's largest body of brackish water, with marine species in the saltier waters at the western end, and species that are intolerant of salt in the fresh water at the eastern end, where there are significant river inputs. The circulation of water in the Baltic is complex, with irregular inflows of salt water from the North Sea approximately every 10 years. The Baltic occupies a basin that was created by glacial erosion and since the removal of the ice sheet the land around and beneath has been rising, making the sea smaller and shallower. In the last century the area has risen by 4 inches (100 mm) and the inner Gulf of Bothnia will rise above sea level within the next 250 years.

THE FACTS	
Area	163,000 square miles (422,200 km²)
Average depth	180 feet (55 m)
Maximum depth	1,380 feet (421 m)
Maximum width	324 miles (540 km)
Maximum length	795 miles (1,280 km)

Kiel Canal (right)
The Kiel Canal was begun in 1887 and completed in 1895. Its construction was driven by the wish of the German navy and merchant shipping interests to have a direct link between the North Sea and the German Baltic ports, avoiding the need to sail around Denmark.

Ice floes (left)
Baltic sea ice usually starts to form in the northern end of the Gulf of Bothnia in mid-November and extends south and westwards so that the open waters of Bothnian Bay are frozen by February. The Gulf of Finland and the Gulf of Riga are frozen by early January.

Gulf of Finland (below)
Fast ice, attached to the shoreline, develops first, and then thinner more mobile pack or rafter ice forms in open water. This satellite image shows the pack ice, driven by the wind into fast ice, piling up into ridges up to 50 feet (15 m) high.

SURFACE CURRENTS (left)
Apart from the well-defined outflow of brackish water through the Danish straits, there is no clearly defined pattern of surface currents within the Baltic. Local surface currents are generated by prevailing winds and by the outflows of the larger rivers that discharge into the Baltic.

→ Outflow through Danish straits
→ Riverine inputs

Wind farms

Shallow coastal waters are good sites for wind farms because of the winds produced by convection created by the differential heating of land and sea each day. Wind speeds in these zones share the characteristics of both onshore and offshore wind, depending on the prevailing wind direction.

U   V   W   X   Y   Z

25°   Longitude east of Greenwich   30°
Arctic Circle

1

BATHYMETRIC DEPTHS

Feet	Meters
Sea level	Sea level
656	200
1640	500
3281	1000
6562	2000
9842	3000
13,123	4000
16,404	5000
19,685	6000
26,246	8000

2

65°

Bottenviken
(Bay of Bothnia)

Hailuoto

3

Gulf of Bothnia

FINLAND

Ängesön

4

Raippaluoto

SCALE 1:10,000,000
Miller Projection

0   200 kilometers
0   200 statute miles
0   200 nautical miles

5

15°

Gräsö   Åland
Ålands Hav

Turku

6

NORWAY

HELSINKI

Gulf of Finland

St Petersburg

60° *OSLO

60°

SWEDEN

STOCKHOLM

Kolga
laht

Purekkari neem

*Narva
Bay*

TALLINN

7

*Gotland
Basin*

Hiiumaa

Väinameri

Vormsi

Soela Väin   Muhu

ESTONIA

**RUSSIAN
FEDERATION**

Gotska Sandön

Saaremaa

8

Oslofjorden

Orust
Tjörn

Gothenburg

Fårösund

Abruka

Kihnu

Ruhnu

Pärnu
laht

Irbe Strait

*Gulf
of
Riga*

LATVIA

Skagerrak

9

Laesø

Kattegat

Anholt

Öland

Liepaja

RIGA

25°

30°

DENMARK

COPENHAGEN

Malmö

Hanöbukten

LITHUANIA

10

F y n

Sjaelland

Baltic Sea

Møn

Fakse Bugt

Lolland   Falster

Bornholm

Klaipeda

55°

11

Kiel

Kiel
Canal

*Zatoka
Pomorska*

Gulf of
Gdansk

Kaliningrad

**RUSSIAN
FEDERATION**

55°

Gdansk

NATURAL RESOURCES

12

GERMANY

POLAND

10°

15°

20°

Fishing

Tourism

Stockholm (left)

Stockholm is sometimes known as the "Venice of the North" as the city stands on 14 islands connected by more than 50 bridges, with ocean-going vessels able to dock in the city center. Stockholm is part of an archipelago of 24,000 islands.

GULF OF ST. LAWRENCE

The Gulf of St. Lawrence is considered the world's largest estuary, where the fresh water of the Great Lakes meets North Atlantic seawater. It has a distinct ecosystem, characterized by partial isolation from the North Atlantic, a large freshwater runoff, a deep trough running along its length, seasonal ice, the presence of a cold intermediate layer, shallow depths, and high biological productivity and diversity. The deep submarine trough, the Laurentian Channel, is a crucial component of the gulf's biology as it brings in cold, nutrient-rich Atlantic water that slowly mixes with the less dense overlying waters.

Gulf structure (below)
The St. Lawrence River flows northeastward, entering the gulf either side of Anticosti Island. The round shape in the upper middle of the image is Reservoir Manicouagan, which occupies a meteoric impact crater that was created 214 million years ago.

SURFACE CURRENTS (right)
Each spring, as the winter snows melt, the increased fresh water flows into the gulf from the St. Lawrence River, the Saguenay River, and other rivers along the shores. This produces a low-salinity, higher-temperature surface layer of water that begins to flow toward the Atlantic Ocean.

—→ Seasonal currents

Navigation (above)
Within the Gulf of St. Lawrence, the complex currents, numerous small islands, and the formation of winter ice are major hazards to navigation. The control of shipping movements and the provision of buoys, lighthouses, and other navigational aids are the responsibility of the Canadian Coast Guard.

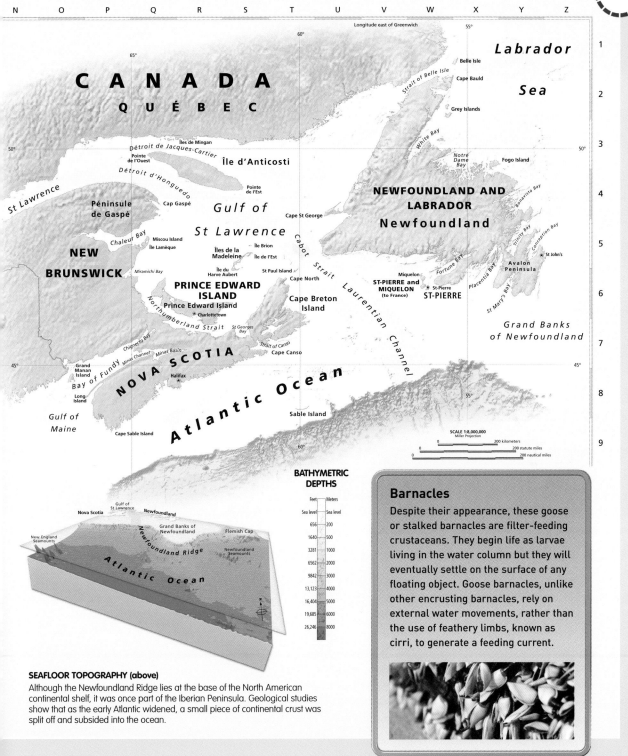

N O P Q R S T U V W X Y Z

Longitude east of Greenwich

60° 55°

Labrador

1

Belle Isle

Cape Bauld

65°

C A N A D A

Strait of Belle Isle

Grey Islands

Sea

2

Q U É B E C

White Bay

50°

Détroit de Jacques-Cartier

Îles de Mingan

Notre
Dame
Bay

Fogo Island

50°

3

Pointe
de l'Ouest

Île d'Anticosti

Détroit d'Honguedo

Pointe
de l'Est

St Lawrence

Péninsule
de Gaspé

Cap Gaspé

Gulf of

Cape St George

**NEWFOUNDLAND AND
LABRADOR
Newfoundland**

Bonavista Bay

4

St Lawrence

Chaleur Bay

Miscou Island

Îles de la
Madeleine

Île Brion

Trinity Bay

Conception Bay

St John's

5

NEW

Île Lamèque

Île de l'Est

Fortune Bay

Avalon
Peninsula

BRUNSWICK

Miramichi Bay

Île du
Harve Aubert

St Paul Island

Miquelon

**ST-PIERRE and
MIQUELON
(to France)**

St-Pierre

ST-PIERRE

Placentia Bay

6

**PRINCE EDWARD
ISLAND**

Prince Edward Island

Cape North

Cabot Strait

St Mary's Bay

Charlottetown

**Cape Breton
Island**

**Grand Banks
of Newfoundland**

7

Northumberland Strait

St Georges
Bay

Laurentian Channel

Chignecto Bay

Strait of Canso

Minas Basin

Cape Canso

45°

Grand
Manan
Island

Bay of Fundy

Minas Channel

N O V A   S C O T I A

55°

45°

8

Long
Island

Halifax

Atlantic   Ocean

**Gulf of
Maine**

Sable Island

9

Cape Sable Island

60°

SCALE 1:8,000,000
Miller Projection

0   200 kilometers
0   200 statute miles
0   200 nautical miles

**BATHYMETRIC
DEPTHS**

Feet   Meters

Nova Scotia

Gulf of
St Lawrence

Newfoundland

Sea level   Sea level

656   200

New England
Seamounts

Newfoundland Ridge

Grand Banks
of Newfoundland

Flemish Cap

Newfoundland
Seamounts

1640   500

3281   1000

Atlantic   Ocean

6562   2000

9842   3000

13,123   4000

16,404   5000

19,685   6000

26,246   8000

Barnacles

Despite their appearance, these goose
or stalked barnacles are filter-feeding
crustaceans. They begin life as larvae
living in the water column but they will
eventually settle on the surface of any
floating object. Goose barnacles, unlike
other encrusting barnacles, rely on
external water movements, rather than
the use of feathery limbs, known as
cirri, to generate a feeding current.

SEAFLOOR TOPOGRAPHY (above)
Although the Newfoundland Ridge lies at the base of the North American
continental shelf, it was once part of the Iberian Peninsula. Geological studies
show that as the early Atlantic widened, a small piece of continental crust was
split off and subsided into the ocean.

GULF OF MEXICO

The Gulf of Mexico is the ninth largest body of water on the planet and occupies a roughly circular basin whose formation continues to be the subject of geological debate. The gulf receives huge volumes of fresh water from the river systems that drain into it, the largest being the Mississippi. However, excessive nutrients brought down by the rivers have caused algal blooms that create anoxic "dead zones" when they die. The wide continental margins of the gulf contain large amounts of oil and gas that contribute a quarter of the United States' gas production and one-eighth of its oil production.

Mississippi Delta (left)
This satellite image shows the algal blooms created by the upwelling of cold, nutrient-rich bottom water, caused by the plume of fresh water discharged from the Mississippi Delta. This river water does not fully mix with the surrounding seawater until it passes through the Straits of Florida.

SURFACE CURRENTS (below)
The principal surface current is the Loop Current that enters through the Straits of Yucatan. The path of the loop is variable and beyond a certain length it becomes unstable and "buds off" large eddies with a clockwise spin.

NATURAL RESOURCES

- ➤ Fishing
- ➤ Shellfish
- ▓ Oil production
- ♦ Gas production
- ▭ Tourism

→ Eddies
→ Florida Current
→ Loop Current
→ Mexican Current
→ Yucatan Current

⚡ Giant grouper
The giant grouper (*Epinephelus itajara*) is found in the Gulf of Mexico. However, this species is classified by the International Union for Conservation of Nature (IUCN) as critically endangered throughout its range. Its slow growth, low reproductive rate, and spawning behavior have made it especially susceptible to overfishing.

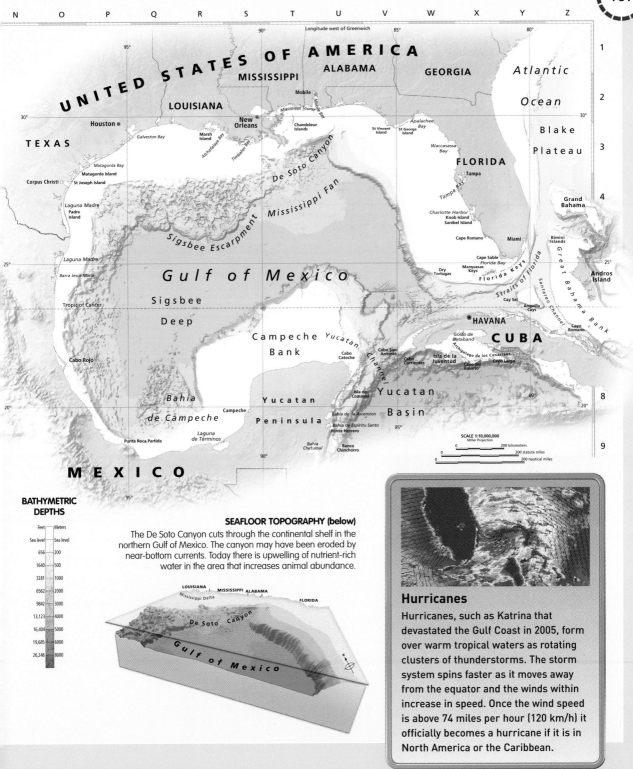

N   O   P   Q   R   S   T   U   V   W   X   Y   Z

1

UNITED STATES OF AMERICA

Longitude west of Greenwich

90°   85°   80°

95°

MISSISSIPPI   **ALABAMA**   **GEORGIA**

Atlantic

2

LOUISIANA

Mobile

Ocean

Mississippi Sound

Mobile Bay

30°   30°

Houston

New Orleans

Chandeleur
Islands

St Vincent
Island

St George
Island

Apalachee
Bay

Blake

TEXAS

Marsh
Island

Atchafalaya Bay

Timbalier Bay

Waccasassa
Bay

Plateau

3

Galveston Bay

FLORIDA

Matagorda Bay

Tampa

Grand
Bahama

Matagorda Island

St Joseph Island

Corpus Christi

De Soto Canyon

Mississippi Fan

Tampa Bay

4

Laguna Madre

Padre
Island

Sigsbee Escarpment

Charlotte Harbor

Knob Island

Sanibel Island

Bimini
Islands

Cape Romano

Miami

Laguna Madre

Gulf of Mexico

Sigsbee

Cape Sable

Florida Bay

Dry
Tortugas

Marquesas
Keys

*Andros
Island*

25°   25°

Barra Jesús María

Deep

Florida Keys

Cay Sal

Straits of Florida

Great Bahama Bank

Santaren Channel

Anguilla
Cays

Tropic of Cancer

HAVANA

CUBA

Campeche
Bank

Yucatan

Cabo San
Antonio

Golfo de
Batabanó

Archipelago de los Canarreos

Cayo
Romano

Cabo Rojo

Cabo
Catoche

Channel

Cabo
Corrientes

Isla de la
Juventud

Cayo Largo

Cayo del
Rosario

Bahía

Yucatan

Isla de
Cozumel

80°   20°   8

20°   20°

de Campeche

Campeche

Yucatan

Basin

85°

Bahía de la Ascensión

Peninsula

Punta Roca Partida

Laguna
de Términos

Bahía de Espíritu Santo

Punta Herrero

SCALE 1:10,000,000

Miller Projection

0   200 kilometers

9

Bahía
Chetumal

Banco
Chinchorro

0   200 statute miles

0   200 nautical miles

90°

M E X I C O

95°

BATHYMETRIC DEPTHS

Feet	Meters
Sea level	Sea level
656	200
1640	500
3281	1000
6562	2000
9842	3000
13,123	4000
16,404	5000
19,685	6000
26,246	8000

SEAFLOOR TOPOGRAPHY (below)

The De Soto Canyon cuts through the continental shelf in the northern Gulf of Mexico. The canyon may have been eroded by near-bottom currents. Today there is upwelling of nutrient-rich water in the area that increases animal abundance.

LOUISIANA   MISSISSIPPI   ALABAMA

Mississippi Delta

FLORIDA

De Soto   Canyon

Gulf of Mexico

N

Hurricanes

Hurricanes, such as Katrina that devastated the Gulf Coast in 2005, form over warm tropical waters as rotating clusters of thunderstorms. The storm system spins faster as it moves away from the equator and the winds within increase in speed. Once the wind speed is above 74 miles per hour (120 km/h) it officially becomes a hurricane if it is in North America or the Caribbean.

CARIBBEAN SEA

The Caribbean Sea is relatively shallow, but there are deep trenches such as the Cayman Trench. The Caribbean Sea has a counterclockwise current that brings in Atlantic water between the Lesser Antilles. Once in the Caribbean the water is warmed, and exits via the Yucatan Channel, where it eventually forms the Gulf Stream. The waters of the Caribbean are clear, warm, and less salty than the Atlantic, and the basin has a very low tidal range. These conditions are ideal for reef-building corals, giving the Caribbean 9 percent of the world's coral reefs.

THE FACTS	
Area	1.1 million square miles (2.7 million km²)
Average depth	8,685 feet (2,647 m)
Maximum depth	25,218 feet (7,686 m)
Maximum width	840 miles (1,400 km)
Maximum length	1,678 miles (2,700 km)

→ Caribbean Current
→ Eddy
→ Guiana Current
→ Yucatan Current

SURFACE CURRENTS (above left)
Water from the equatorial Atlantic is carried by the North Equatorial, North Brazil, and Guiana Currents between the Antilles to become the Caribbean Current. This carries large amounts of water northwestward, eventually entering the Gulf of Mexico and becoming part of the Yucatan Current.

Schooling barracuda (left)
Juvenile barracuda (*Sphyraena barracuda*) are frequently found in large schools. They are reputed to be good eating but there is an increasing problem with the toxin from the alga Ciguatera which accumulates in the barracudas' muscles and causes severe food poisoning.

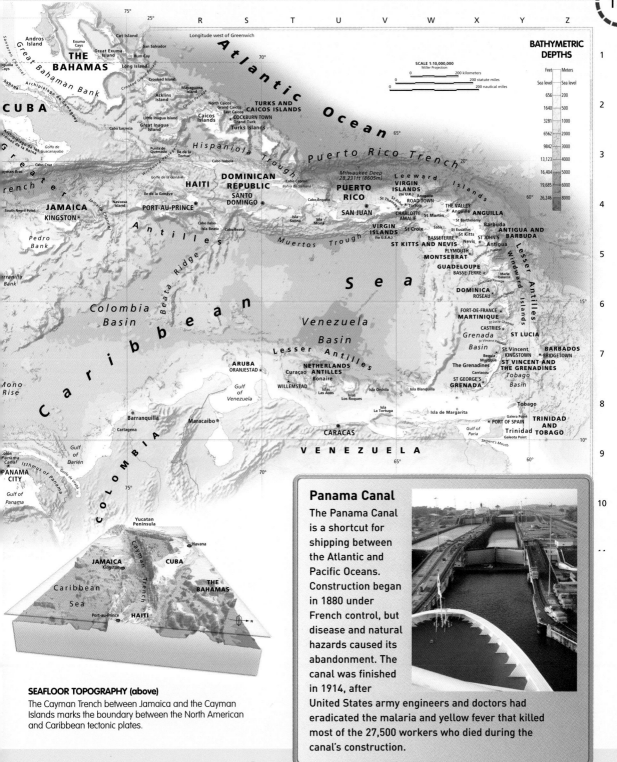

THE BAHAMAS

Andros Island
Exuma Cays
Cat Island
Great Exuma Island
San Salvador
Rum Cay
Long Island
Crooked Island
Acklins Island
Mayaguana Island
North Caicos
Grand Caicos
East Caicos
Little Inagua Island
Caicos Islands
Great Inagua Island
Cabo Lucrecia
TURKS AND CAICOS ISLANDS
COCKBURN TOWN
Grand Turk
Turks Islands

Longitude west of Greenwich

Atlantic Ocean

Great Bahaman Bank

CUBA

Santaren Channel
Anguilla Cays
Sabana
Archipiélago de Camagüey
Golfo de Guacanayabo
Cabo Cruz
Cayman Brac

Greater

Antilles

Cayman Trench

JAMAICA
KINGSTON

Pedro Bank

Barranquilla Bank

Mono Rise

Caribbean

Colombia Basin

Beata Ridge

Jardines de la Reina
Golfo de Guacanayabo

Hispaniola Trough

Punta de Quemado
Île de la Tortue
HAITI
Golfe de la Gonâve
Île de la Gonâve
PORT-AU-PRINCE
Cabo Falso
Isla Beata
Cabo Beata

DOMINICAN REPUBLIC
SANTO DOMINGO
Cabo Isabela
Cabo Cabrón
Bahía de Samaná
Cabo Engaño
Isla Saona
Isla Mona

Windward Passage
Navassa Island
Jamaica Channel

Puerto Rico Trench
Milwaukee Deep 28,231ft (8605m)

PUERTO RICO
SAN JUAN

Muertos Trough

Leeward Islands

VIRGIN ISLANDS (to U.K.)
St Thomas
St John
ROAD TOWN
Tortola
CHARLOTTE AMALIE
VIRGIN ISLANDS (to U.S.A.)
St Croix

Anegada
THE VALLEY
ANGUILLA
St Martin
St Barthélemy
Saba
St Eustatius
BASSETERRE
ST KITTS AND NEVIS
St Kitts
Nevis
PLYMOUTH
MONTSERRAT
Barbuda
ANGUILLA
ST JOHN'S
Antigua
ANTIGUA AND BARBUDA

Guadeloupe Passage
GUADELOUPE
BASSE-TERRE
Marie-Galante
Dominica Passage
DOMINICA
ROSEAU

Lesser Antilles
Windward Islands

Caribbean Sea

Venezuela Basin

Lesser Antilles

FORT-DE-FRANCE
MARTINIQUE
St Lucia Channel
CASTRIES
ST LUCIA

Grenada Basin

Grenada
St Vincent Passage
St Vincent
KINGSTOWN
Bequia
Mustique
The Grenadines
Carriacou
ST VINCENT AND THE GRENADINES

BARBADOS
BRIDGETOWN

Tobago Basin

ST GEORGE'S
GRENADA

Antilles

ARUBA
ORANJESTAD

NETHERLANDS ANTILLES
Curaçao
Bonaire
WILLEMSTAD

Gulf of Venezuela

Islas Las Aves
Islas Los Roques
Isla Orchila
Isla Blanquilla

Isla La Tortuga
Isla de Margarita

Gulf of Paria
Serpent's Mouth
Galera Point
PORT OF SPAIN
Trinidad
Galeota Point
TRINIDAD AND TOBAGO
Tobago

COLOMBIA

Barranquilla
Cartagena
Maracaibo

Gulf of Darién
Golfo de Urabá
Isthmus of Panama

Colón
Panama Canal
PANAMA CITY
Gulf of Panama

CARACAS

VENEZUELA

BATHYMETRIC DEPTHS

Feet	Meters
Sea level	Sea level
656	200
1640	500
3281	1000
6562	2000
9842	3000
13,123	4000
16,404	6000
19,685	6000
26,246	8000

SCALE 1:10,000,000
Miller Projection

0   200 kilometers
0   200 statute miles
0   200 nautical miles

Yucatan Peninsula

CUBA
Havana

JAMAICA
Kingston

Cayman Trench

THE BAHAMAS

Caribbean Sea

Port-au-Prince
HAITI

N

SEAFLOOR TOPOGRAPHY (above)

The Cayman Trench between Jamaica and the Cayman Islands marks the boundary between the North American and Caribbean tectonic plates.

Panama Canal

The Panama Canal is a shortcut for shipping between the Atlantic and Pacific Oceans. Construction began in 1880 under French control, but disease and natural hazards caused its abandonment. The canal was finished in 1914, after United States army engineers and doctors had eradicated the malaria and yellow fever that killed most of the 27,500 workers who died during the canal's construction.

SARGASSO SEA

The Sargasso Sea does not have limits defined by coasts or other geographic features. Instead, it is an area of the Atlantic Ocean characterized by large, floating masses of sargassum seaweed that accumulate there. The sea is at the center of the North Atlantic Gyre, a group of clockwise north-Atlantic currents—the Gulf Stream, North Atlantic Current, Canary Current, and North Equatorial Current—which form a single, closed-circulation cell. This circulation causes everything that floats to become concentrated in the center of the gyre. Several animals have co-evolved with the sargassum, taking on its brown-yellow coloration and living their lives in its camouflage.

THE FACTS	
Area	1.4 million square miles (3.75 million km²)
Average depth	16,405 feet (5000 m)
Maximum depth	21,005 feet (6,402 m)
Maximum width	994 miles (1,600 km)
Maximum length	1,864 miles (3,000 km)

NATURAL RESOURCES

- Fishing
- Shellfish
- Tourism

BATHYMETRIC DEPTHS

Feet	Meters
Sea level	Sea level
656	200
1640	500
3281	1000
6562	2000
9842	3000
13,123	4000
16,404	5000
19,685	6000
26,246	8000

Sargassum crab (left)
The ends of the fifth pair of legs of the sargassum crab (*Portunus sp.*) are modified into paddles so that it is able to swim between clumps of sargassum weed. The mottled shell is an effective camouflage when the crab is covered by strands of weed.

Sargassum refuge (right)
Sargassum, a brown seaweed, is covered with gas-filled, grape-shaped floats. This enables the plant to live on the ocean's surface. It provides a floating refuge for invertebrates and fish, such as this sargassumfish (*Histrio histrio*).

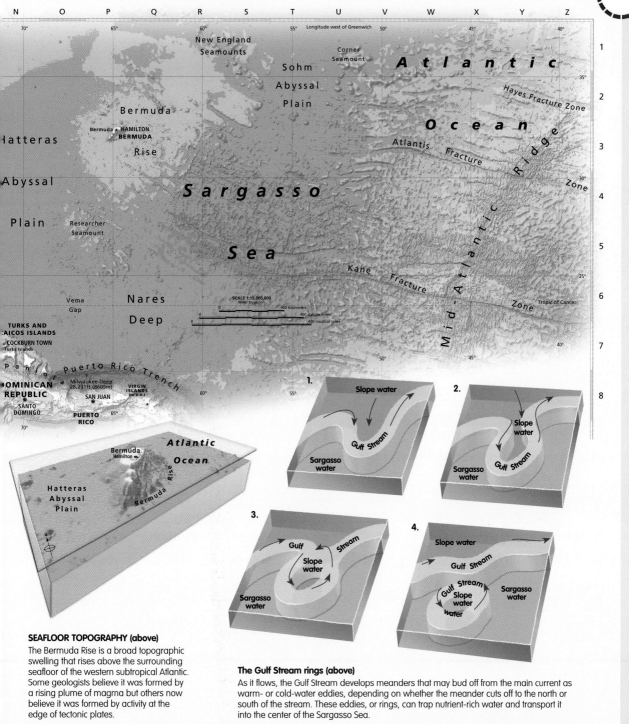

N O P Q R S T U V W X Y Z

70° 65° 60° 55° Longitude west of Greenwich 50° 45° 40°

New England
Seamounts

Corner
Seamount

Sohm

A t l a n t i c

Abyssal

Plain

Hayes Fracture Zone

Bermuda

O c e a n

Bermuda · HAMILTON
BERMUDA

Atlantis Fracture

Hatteras

Rise

Zone

Abyssal

S a r g a s s o

Mid-Atlantic Ridge

Plain

Researcher
Seamount

S e a

Kane Fracture

Vema
Gap

Nares

Zone

Tropic of Cancer

Deep

SCALE 1:15,000,000
Miller Projection

400 kilometers

TURKS AND
AICOS ISLANDS

400 statute miles

COCKBURN TOWN
Turks Islands

400 nautical miles

50° 45°

P a n l o f Puerto Rico Trench

**OMINICAN
REPUBLIC**

Milwaukee Deep
28,231ft (8605m)

VIRGIN
ISLANDS
(to U.K.)

SANTO
DOMINGO

SAN JUAN

**PUERTO
RICO**

65°

70° 60° 55°

35°

30°

25°

40°

1

2

3

4

5

6

7

8

1.

Slope water

Gulf Stream

Sargasso
water

2.

Slope
water

Gulf Stream

Sargasso
water

3.

Gulf   Stream

Slope
water

Sargasso
water

4.

Slope water

Gulf Stream

Gulf Stream
Slope
water
water

Sargasso
water

Atlantic

Bermuda
Hamilton

Ocean

Rise

Hatteras
Abyssal
Plain

Bermuda

z

SEAFLOOR TOPOGRAPHY (above)
The Bermuda Rise is a broad topographic
swelling that rises above the surrounding
seafloor of the western subtropical Atlantic.
Some geologists believe it was formed by
a rising plume of magma but others now
believe it was formed by activity at the
edge of tectonic plates.

The Gulf Stream rings (above)
As it flows, the Gulf Stream develops meanders that may bud off from the main current as
warm- or cold-water eddies, depending on whether the meander cuts off to the north or
south of the stream. These eddies, or rings, can trap nutrient-rich water and transport it
into the center of the Sargasso Sea.

BAY OF BISCAY

The Bay of Biscay is a semi-enclosed area of the northeast Atlantic that contains a wider than usual portion of continental shelf. This has made the bay relatively shallow, which—combined with the prevailing westerly winds that bring in waves that have traveled across most of the Atlantic—often makes its waters exceptionally rough. Circulation patterns are seasonal. From October to March, the Navidad Current, so-called because it is present through Christmas, flows eastward along the north coast of Spain, and is an extension of the northward Portugal Countercurrent. Where the current encounters irregularities on the continental slope, such as the Santander Canyon, it generates eddies, meanders, and warm-water lenses.

THE FACTS	
Area	86,000 square miles (223,000 km²)
Average depth	7,874 feet (2,400 m)
Maximum depth	15,525 feet (4,735 m)
Maximum width	342 miles (550 km)
Maximum length	317 miles (510 km)

Quiet inlet (right)
Pont Goulphar is one of the numerous secluded inlets along the southwest coast of Brittany. The inlet and the surrounding rugged cliffs inspired the Impressionist painter Claude Monet to produce a series of famous seascapes. The area continues to attract large numbers of summer visitors.

La Rochelle Harbor (left)
There has been a port at La Rochelle since the tenth century. Although always prosperous, as the most westerly Atlantic port in France the port also became strategically important in the eighteenth century when trade with French possessions in the New World expanded.

Gannet (below)
The northern gannet (*Morus bassanus*) is the largest seabird in the North Atlantic, having a wingspan of up to 6 feet (2 m). Adults of the species are seen throughout the Bay of Biscay although they breed farther north.

SURFACE CURRENTS (left)
The surface currents of the Bay of Biscay have a clockwise circulation that is linked to the clockwise surface circulation pattern in the main part of the North Atlantic. In addition, there are strong coastal currents driven by the high tidal range within the bay.

→ Inshore tidal movement
→ North Atlantic Drift
→ Seasonal Navidad Current
→ Surface circulation

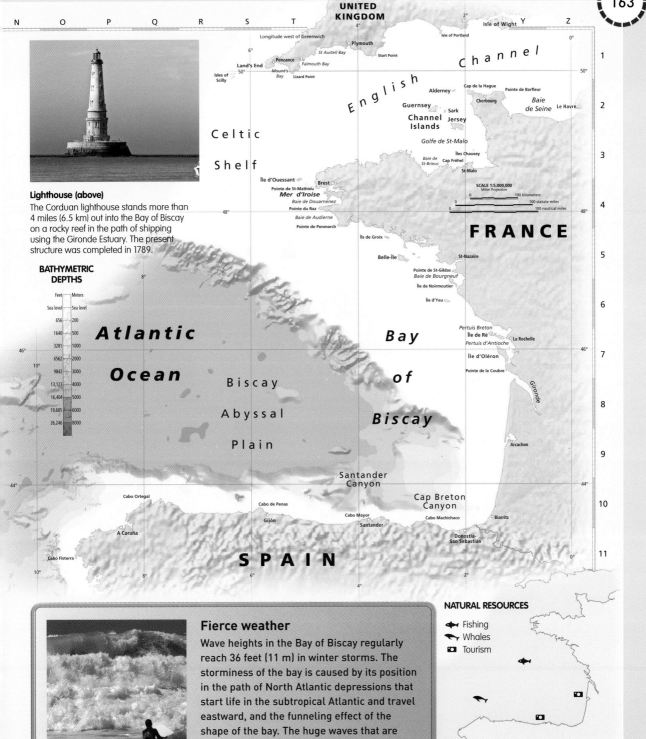

Lighthouse (above)

The Corduan lighthouse stands more than 4 miles (6.5 km) out into the Bay of Biscay on a rocky reef in the path of shipping using the Gironde Estuary. The present structure was completed in 1789.

BATHYMETRIC DEPTHS

Feet	Meters
Sea level	Sea level
656	200
1640	500
3281	1000
6562	2000
9842	3000
13,123	4000
16,404	5000
19,685	6000
26,246	8000

UNITED KINGDOM

Longitude west of Greenwich

Isle of Wight
Isle of Portland
Plymouth
St Austell Bay
Start Point
Penzance
Land's End
Falmouth Bay
Mount's Bay
Lizard Point
Isles of Scilly

English Channel

Celtic Shelf

Cap de la Hague
Alderney
Pointe de Barfleur
Cherbourg
Baie de Seine
Le Havre
Guernsey
Sark
Jersey
Channel Islands
Golfe de St-Malo
Îles Chausey
Baie de St-Brieuc
Cap Fréhel
St-Malo

Île d'Ouessant
Brest
Pointe de St-Mathieu
Mer d'Iroise
Baie de Douarnenez
Pointe du Raz
Baie de Audierne
Pointe de Penmarch

SCALE 1:5,000,000
Miller Projection
100 kilometers
100 statute miles
100 nautical miles

FRANCE

Îls de Groix
Belle-Île
St-Nazaire
Pointe de St-Gildas
Baie de Bourgneuf
Île de Noirmoutier
Île d'Yeu

Atlantic Ocean

Biscay Abyssal Plain

Bay of Biscay

Pertuis Breton
Île de Ré
Pertuis d'Antioche
La Rochelle
Île d'Oléron
Pointe de la Coubre
Gironde

Arcachon

Santander Canyon

Cap Breton Canyon

Cabo Ortegal
Cabo de Penas
Cabo Mayor
Cabo Machichaco
Biarritz
Gijón
Santander
Donostia-San Sebastián
A Coruña

Cabo Fisterra

SPAIN

NATURAL RESOURCES

- Fishing
- Whales
- Tourism

Fierce weather

Wave heights in the Bay of Biscay regularly reach 36 feet (11 m) in winter storms. The storminess of the bay is caused by its position in the path of North Atlantic depressions that start life in the subtropical Atlantic and travel eastward, and the funneling effect of the shape of the bay. The huge waves that are generated are, however, enjoyed by surfers.

MEDITERRANEAN SEA

The Mediterranean Sea's only link with the Atlantic is through the Strait of Gibraltar, where dense salty Mediterranean water flows out beneath less dense Atlantic water. As a consequence, the tidal range in the Mediterranean is short and the circulation patterns are driven by evaporation and freshwater inputs. The Mediterranean Sea is largely populated by species that have entered via the Strait of Gibraltar and adapted to warmer, more saline water. However, since the opening of the Suez Canal in 1869, Red Sea species have begun to colonize the eastern Mediterranean.

THE FACTS	
Area	959,210 square miles (2,484,342 km²)
Average depth	4,920 feet (1,500 m)
Maximum depth	16,897 feet (5,150 m)
Maximum width	497 miles (800 km)
Maximum length	1,250 miles (2,000 km)

City of Venice (left)
Venice stands on 118 small islands within a saltwater lagoon bounded by the mouths of the River Piave to the north and the River Po to the south. During the Middle Ages and Renaissance, Venice was the dominant political and military power in the Mediterranean.

Aegean Sea (below)
The Aegean Sea is an embayment of the Mediterranean separating the Greek and Turkish mainlands. It was known to the Greeks as "Archipelago," referring to the large number of islands within it, though the term is now used to refer to island groups throughout the world.

SEAFLOOR TOPOGRAPHY (left)
The Strait of Gibraltar is the only natural connection between the Mediterranean Sea and the world ocean. It is 36 miles (58 km) long and narrows to 8 miles (13 km). Depths in the strait range between 980 and 3,000 feet (300 and 900 m).

Monk seal

The Mediterranean monk seal (*Monachus monachus*) is one of the world's most endangered animals; less than 500 individuals survive. Centuries of hunting, and pollution and disturbance in the sea in the past century, have brought them close to extinction. They are one of only three species of warm-water seals.

SCALE 1:15,000,000
Miller Projection
0   400 kilometers
0   400 statute miles
0   400 nautical miles

EUROPE

Venice
Gulf of Venice

Genoa
Gulf of Genoa
Ligurian Sea Basin
Corso-Ligurian Basin
Corsica
Isola d'Elba
Rome
Adriatic Sea
Mid-Adriatic Basin
South Adriatic Basin
Dubrovnik

Sardinia
Strait of Bonifacio
Sardinia-Corsica Trough
Tyrrhenian Sea
Golfo di Gaeta
Naples
Golfo di Salerno
Tyrrhenian Basin
Isole Lipari
Cefalù Basin
Golfo di Taranto
Corfu
Apulian Plateau
Strait of Otranto
Otranto Valley
Taranto Valley

Sardino-Balearic Abyssal Plain

Cap de Fer   Cap Blanc
Tunis
Golfe de Tunis
Sicilian Basin
Adventure Bank
Sicily
Isola di Pantelleria
Golfe de Hammamet
Ras Kaboudia
Iles Kerkenah
Golfe de Gabès
Ile de Jerba

Malta
Isole Pelagie
Malta Plateau
Medina Bank
Tunisian Plateau

De la Basin
Malta Trough
Malta Ridge
Medina Escarpment
Melita Valley
Misrata Valley
Misurata Valley

Ionian Sea
Ionian Islands
Ionian Basin
Calabrian Rise
East Mediterranean Ridge
Ptolemy Trench
Hellenic Trench
Herodotus Trough
Herodotus Rise
Mediterranean
Sirte Rise
Banghazi
Gulf of Sirte

Thessalonika
Samothraki Plateau
Thracian Plateau
Thermaikos Kolpos
Thermaikos Sea
North Aegean Trough
Limnos
Lesbós
Chios
Izmir
Voreioi Sporades
Evvoia
Athens
Aegean Sea
Mirtoon Basin
North Ikaria Basin
Samos
Kiklades
South Ikaria Basin
Cyclades
Sea of Crete
Cretan Trough
Crete
Mitsos Trench
Strabo Trench
Herodotus Abyssal Plain
Herodotus Basin

Istanbul
Bosphorus
Marmara Trough
Sea of Marmara
Samsun

Black Sea

ASIA

Rhodes
Rhodes Basin
Dodecanese
Anaximander Mountains
Antalya Basin
Cape Arnaoutis
Adana
Adana Trough
Latakia Basin
Cyprus
Cyprus Basin
Beirut
Eratosthenes Seamount
Beirut Escarpment
Tel Aviv-Jaffa

Khalij Bumbah
Gulf of Salum
Levantine Basin
Khalig el 'Arab
Nile Fan
Cairo

Sea

AFRICA

Gulf of Suez
Gulf of Aqaba
Red Sea

Longitude east of Greenwich

SURFACE CURRENTS (below)

Surface circulation of the Mediterranean consists of separate counterclockwise movements of the water in each of the two basins. The complexity of the northern coastline and of the numerous islands generates many small eddies and other local currents.

→ Atlantic surface inflow
→ Surface circulation

BATHYMETRIC DEPTHS

Feet	Meters
Sea level	Sea level
656	200
1640	500
3281	1000
6562	2000
9842	3000
13,123	4000
16,404	5000
19,685	6000
26,246	8000

NATURAL RESOURCES

🐟 Fishing
⛏ Oil production
📷 Tourism

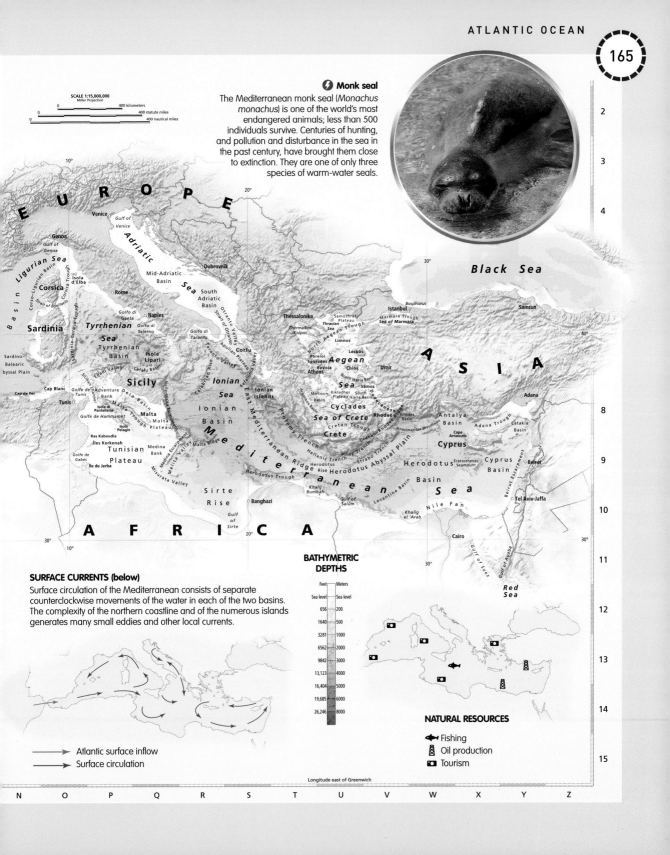

BLACK SEA

The Black Sea is believed by many geologists to have been a freshwater lake until about 8,000 years ago, when the post-glacial rise in sea levels allowed seawater from the Aegean Sea to break through the Turkish straits system (the Bosporus, Sea of Marmara, and Dardenelles). The salinity of the Black Sea is only half that of full-strength seawater. The freshwater input of major rivers means that much of the Black Sea is stratified so that the deeper layers do not mix with the surface and become hypoxic and devoid of life. Most marine life is found in the surface waters and the shallow coastal margins, though these areas have been severely affected by pollution.

THE FACTS	
Area	196,000 square miles (508,000 km²)
Average depth	4,062 feet (1,240 m)
Maximum depth	7,365 feet (2,245 m)
Maximum width	160 miles (260 km)
Maximum length	730 miles (1,175 km)

Moon jellyfish (right)
In the 1970s there was a dramatic rise in the number of moon jellyfish (*Aurelia aurita*) in the Black Sea and it was suggested that this species, alone, was consuming 62 percent of all zooplankton produced in the surface waters. The zooplankton was food that previously supported important fisheries.

First Bosporus bridge (below)
The Bosporus is less than half a mile (700 m) at its narrowest point. The first bridge, completed in 1973, stands beside the Oratokoy mosque. There are now also two other bridges.

Scorpionfish (below)
The black scorpionfish (*Scorpaena porcus*) is found in shallow waters throughout the Mediterranean and Black seas. It is an ambush predator that sits motionless among weed and rocks waiting to seize small fish and crustaceans; its sharp poisonous dorsal spine stops it being eaten by larger fish.

Sea of Azov (above)
The Sea of Azov is a body of brackish water that connects to the Black Sea via the Kerch Strait and is the shallowest sea in the world. It has a maximum depth of 50 feet (15.3 m).

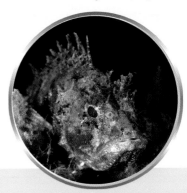

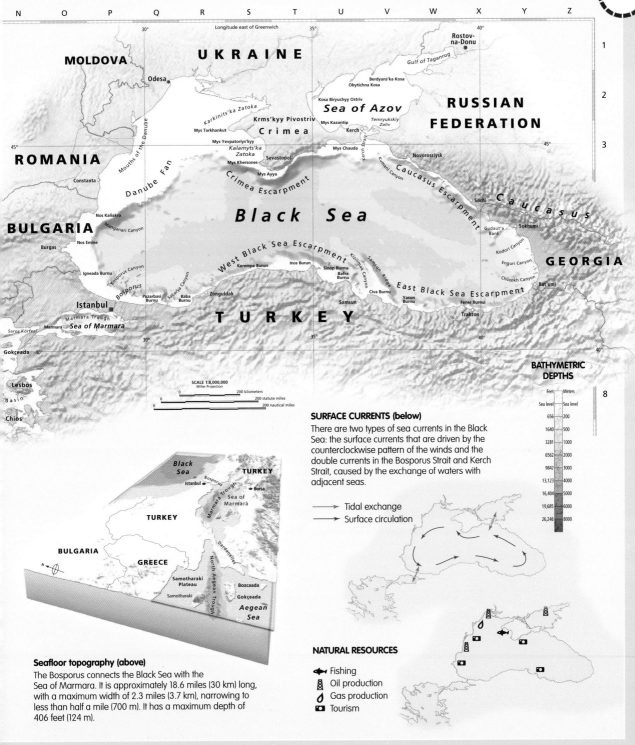

N   O   P   Q   R   S   T   U   V   W   X   Y   Z

MOLDOVA

UKRAINE

Longitude east of Greenwich   30°   35°   40°

Rostov-na-Donu

Gulf of Taganrog

Odesa

Berdyans'ka Kosa
Obytichna Kosa

Kosa Biryuchyy Ostriv

RUSSIAN

Karkinits'ka Zatoka

Sea of Azov

FEDERATION

Krms'kyy Pivostriv

Mys Tarkhankut

Crimea

Mys Kazantip

Temryukskiy Zaliv

Kerch

45°   Mys Yevpatoriys'kyy

ROMANIA

Kalamyts'ka Zatoka

Mys Khersones

Sevastopol

Mys Chauda

Kerch Strait

Novorossiysk   45°   3

Kumani Canyon

Caucasus Escarpment

Sochi

C a u c a s u s

Mys Ayya

Crimea Escarpment

Constanta

Danube Fan

Mouths of the Danube

Black   Sea

Gudaut'a Bank

Sokhumi

Kodori Canyon

GEORGIA

BULGARIA

Nos Kaliakra

Manganari Canyon

West Black Sea Escarpment

Enguri Canyon

Nos Emine

Burgas

Kerempe Burun   Ince Burun

Sinop Burnu

Kizilirmak Canyon

Samsun Ridge

East Black Sea Escarpment

Chorokh Canyon   Bat'umi

Igneada Burnu

Bosporus Canyon

Bafra Burnu

Sakarya Canyon

Pazarbasi Burnu

Baba Burnu

Zonguldak

Civa Burnu

Yasun Burnu

Fener Burnu

Istanbul

Marmara Trough

Sea of Marmara

Samsun

T U R K E Y

Trabzon

Saros Körfezi   Marmara

30°   35°   40°

Gokçeada   40°   40°

Lesbos

Basin

Chios

SCALE 1:8,000,000
Miller Projection

0   200 kilometers
0   200 statute miles
0   200 nautical miles

BATHYMETRIC DEPTHS

Feet	Meters
Sea level	Sea level
656	200
1640	500
3281	1000
6562	2000
9842	3000
13,123	4000
16,404	5000
19,685	6000
26,246	8000

8

SURFACE CURRENTS (below)

There are two types of sea currents in the Black Sea: the surface currents that are driven by the counterclockwise pattern of the winds and the double currents in the Bosporus Strait and Kerch Strait, caused by the exchange of waters with adjacent seas.

→ Tidal exchange
→ Surface circulation

Seafloor topography (above)

Black Sea

TURKEY

Bosporus

Istanbul   Bursa

Marmara Trough

Sea of Marmara

TURKEY

Dardanelles

BULGARIA

North Aegean Trough

GREECE

Samothraki Plateau

Samothraki

Bozcaada

Gokçeada

Aegean Sea

N

The Bosporus connects the Black Sea with the Sea of Marmara. It is approximately 18.6 miles (30 km) long, with a maximum width of 2.3 miles (3.7 km), narrowing to less than half a mile (700 m). It has a maximum depth of 406 feet (124 m).

NATURAL RESOURCES

🐟 Fishing
🛢 Oil production
💧 Gas production
📷 Tourism

SOUTHERN ATLANTIC OCEAN

Like the North Atlantic, the South Atlantic has a central gyre of surface currents, but these flow counterclockwise. The Brazil Current flows south from the equator, eventually turning eastward to become the South Atlantic Current, which meets the Agulhas Current around the Cape of Good Hope. This creates an upwelling zone that brings cold, nutrient-rich waters to the surface. The cold water that continues north along the Namibian coast reduces the water vapor in the air, making it an arid desert known as the "Skeleton Coast."

Great white shark (right)
The great white shark (*Carcharodon carcharias*) is found in warm coastal waters. The best-known Atlantic great whites are those around Seal Island, South Africa, during the seal breeding season, breaching spectacularly from the depths.

SURFACE CURRENTS (below)
The counterclockwise gyre that covers the central South Atlantic is made up of four components: the South Equatorial Current, Brazil Current, Antarctic Circumpolar Current and Benguela Current. The waters that are isolated in the central portion of the gyre are nutrient-poor, forming a "blue desert."

- - - - → Equatorial Countercurrent
——→ South Equatorial Current
——→ Brazil Current
- - - - → South Atlantic Current
——→ Falklands Current
——→ Antarctic Circumpolar Current
- - - - → Agulhas Current
——→ Benguela Current

Paramaribo
Cayenne
50° Amazon Cone
Cear
Equator
0°

SOUTH

AMERICA

10°

20°

Tropic of Capricorn
Rio de Janeiro
Sao Paulo

30°

Santo
Platea

Buenos Aires
Montevideo

Golfo San Matias

Argentine
Basin

Zapiola

Golfo de San Jorge

Argentine Abyssal Plain

Falkland Esca

Falkland
Islands
Falkland
Plateau

Tierra del
Fuego
Burdwood Bank
North Scotia Ridge

Cape
Horn
Yaghan
Basin
Endurance Fracture Zone

Shackleton Fracture Zone
West Scotia Ridge
Scotia

Drake Passage
Ona Basin
Protector
Basin

Hero Fracture Zone
South Shetland Trough
South Orkney
Islands

South Shetland Islands
Powell
Basin

Scotia

70°   60°   50°

G   H   I   J   K   L   M

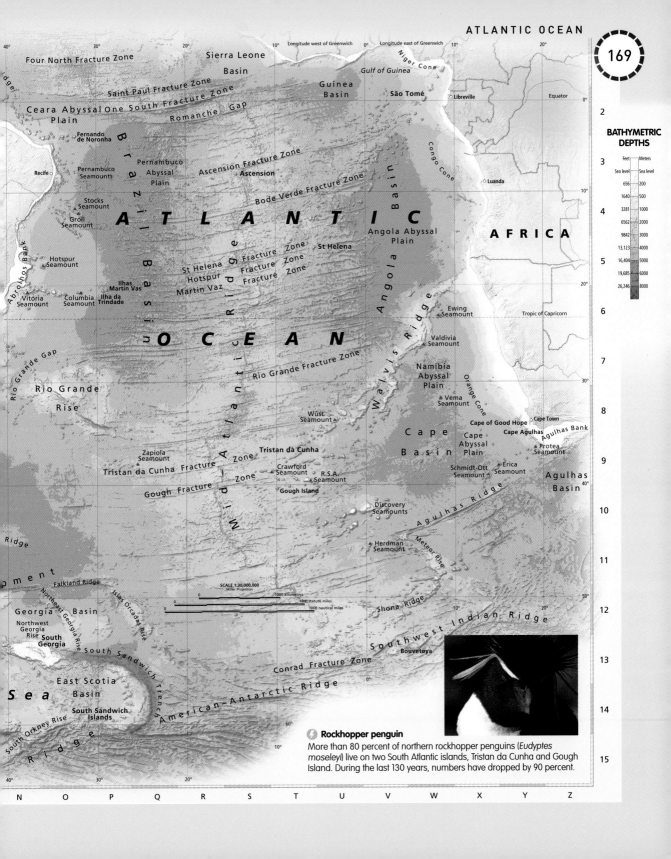

ATLANTIC OCEAN

Four North Fracture Zone
Sierra Leone
Basin
Longitude west of Greenwich
Longitude east of Greenwich
Niger Cone
Gulf of Guinea
Saint Paul Fracture Zone
Guinea
Basin
São Tomé
Libreville
Equator
Ceara Abyssal One South Fracture Zone
Plain
Romanche Gap
Fernando
de Noronha
Pernambuco
Congo Cone
Recife
Pernambuco
Seamounts
Pernambuco
Abyssal
Plain
Ascension Fracture Zone
Ascension
Luanda
Stocks
Seamount
Bode Verde Fracture Zone

A T L A N T I C

Groll
Seamount
Angola Abyssal
Plain
A F R I C A
Abrolhos
Bank
Hotspur
Seamount
St Helena   Fracture   Zone
Hotspur   Fracture   Zone
St Helena
Ilhas
Martin Vas
Martin Vaz   Fracture   Zone
Vitória
Seamount
Columbia
Seamount
Ilha da
Trindade

O C E A N
Ewing
Seamount
Tropic of Capricorn
Valdivia
Seamount
Rio Grande Gap
Rio Grande Fracture Zone
Namibia
Abyssal
Plain
Rio Grande
Rise
Vema
Seamount
Orange Cone
Wüst
Seamount
Cape of Good Hope
Cape Town
Cape Agulhas
Agulhas Bank
Zapiola
Seamount
Tristan da Cunha
Cape
Basin
Cape
Abyssal
Plain
Protea
Seamount
Tristan da Cunha Fracture   Zone
Crawford
Seamount
R.S.A.
Seamount
Schmidt-Ott
Seamount
Erica
Seamount
Agulhas
Basin
Gough Fracture   Zone
Gough Island
Agulhas Ridge
Discovery
Seamounts
Ridge
Herdman
Seamount
Meteor Rise
Falkland Ridge
Islas Orcadas Rise
SCALE 1:30,000,000
Miller Projection
Shona Ridge
Georgia Basin
Northeast Georgia Rise
1000 kilometers
1000 statute miles
1000 nautical miles
Southwest Indian Ridge
Northwest
Georgia
Rise
South
Georgia
South Sandwich Trench
Bouvetøya
East Scotia
Basin
Conrad Fracture Zone
S e a
South Sandwich
Islands
American–Antarctic Ridge
South Orkney Rise
Ridge

Rockhopper penguin
More than 80 percent of northern rockhopper penguins (*Eudyptes moseleyi*) live on two South Atlantic islands, Tristan da Cunha and Gough Island. During the last 130 years, numbers have dropped by 90 percent.

BATHYMETRIC DEPTHS

Feet	Meters
Sea level	Sea level
656	200
1640	500
3281	1000
6562	2000
9842	3000
13,123	4000
16,404	5000
19,685	6000
26,246	8000

GULF OF GUINEA

The coastline of the Gulf of Guinea forms part of the western edge of the African tectonic plate and corresponds remarkably to the continental margin of South America running from Brazil to the Guianas. The coincidence between the geology and the geomorphology of these two coastlines constitutes one of the clearest confirmations of the theory of continental drift. The continental shelf within the gulf is narrower than that of most of the Atlantic margins but contains large and valuable oil and mineral resources, the best known being the oil and gas fields of the Niger Delta.

NATURAL RESOURCES

- Fishing
- Oil production
- Gas production
- Tourism

Coast of Togo (above)
The lagoon at Aneho, on the Togolese coast, is part of a 31-mile (50 km) system of dunes and lagoons. These have been built up from sediments carried westward by strong clockwise coastal currents and longshore drift along this part of the Gulf of Guinea.

SURFACE CURRENTS (below)
The major surface current systems of the Gulf of Guinea are the Benguela, the South Equatorial and the Guinea Currents. The latter flows eastward from Senegal to the Bight of Biafra and is fed by the Equatorial Countercurrent and a branch of the Canary Current.

Angola Current

Benguela Current

Guinea Current

Equatorial Countercurrent

South Equatorial Current

Spiny lobster (left)
The royal spiny lobster (*Panulirus regius*) lives mainly on rocky ground down to depths of about 130 feet (40 m) but is most often found between 15 and 50 feet (5 and 15 m). In the Gulf of Guinea it is an important part of inshore fisheries.

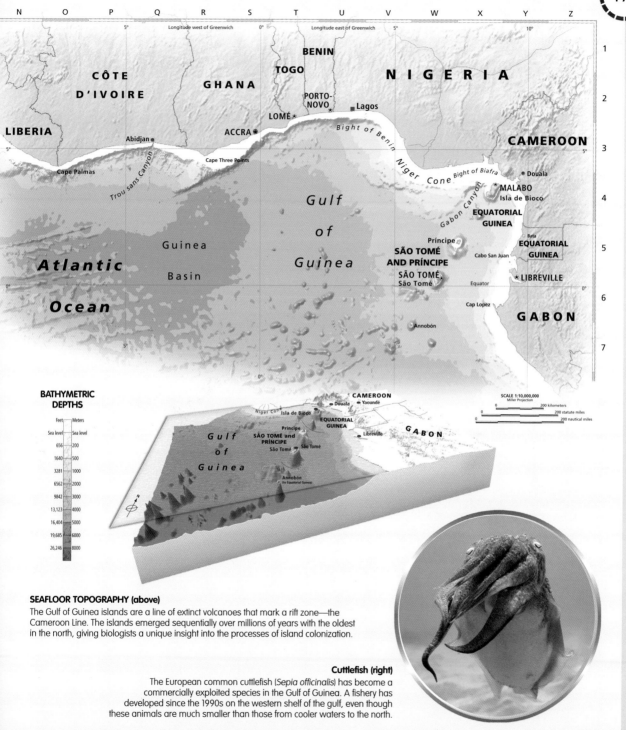

N O P Q R S T U V W X Y Z

5°   Longitude west of Greenwich   0°   Longitude east of Greenwich   5°   10°

BENIN

TOGO

CÔTE D'IVOIRE

GHANA

PORTO-NOVO

LOMÉ

N I G E R I A

Lagos

LIBERIA

ACCRA

Abidjan

Bight of Benin

CAMEROON

Cape Palmas

Cape Three Points

Niger Cone

Bight of Biafra

Douala

MALABO

Isla de Bioco

Trou sans Canyon

Gulf

of

Guinea

Gabon Canyon

EQUATORIAL GUINEA

Guinea

Basin

Príncipe

SÃO TOMÉ AND PRÍNCIPE

Cabo San Juan

Bata

EQUATORIAL GUINEA

A t l a n t i c

SÃO TOMÉ

São Tomé

Equator

LIBREVILLE

O c e a n

Cap Lopez

G A B O N

Annobón

5°

3°

5°

0°

6°

7°

1

2

3

4

5

6

7

BATHYMETRIC DEPTHS

Feet	Meters
Sea level	Sea level
656	200
1640	500
3281	1000
6562	2000
9842	3000
13,123	4000
16,404	5000
19,685	6000
26,246	8000

CAMEROON

Douala

Yaoundé

Niger Cone

Isla de Bioco

Príncipe

EQUATORIAL GUINEA

SÃO TOMÉ and PRÍNCIPE

Gulf

of

Guinea

São Tomé

São Tomé

G A B O N

Libreville

Annobón
(to Equatorial Guinea)

SCALE 1:10,000,000
Miller Projection

0   200 kilometers

0   200 statute miles

0   200 nautical miles

SEAFLOOR TOPOGRAPHY (above)

The Gulf of Guinea islands are a line of extinct volcanoes that mark a rift zone—the Cameroon Line. The islands emerged sequentially over millions of years with the oldest in the north, giving biologists a unique insight into the processes of island colonization.

Cuttlefish (right)

The European common cuttlefish (*Sepia officinalis*) has become a commercially exploited species in the Gulf of Guinea. A fishery has developed since the 1990s on the western shelf of the gulf, even though these animals are much smaller than those from cooler waters to the north.

WEST AFRICAN COAST

The surface waters of the southwest African coast are some of the most productive in the world. The abundant plankton sustains both fin fish and crustacean fisheries. This intense biological activity depends on cold, nutrient-rich water brought northward by the Benguela Current and brought to the surface by the upwelling produced by the prevailing south and southeasterly winds blowing over the sea surface. Suction dredging of offshore diamond deposits causes major damage to seabed communities.

Skeleton Coast (right)
This part of the Namibian coast got its name from the bleached bones that once covered the shore, left by whaling and seal hunting. There are also more than a thousand rusting hulks from the numerous shipwrecks caused by the dense fogs and offshore rocks.

Ocean fog (below)
On the west African coast the upwelling of the cold Benguela Current cools the air above it to the point where the water vapor in it starts to condense. This gives rise to dense ocean fogs, known locally as "cassimbo," that occur for most of the year.

Cape gannet colony (above)
Bird Island at Lamberts Bay on the west coast of South Africa is famed for its colony of Cape gannets (*Morus capensis*). Apart from some small cormorant colonies on rock stacks, there are no large seabird breeding colonies north of Lamberts Bay until the Namibian islands.

Black oystercatcher (right)
The African black oystercatcher (*Haematopus moquini*) lives and breeds on the rocky coasts and islands of southern Africa. It uses its strong beak to open bivalves or to probe for worms.

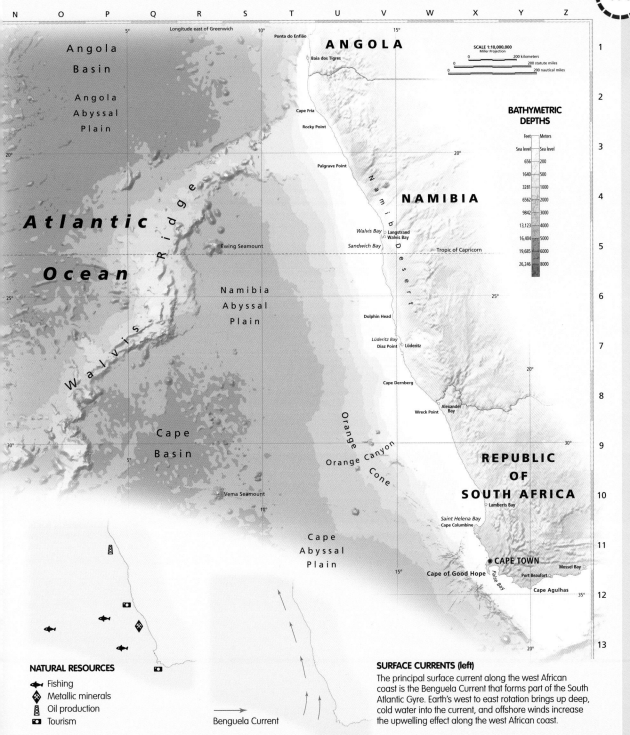

N O P Q R S T U V W X Y Z

5°   Longitude east of Greenwich   10°   15°

Ponta do Enfião

ANGOLA

○ Baia dos Tigres

SCALE 1:10,000,000
Miller Projection

0   200 kilometers
0   200 statute miles
0   200 nautical miles

Angola
Basin

Cape Fria

Rocky Point

BATHYMETRIC
DEPTHS

Feet	Meters
Sea level	Sea level
656	200
1640	500
3281	1000
6562	2000
9842	3000
13,123	4000
16,404	5000
19,685	6000
26,246	8000

Angola
Abyssal
Plain

20°

Palgrave Point

20°

NAMIBIA

A t l a n t i c

Ewing Seamount

Walvis Bay   Langstrand
    Walvis Bay
Sandwich Bay

Tropic of Capricorn

O c e a n

25°

Namibia
Abyssal
Plain

25°

Dolphin Head

Lüderitz Bay
Diaz Point   Lüderitz

20°

Cape Dernberg

Cape
Basin

Alexander
Bay
Wreck Point

30°

Vema Seamount

Orange Canyon
Cone

30°

REPUBLIC
OF
SOUTH AFRICA

10°

Lamberts Bay

Saint Helena Bay
Cape Columbine

Cape
Abyssal
Plain

15°

● **CAPE TOWN**   Mossel Bay

Port Beaufort

Cape of Good Hope   False Bay

Cape Agulhas   35°

20°

NATURAL RESOURCES

Fishing
Metallic minerals
Oil production
Tourism

Benguela Current

SURFACE CURRENTS (left)

The principal surface current along the west African coast is the Benguela Current that forms part of the South Atlantic Gyre. Earth's west to east rotation brings up deep, cold water into the current, and offshore winds increase the upwelling effect along the west African coast.

CAPE HORN

Until the opening of the Panama Canal in 1914, the only route for ships between the Pacific and Atlantic Oceans was around Cape Horn, which meant facing the mountainous seas and year-round storms found there. At latitudes below 40°S, prevailing winds blow from west to east around the world, almost uninterrupted by land, giving rise to the "roaring forties" and the "furious fifties." The turbulence and speed of these winds intensify around Cape Horn as the Andes and the Antarctic Peninsula channel the winds into the Drake Passage. An area of shallow water around Cape Horn increases wave heights and "rogue waves" can reach 100 feet (30 m).

Whale migration (right)
The southern right whale (*Eubalaena australis*) migrates northward to breed during the austral winter and is seen as far north as Brazil and Namibia. The population is estimated to be 12,000 animals and, since the hunting ban, stocks are estimated to have grown by 7 percent a year.

Tierra del Fuego (below)
Tierra del Fuego (Land of Fire) is an archipelago whose southern tip is Cape Horn. The islands have an inhospitable subpolar climate. The archipelago gets its name from the fires lit by the indigenous people that were seen by the explorer Magellan in 1520.

Magellanic penguins (above)
Magellanic penguins (*Spheniscus magellanicus*) have their main breeding grounds around Cape Horn, Tierra del Fuego and the Falkland Islands. During the austral winter the penguins from the Atlantic coast of South America and the Falkland Islands all migrate northward to the coast of Brazil.

SURFACE CURRENTS (below)
The Antarctic Circumpolar Current is a wind-driven current that is able to circle the globe unimpeded by landmasses. However, the Drake Passage is a choke point so that some water is diverted northward into the Peru Current, the rest eventually linking with the South Atlantic Gyre.

→ Antarctic Circumpolar Current

→ Cape Horn Current

→ Falklands Current

NATURAL RESOURCES
- Whales
- Metallic minerals
- Oil production
- Tourism

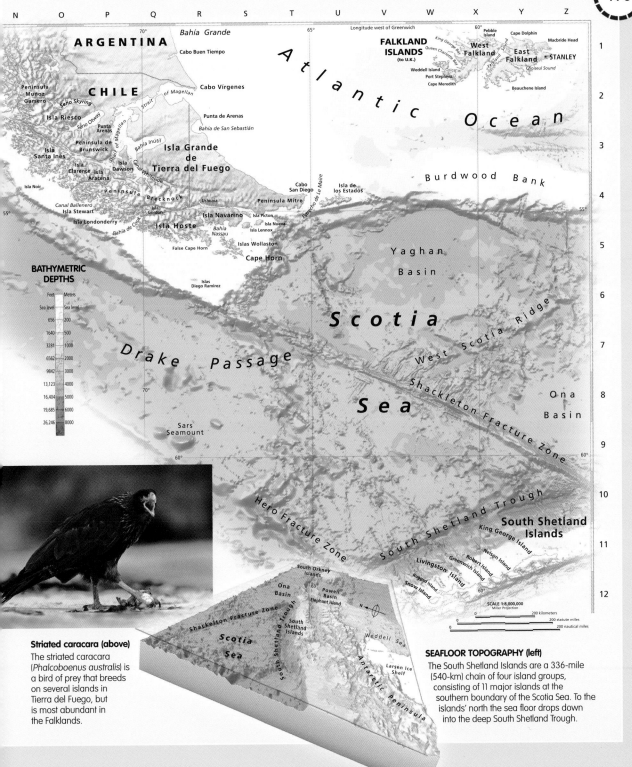

N O P Q R S T U V W X Y Z

ARGENTINA

Bahía Grande

70°

Cabo Buen Tiempo

65°

Longitude west of Greenwich

60°

FALKLAND ISLANDS
(to U.K.)

King George Bay

Pebble Island

Cape Dolphin

Macbride Head

West Falkland

East Falkland

★ STANLEY

CHILE

Península Muñoz Gamero

Seno Skyring

Isla Riesco

Seno Otway

Cabo Vírgenes

Queen Charlotte Bay

Weddell Island

Port Stephens

Cape Meredith

Choiseul Sound

Beauchene Island

Punta de Arenas

Bahía de San Sebastián

Península de Brunswick

Isla Santa Inés

Isla Clarence

Isla Araçena

Isla Dawson

Isla Grande de Tierra del Fuego

Isla Noir

Península Brecknock

Ushuaia

Cabo San Diego

Isla de los Estados

B u r d w o o d   B a n k

Canal Ballenero

Isla Stewart

Isla Gordon

Peninsula Mitre

55°

Isla Londonderry

Bahía de Cook

Isla Hoste

Isla Navarino

Isla Picton

Isla Nueva

Isla Lennox

55°

A t l a n t i c

O c e a n

Estrecho de Le Maire

Bahía Nassau

Islas Wollaston

False Cape Horn

Cape Horn

Islas Diego Ramírez

Y a g h a n   B a s i n

BATHYMETRIC DEPTHS

Feet	Meters
Sea level	Sea level
656	200
1640	500
3281	1000
6562	2000
9842	3000
13,123	4000
16,404	5000
19,685	6000
26,246	8000

S c o t i a

West Scotia Ridge

D r a k e   P a s s a g e

70°

Shackleton Fracture Zone

O n a   B a s i n

S e a

Sars Seamount

60°

60°

Hero Fracture Zone

South Shetland Trough

South Shetland Islands

King George Island

Nelson Island

Robert Island

Greenwich Island

South Orkney Islands

Ona Basin

Powell Basin

Elephant Island

Livingston Island

Rugged Island

Snow Island

60°

South Shetland Trough

Shackleton Fracture Zone

Scotia Sea

Weddell Sea

Larsen Ice Shelf

Antarctic Peninsula

SCALE 1:8,000,000
Miller Projection

200 kilometers

200 statute miles

200 nautical miles

Striated caracara (above)

The striated caracara (*Phalcoboenus australis*) is a bird of prey that breeds on several islands in Tierra del Fuego, but is most abundant in the Falklands.

SEAFLOOR TOPOGRAPHY (left)

The South Shetland Islands are a 336-mile (540-km) chain of four island groups, consisting of 11 major islands at the southern boundary of the Scotia Sea. To the islands' north the sea floor drops down into the deep South Shetland Trough.

CHAPTER TEN

INDIAN OCEAN

Indian elephant

The Andaman Islands, set in the tropical waters of the Indian Ocean's Andaman Sea, are fringed by coral reefs. The submarine scenery is spectacular and divers who make the trip to this site are richly rewarded. One of the group, Havelock Island, is home to some domesticated Indian elephants (*Elephas maximus*) that also relish a swim in the warm sea.

INDIAN OCEAN

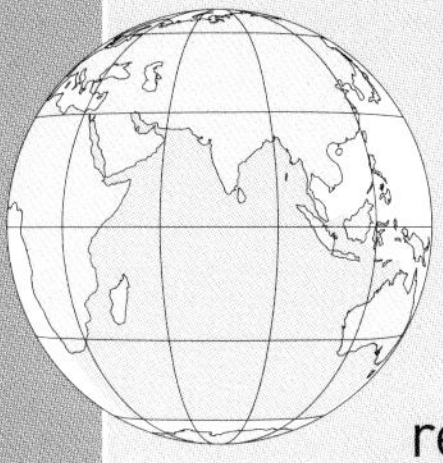

Unlike the Atlantic and Pacific, the Indian Ocean is completely closed to the north, by Asia, and it hosts a major current, the Somali, that reverses direction seasonally. Other subtropical basins, such as the South Atlantic and the North Pacific, have a strong western boundary current flowing poleward and a weak, wide drift as an eastern boundary current. By contrast, the South Indian Ocean has a strong poleward current as well, the Leeuwin, along the west coast of Australia.

THE FACTS

Area	26.5 million square miles (68.6 million km²)
Average depth	12,644 feet (3,854 m)
Maximum depth	23,376 feet (7,125 m)
Maximum width	6,300 miles (10,200 km)
Maximum length	5,800 miles (9,400 km)

NATURAL RESOURCES

- Fishing
- Shellfish
- Metallic minerals
- Mining
- Oil production
- Gas production
- Tourism

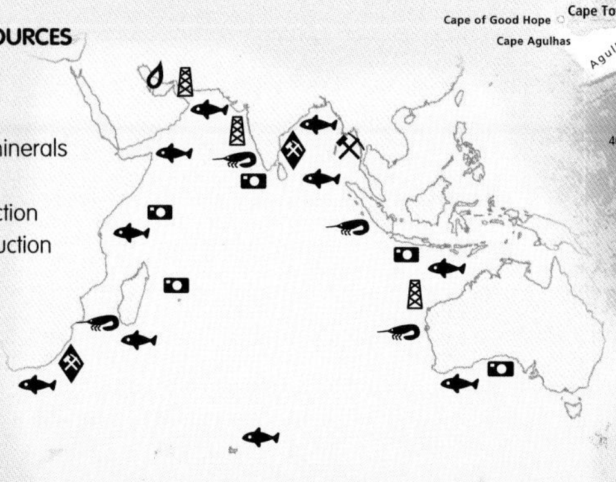

⚡ Endangered species

Hawksbill turtles (*Eretmochelys imbricata*) and coral reefs are both endangered entities in the Indian Ocean. The former are being caught for the high quality of their tortoiseshell and meat; the latter are at risk because of overexploitation, pollution, and ocean acidification.

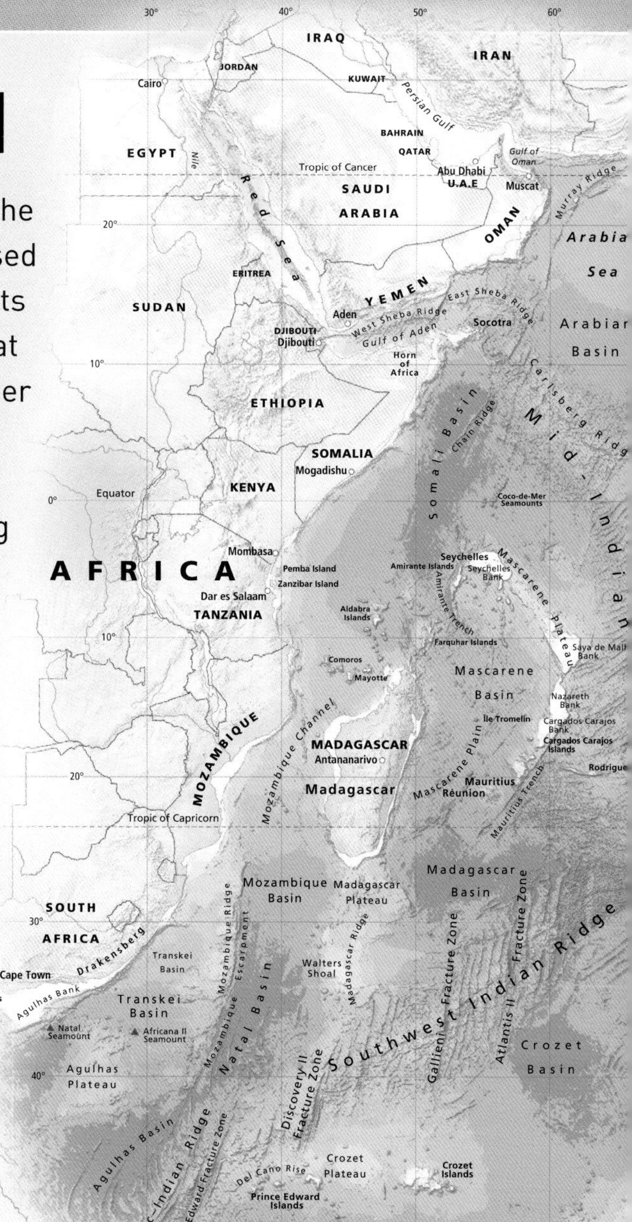

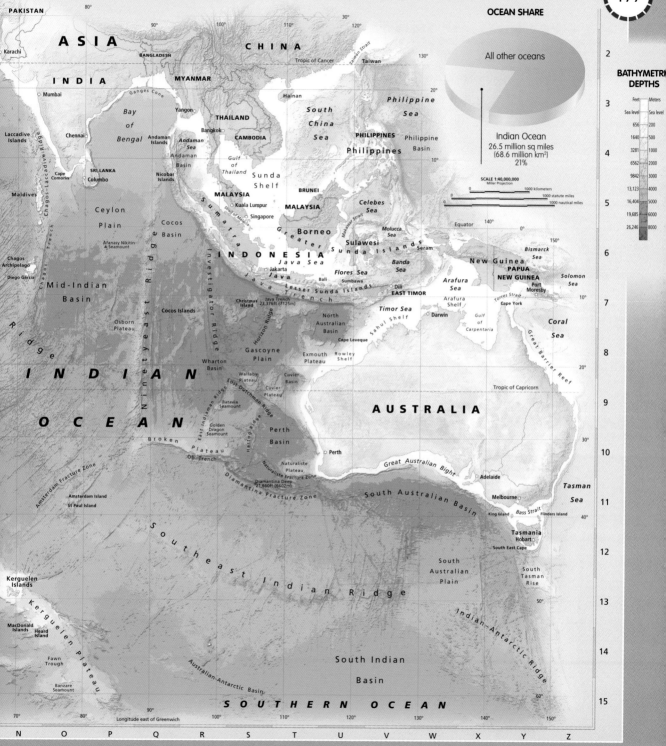

ASIA

PAKISTAN

Karachi

INDIA

Mumbai

CHINA

Tropic of Cancer

Taiwan

Taiwan Strait

80° 90° 100° 110° 30° 120° 130°

70°

BANGLADESH

MYANMAR

Ganges Cone

Yangon

Bay
of
Bengal

Andaman
Islands

THAILAND

Bangkok

CAMBODIA

Hainan

South
China
Sea

20°

Chennai

Laccadive
Islands

Andaman
Sea

Andaman

Nicobar
Islands

Gulf
of
Thailand

Sunda
Shelf

MALAYSIA

Kuala Lumpur

Singapore

BRUNEI

MALAYSIA

Borneo

PHILIPPINES

Philippines

*Philippine
Sea*

Philippine
Basin

*Celebes
Sea*

10°

SRI LANKA

Columbo

Cape
Comorin

Maldives

Chagos-Laccadive Ridge

Ceylon
Plain

Cocos
Basin

Afanasy Nikitin
Seamount

Chagos
Archipelago

Diego Garcia

Mid-Indian
Basin

Sumatra

Strait of Malacca

Greater Sunda Islands

INDONESIA

Java Sea

Jakarta

Java

Bali

Sumbawa

*Molucca
Sea*

Seram

Sulawesi

*Banda
Sea*

Flores Sea

*Arafura
Sea*

New Guinea

**PAPUA
NEW GUINEA**

Port
Moresby

*Bismarck
Sea*

*Solomon
Sea*

150°

140°

Equator

0°

OCEAN SHARE

All other oceans

Indian Ocean
26.5 million sq miles
(68.6 million km²)
21%

SCALE 1:40,000,000
Miller Projection

0   1000 kilometres
0   1000 statute miles
0   1000 nautical miles

**BATHYMETRIC
DEPTHS**

Feet	Meters
Sea level	Sea level
656	200
1640	500
3281	1000
6562	2000
9842	3000
13,123	4000
16,404	5000
19,685	6000
26,246	8000

2

3

4

5

6

7

Investigator Ridge

Ninetyeast Ridge

Java Trench

Lesser Sunda Islands

Christmas
Island

Java Trench
23,376ft (7125m)

Horizon Ridge

Dili
EAST TIMOR

Timor Sea

North
Australian
Basin

Arafura
Shelf

Torres Strait

Cape York

Darwin

Gulf of
Carpentaria

*Coral
Sea*

Great Barrier Reef

10°

Cocos Islands

Gascoyne
Plain

Exmouth
Plateau

Rowley
Shelf

Sahul Shelf

Cape Leveque

8

Osborn
Plateau

Wharton
Basin

Wallaby
Plateau

Cuvier
Basin

Cuvier
Plateau

AUSTRALIA

Tropic of Capricorn

9

INDIAN

East Indian Ridge

Lost Dutchmen Ridge

Batavia
Seamount

Golden
Dragon
Seamount

Perth
Basin

Perth

30°

OCEAN

Ridge

Broken
Plateau

Ob Trench

Naturaliste
Plateau

Naturaliste
Fracture Zone

Diamantina Deep
21,600ft (6602m)

Great Australian Bight

Adelaide

Melbourne

King Island

Bass Strait

Flinders Island

*Tasman
Sea*

40°

10

Amsterdam Fracture Zone

Amsterdam Island

St Paul Island

Diamantina Fracture Zone

South Australian Basin

11

Kerguelen
Islands

Southeast Indian Ridge

South
Australian
Plain

South
Tasman
Rise

Tasmania

Hobart

South East Cape

12

MacDonald
Islands

Heard
Island

Kerguelen Plateau

Fawn
Trough

Banzare
Seamount

Australian-Antarctic Basin

South Indian

Basin

Indian-Antarctic Ridge

50°

13

14

60°

15

S O U T H E R N   O C E A N

Longitude east of Greenwich

70° 80° 90° 100° 110° 120° 130° 140° 150°

N   O   P   Q   R   S   T   U   V   W   X   Y   Z

NORTHERN INDIAN OCEAN

The waters of the northern Indian Ocean support coral reefs and extensive areas of mangroves. Sea turtles nest on the Indian coast and many shark species thrive. At the center of this expanse of ocean are the Indian subcontinent and its extension, the Chagos-Laccadive Ridge. These geographical features split this ocean into two roughly equal parts: the Arabian Sea and the Bay of Bengal. Adjacent seas, the Red Sea and the Persian Gulf, contribute highly saline waters.

Lionfish (left)
Lionfish (*Pterois miles*) are a venomous marine species; they have long poisonous dorsal spines. An Indo-Pacific fish, they have been displaced to the Atlantic where they are now an invasive species.

SURFACE CURRENTS (above)
Northern Indian Ocean currents are influenced by monsoonal winds. The southwest monsoon blows from June to October, the northeast monsoon from December to April. The latter causes the reversal of the Somali Current and the formation of the Equatorial Countercurrent.

----> Equatorial Countercurrent
——— North Equatorial Current
——— Northeast monsoon

NATURAL RESOURCES
Fishing
Shellfish
Metallic minerals
Mining
Oil production
Tourism

N O P Q R S T U V W X Y Z

PAKISTAN

Karachi

Longitude east of Greenwich

SCALE 1:20,000,000
Miller Projection

ASIA

BANGLADESH
DHAKA

Tropic of Cancer

Murray Ridge

Basin

Gulf of Kachchh

INDIA

MYANMAR

Gulf of Khambhat

Indus Cone

Mumbai

Ganges Cone

YANGON

Arabian

Sea

Deccan

Plateau

Bay

of

Bengal

THAILAND

BANGKOK

Arabian

Basin

Laccadive
Islands

Chennai

Andaman
Islands

Andaman
Sea

CAMBODIA

PHNOM PENH

Gulf

of

Thailand

Andaman

Basin

Kanniyakumari
Cape Comorin

SRI LANKA

*COLOMBO

Nicobar
Islands

Sunda

Shelf

Ridge

Maldives

Ceylon

ACEH

MALAYSIA

KUALA LUMPUR

Strait of Malacca

SINGAPORE

INDIAN

Plain

Cocos

Equator

Basin

OCEAN

Sunda Trench

Sumatra

INDONESIA

Chagos–Laccadive Ridge

Chagos Trench

Ninetyeast Ridge

BATHYMETRIC
DEPTHS

Feet | Meters
Sea level | Sea level
656 | 200
1640 | 500
3281 | 1000
6562 | 2000
9842 | 3000
13,123 | 4000
16,404 | 5000
19,685 | 6000
26,246 | 8000

Oman coastline (above)
An abandoned fishing boat lies on the beach near Musandam, Oman. Subsistence and artisanal fisheries still play a major role in the economies of coastal communities around the northern Indian Ocean.

Surgeonfish (below)
There are many species of surgeonfish, here the powder blue (*Acanthurus leucosternon*). Surgeonfish are brightly colored, grow to 6–16 inches (15–40 cm), and are found among coral reefs in the tropics, where they graze on algae.

BAY OF BENGAL

This ocean region is not a bay in the usual coastal sense of the word, but constitutes the sea between India and Southeast Asia. A substantial part of the Bay of Bengal is less than 9,840 feet (3,000 m) deep, including all of the Andaman Sea along its eastern side. Much of the seafloor is flat, the result of sediment from the main rivers of the Indian subcontinent accumulating here over millenia.

THE FACTS	
Area	838,613 square miles (2,172,000 km²)
Average depth	8,500 feet (2,600 m)
Maximum depth	15,400 feet (4,694 m)
Maximum width	1,000 miles (1,610 km)
Maximum length	1,300 miles (2,090 km)

NATURAL RESOURCES

 Fishing
 Metallic minerals

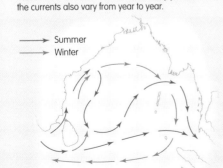

Chlorophyll (right)
In this satellite image of the Bay of Bengal, the green coloration gives a good indication of the density of chlorophyll in the water, which in turn can be related to the presence of phytoplankton, marine algae. Regions colored red show where phytoplankton is abundant.

Subsistence fisheries (below)
Fishermen in Orissa, India, remove a meager catch from their nets while others wait to take the fish to market. Subsistence or artisanal fisheries are found along the whole coastline of the Bay of Bengal, but in many places overfishing has caused fish stocks to collapse.

SURFACE CURRENTS (below)

The surface currents here are affected by monsoonal winds. The currents off the northeastern coast of the Indian subcontinent reverse direction seasonally. However, the duration and intensity of monsoonal winds are not identical every year, so the currents also vary from year to year.

 Summer
 Winter

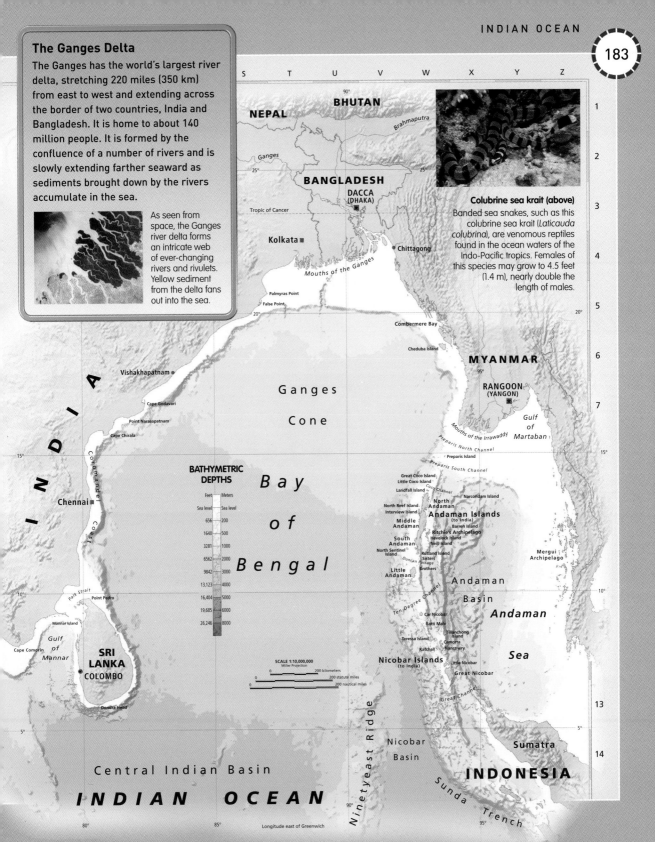

The Ganges Delta

The Ganges has the world's largest river delta, stretching 220 miles (350 km) from east to west and extending across the border of two countries, India and Bangladesh. It is home to about 140 million people. It is formed by the confluence of a number of rivers and is slowly extending farther seaward as sediments brought down by the rivers accumulate in the sea.

As seen from space, the Ganges river delta forms an intricate web of ever-changing rivers and rivulets. Yellow sediment from the delta fans out into the sea.

Colubrine sea krait (above)

Banded sea snakes, such as this colubrine sea krait (*Laticauda colubrina*), are venomous reptiles found in the ocean waters of the Indo-Pacific tropics. Females of this species may grow to 4.5 feet (1.4 m), nearly double the length of males.

S T U V W X Y Z

90°

BHUTAN

NEPAL

Brahmaputra

Ganges

25°   25°

BANGLADESH

Tropic of Cancer

DACCA
(DHAKA)

Kolkata

Chittagong

Mouths of the Ganges

Palmyras Point

False Point

20°   20°

Combermere Bay

Cheduba Island

95°

MYANMAR

Vishakhapatnam

Ganges

RANGOON
(YANGON)

Cape Godavari

Cone

Gulf
of
Martaban

Point Narasapatnam

Cape Chirala

Mouths of the Irrawaddy

Preparis North Channel

15°   15°

Preparis Island

Preparis South Channel

I N D I A

BATHYMETRIC
DEPTHS

Great Coco Island
Little Coco Island

Coco Channel

Narcondam Island

Landfall Island

Feet | Meters

Bay

North Reef Island
Interview Island

North
Andaman

Sea level | Sea level

Andaman Islands
(to India)

Chennai

656 | 200

of

Middle
Andaman

Barren Island

1640 | 500

Ritchie's Archipelago
Havelock Island

3281 | 1000

South
Andaman

Neill Island

6562 | 2000

North Sentinel
Island

Rutland Island

Mergui
Archipelago

9842 | 3000

Bengal

Sisters
Duncan Passage
Brothers

13,123 | 4000

Little
Andaman

Andaman

10°   10°

Palk Strait

16,404 | 5000

Basin

Point Pedro

19,685 | 6000

Ten Degree Channel

Andaman

Mannar Island

26,246 | 8000

Car Nicobar

Gulf
of
Mannar

Batti Malv

Tillanchong
Island

Sea

Cape Comorin

Teressa Island

Camorta
Nancowry

SRI
LANKA

Katchall

Little Nicobar

COLOMBO

SCALE 1:10,000,000
Miller Projection

Nicobar Islands
(to India)

Great Nicobar

0   200 kilometers

Dondra Head

0   200 statute miles

0   200 nautical miles

Great Channel

13

5°   5°

Nicobar
Basin

14

Central Indian Basin

Sumatra

INDONESIA

I N D I A N   O C E A N

Ninetyeast Ridge

80°   85°   Longitude east of Greenwich   90°   Sunda Trench   95°

RED SEA

The Red Sea is part of a rift valley that formed when Africa separated from Arabia. Lying between two desert regions, the Red Sea receives little runoff from land but has high levels of evaporation; some of the most saline waters in the world's seas are to be found here. Access to the open sea is over a sill at the Bab al Mandab strait that is only 360 feet (110 m) deep. As a result of this, fresher water moves in at the surface and dense, highly saline water with a low oxygen content escapes below the inflow.

THE FACTS	
Area	169,100 square miles (438,000 km²)
Average depth	1,608 feet (490 m)
Maximum depth	9,974 feet (3,040 m)
Maximum width	220 miles (355 km)
Maximum length	1,398 miles (2,250 km)

SURFACE CURRENTS (below)
Surface currents in the Red Sea are largely driven by the dominant winds. In winter the flow is northward. In summer the winds blow from the opposite direction, but in general only weaken the northward flow.

→ Summer
→ Winter

Twobar anemonefish (above)
Among the tentacles of the sea anemone, the twobar anemonefish (*Amphiprion bicinctus*) is safe from predators. Anemonefish are found in warm seas worldwide but particularly on coral or rocky reefs in the Indo-Pacific.

Bottlenose dolphin (left)
The most common of ocean dolphins, bottlenose dolphins (*Tursiops truncatus*), inhabit warm seas worldwide. They live in pods of 15 or more and hunt small fish. They use echolocation to locate prey, and sound for communication.

Suez Canal

Connecting the Mediterranean Sea with the Red Sea, the Suez Canal was opened to shipping in 1869. It is 120 miles (193 km) long and can handle ships of 150,000 tons displacement and 53 feet (16 m) draft. Up to 160 ships pass through it each day. There is a negligible difference in height between the waters of the oceans at each end, so no locks are needed in the canal.

A seagoing freighter sails through the Suez Canal on its way to the Red Sea. Ships pass through the canal at low speeds to avoid creating a bow wash that could erode the shoreline.

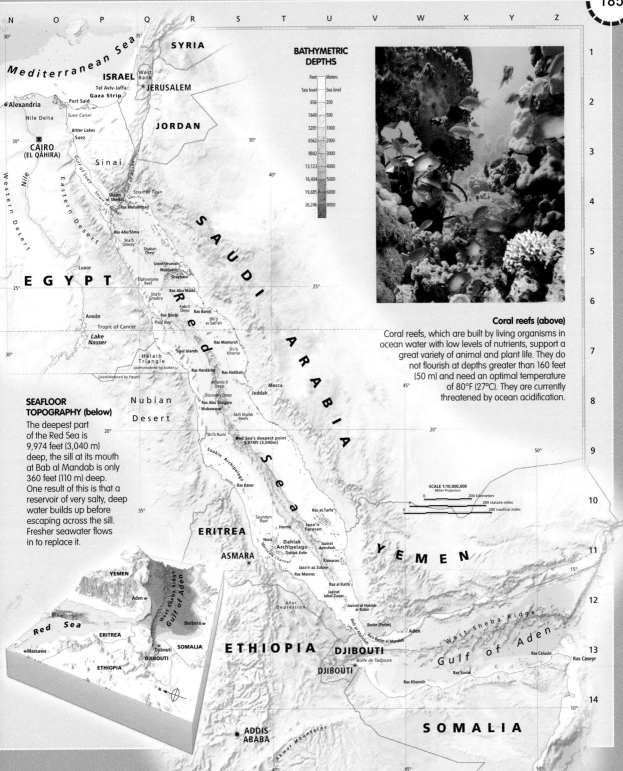

BATHYMETRIC DEPTHS

Feet	Meters
Sea level	Sea level
656	200
1640	500
3281	1000
6562	2000
9842	3000
13,123	4000
16,404	5000
19,685	6000
26,246	8000

Coral reefs (above)

Coral reefs, which are built by living organisms in ocean water with low levels of nutrients, support a great variety of animal and plant life. They do not flourish at depths greater than 160 feet (50 m) and need an optimal temperature of 80°F (27°C). They are currently threatened by ocean acidification.

SEAFLOOR TOPOGRAPHY (below)

The deepest part of the Red Sea is 9,974 feet (3,040 m) deep, the sill at its mouth at Bab al Mandab is only 360 feet (110 m) deep. One result of this is that a reservoir of very salty, deep water builds up before escaping across the sill. Fresher seawater flows in to replace it.

SCALE 1:10,000,000
Miller Projection

0   200 kilometers
0   200 statute miles
0   200 nautical miles

Map labels:

N O P Q R S T U V W X Y Z

Mediterranean Sea
SYRIA
ISRAEL
West Bank
JERUSALEM
Gaza Strip
Tel Aviv-Jaffa
Alexandria
Nile Delta
Port Said
Suez Canal
JORDAN
Bitter Lakes
CAIRO (EL QÂHIRA)
Suez
Sinai
Gulf of Suez
Strait of Tiran
Sharm el Sheikh
Ras Muhammad
Western Desert
Eastern Desert
Ras Abu Sôma
Sha'b Quway'i
Shaban Deep'
EGYPT
Umm Urumah
Mashabih
Shaybara
Luxor
Elphinstone Reef
Sha'b Ghadira
Ras Abu Madd
Kebrit Deep
Aswân
Ras Banâs
Ras Baridi
Foul Bay
Tropic of Cancer
Shi'b as Sab'ah
Lake Nasser
Ras Masturah
Siyal Islands
Shi'b Kharrar
Halaib Triangle (Administered by Sudan)
Ras Hardârba
Ras Hatibah
(Administered by Egypt)
Atlantis II Deep
Mecca
Nubian Desert
Discovery Deep
Jeddah
Ras Abu Shagara
Mukawwar
Abû Shawk Reefs
Shi'b Rumi
Red Sea's deepest point 9,974ft (3,040m)
SAUDI ARABIA
Red Sea
Suakin Archipelago
Ras Kasar
Ras at Tarfa
Jaza'ir Farasan
Saunders Reef
Harmil
Nora
Dahlak Archipelago
Dahlak Kebir
Jazirat Antufash
Kamaran
Jaza'ir az Zubayr
Masarka Channel
Ras Manrec
YEMEN
ERITREA
ASMARA
Ras al Katib
Jazirat Jabal Zuqar
Afar Depression
Jazirat al Hanish al Kabir
Barim (Perim)
Bab al Mandab
Ra's Barim al Mandab
Aden
Berbera
West Sheba Ridge
Gulf of Aden
SOMALIA
ETHIOPIA
DJIBOUTI
DJIBOUTI
Golfe de Tadjoura
Ras Caluula
Ras Caseyr
Ras Surud
Ras Khansiir
ADDIS ABABA
Ahmar Mountains
SOMALIA

Inset map:

YEMEN
Red Sea
Aden
West Sheba Ridge
Gulf of Aden
ERITREA
ETHIOPIA
SOMALIA
Massawa
Djibouti
DJIBOUTI
N

ARABIAN SEA

Maritime trade routes have crossed the Arabian Sea since ancient times, and the modern-day vessels that use the Suez Canal continue to pass through. Lying to the west of the Indian subcontinent and the Chagos-Laccadive Ridge, the Arabian Sea has two Mediterranean seas feeding water into it, the Persian Gulf and the Red Sea. The flow in the Arabian Sea is seasonal: clockwise flow in summer, fed by the Somali Current, and a counterclockwise, weak flow in winter.

THE FACTS	
Area	1.5 million square miles (3.9 million km²)
Average depth	9,022 feet (2,750 m)
Maximum depth	15,262 feet (4,652 m)
Maximum width	1,490 miles (2,400 km)

Dugong (right)
Dugongs (*Dugong dugon*) are large, placid marine mammals found in the Indo-Pacific. They eat seagrasses and are found largely in bays and mangrove channels, where they may be vulnerable to predators. Although capable of living for 70 years, they are now extinct in parts of their former range.

NATURAL RESOURCES

- Fishing
- Shellfish
- Oil production
- Tourism

Fisherman's hut (above)
Simple huts and dugout canoes are still used by villagers on Socotra Island, just off the tip of the Horn of Africa.

→ East Arabian Current
→ Somali Current

SURFACE CURRENTS (left)
The Arabian Sea has surface currents largely influenced by the monsoonal winds and, as these winds may differ in duration from year to year, so do the currents. At depth the waters are influenced by the dense, salty water that emerges from the two adjacent seas, the Red Sea and Persian Gulf.

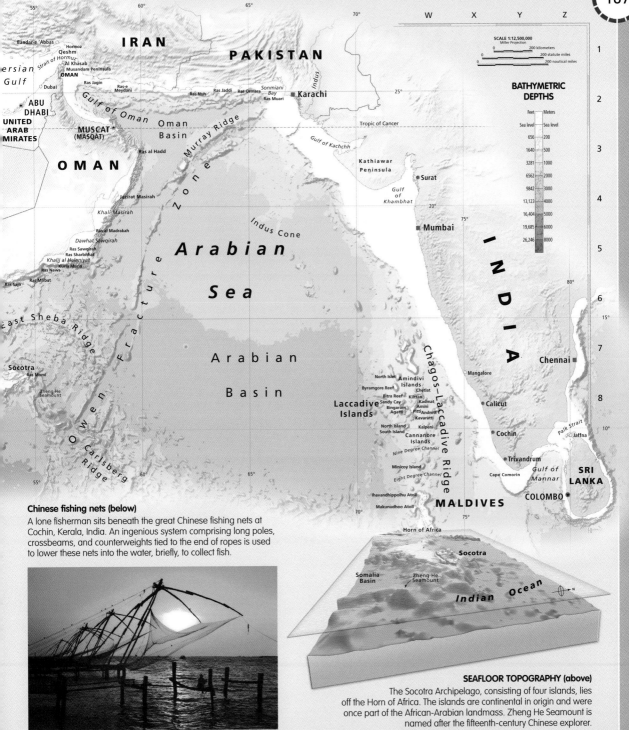

55°   60°   65°   70°

W   X   Y   Z

SCALE 1:12,500,000
Miller Projection

0   200 kilometers
0   200 statute miles
0   200 nautical miles

1

IRAN

PAKISTAN

Bandar-e 'Abbas
Hormoz
Qeshm
Al Khasab
Musandam Peninsula
OMAN

Persian
Gulf

Strait of Hormuz

Dubai

**ABU
DHABI**

**UNITED
ARAB
EMIRATES**

Ras Jagin
Ras-e
Meydani
Ras Nuh   Ras Jaddi   Ras Ormara   Sonmiani
Bay
Ras Muari   **Karachi**

Indus

25°

Tropic of Cancer

2

**BATHYMETRIC
DEPTHS**

Feet   Meters
Sea level   Sea level

Gulf of Oman

**MUSCAT
(MASQAT)**

Oman
Basin

Murray Ridge

Gulf of Kachchh

Kathiawar
Peninsula

656   200
1640   500
3281   1000
6562   2000
9842   3000
13,123   4000
16,404   6000
19,685   6000
26,246   8000

3

OMAN

Ras al Hadd

Surat

Gulf
of
Khambhat

20°

75°

4

Jazirat Masirah

Khali Masirah

Mumbai

Indus Cone

A r a b i a n

Fracture Zone

5

Ras al Madrakah
Ras Sawqirah
Ras Sharbithat
Khalij al Halaniyat
Kuria Muria
Ras Naws

Ras Sajir   Ras Mirbat

S e a

80°

I
N
D
I
A

6

15°

East Sheba Ridge

Yemen Fracture Zone

A r a b i a n

Socotra
Ras Momi

Owen

B a s i n

Chennai

Mangalore

7

Zheng He
Seamount

North Islet   Amindivi
Islands
Byramgore Reef   Chetlat
Bitra Reef   Kiltan
Sandy Cay   Kadmat
Bingaram   Amini
Agatti   Pitti   Andrott
Kavaratti

Calicut

Chagos-Laccadive Ridge

8

Carlsberg Ridge

**Laccadive
Islands**

North Island
South Island

Kalpeni

**Cannanore
Islands**

Nine Degree Channel

Cochin

Minicoy Island

Eight Degree Channel

Trivandrum

Cape Comorin

Gulf of
Mannar

Jaffna

Palk Strait

10°

**SRI
LANKA**

60°   65°

Ihavandhippolhu Atoll

Makunudhoo Atoll

MALDIVES

75°

COLOMBO

55°   70°

Horn of Africa

Chinese fishing nets (below)

A lone fisherman sits beneath the great Chinese fishing nets at Cochin, Kerala, India. An ingenious system comprising long poles, crossbeams, and counterweights tied to the end of ropes is used to lower these nets into the water, briefly, to collect fish.

Socotra

Somalia
Basin

Zheng He
Seamount

Indian   Ocean

N

SEAFLOOR TOPOGRAPHY (above)

The Socotra Archipelago, consisting of four islands, lies off the Horn of Africa. The islands are continental in origin and were once part of the African-Arabian landmass. Zheng He Seamount is named after the fifteenth-century Chinese explorer.

PERSIAN GULF

The Persian Gulf region is the site of vast crude oil and gas reserves. The drilling operations that extract these valuable commodities put pressure on the natural environment. In its geography, the Persian Gulf is in many respects very similar to the Red Sea. It is long and narrow, with a narrow strait at its southern end, and is bordered by land that is predominantly arid. Its waters are also strongly saline because there is an excess of evaporation over rainfall. However, in contrast to the Red Sea, it is very shallow.

THE FACTS	
Area	96,911 square miles (251,000 km²)
Average depth	164 feet (50 m)
Maximum depth	344 feet (119 m)
Maximum width	35 miles (56 km)
Maximum length	615 miles (989 km)

Oil rig (left)
Oil platforms are enormous structures housing machinery for drilling wells into the seafloor in search of oil and gas, processing plants, and accommodation for workers. Platforms may be afloat or attached to the seafloor, depending on the depth of the water.

Sediment flow (below)
A satellite image shows the true color of the sea at the head of the Persian Gulf. Here the combined waters of the Tigris and Euphrates Rivers, laden with sediment, enter the sea. They appear light brown where they enter, and then dissipate into turquoise swirls.

NATURAL RESOURCES (left)

🛢 Oil production
🖤 Gas production
📷 Tourism

SURFACE CURRENTS (right)
The waters of the Persian Gulf are so shallow, less than 82 feet (25 m) in some parts, that the direction of the surface currents is almost entirely determined by the winds. Winds are from the north or northeast for most of the year.

→ Wind-driven currents

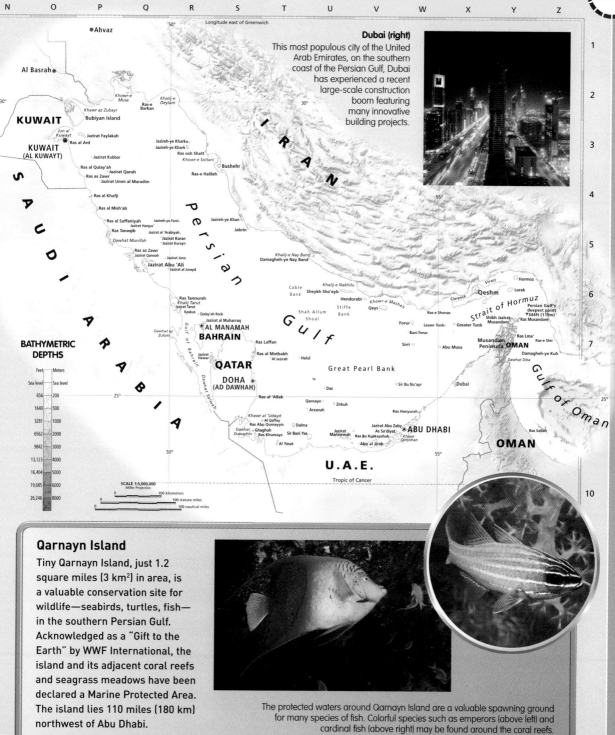

N O P Q R S T U V W X Y Z

1

Dubai (right)
This most populous city of the United Arab Emirates, on the southern coast of the Persian Gulf, Dubai has experienced a recent large-scale construction boom featuring many innovative building projects.

•Ahvaz

Longitude east of Greenwich

50°

Al Basrah

Khowr-e Musa
Khalij-e Deylam
Ras-e Barkan

30°

2

KUWAIT

Bubiyan Island

I R A N

30°

Jun al Kuwayt
Ras al Ard

3

KUWAIT (AL KUWAYT)

Jazirat Faylakah

Jazireh-ye Kharku
Jazireh-ye Khark
Khowr-e Soltani
Ras osh Shatt

Bushehr

S A U D I

Jazirat Kubbar

Ras al Qulay'ah
Jazirat Qaruh
Ras as Zawr
Jazirat Umm al Maradim

Ras-e Halileh

Ras al Khafji

4

55°

Ras al Mish'ab

Ras al Saffaniyah
Jazirat Harqus
Ras Tanaqib

Jazireh-ye Farsi
Jazireh-ye Khan

Jabrin

Dawhat Munifah

Jazirat al 'Arabiyah
Jazirat Karan
Jazirat Kurayn

5

Ras az Zawr
Jazirat Qannah

Jazirat Jana

Khalij-e Nay Band
Damagheh-ye Nay Band

Jazirat Abu 'Ali
Jazirat al Jurayd

A R A B I A

P e r s i a n

Ras Tannurah
Khalij Tarut
Jazirat Tarut

Cable Bank

Khalij-e Nakhilu
Sheykh Sho'eyb

Strait
Hormoz

6

Qeshm
Larak

Kaskus
Qulay'ah Rock

Shah Allum Shoal
Stiffe Bank
Qeys
Hendorabi

Khowr-e Masheh
Clarence

Strait of Hormuz

G u l f

AL MANAMAH

Dawhat az Zulum

G u l f   o f   B a h r a i n

BAHRAIN

Forur
Bani Forur

Lesser Tunb
Ras-e Shenas
Greater Tunb

Shibh Jazirat Musandam
Ras Musandam

Persian Gulf's deepest point ▼344ft (119m)

7

QATAR

Jazirat Hawar

Ras Laffan

Ras al Matbakh
Al Jazirah

Sirri
Abu Musa

Ras Lma'
Musandam Peninsula
OMAN
Ras-e Shir

25°

DOHA (AD DAWHAH)

Dawhat Salwah

Halul

Great Pearl Bank

Damagheh-ye Kuh
Dawhat Diba

G u l f   o f   O m a n

Das

Dubai

25°

Ras al 'Allak

Qarnayn
Zirkuh

Sir Bu Nu'ayr

Ras Hanyurah

BATHYMETRIC DEPTHS

Feet	Meters
Sea level	Sea level
656	200
1640	500
3281	1000
6562	2000
9842	3000
13,123	4000
16,404	5000
19,685	6000
26,246	8000

Khawr al 'Udayd
Al Qaffay
Ras Abu Qumayyis
Dawhat Duwayhin
Ghaghah
Ras Khumays

Dalma

Arzanah

Jazirat Abu Zaby
As Sa'diyat
Ras Bu Kuskayshah

ABU DHABI

Ras Sallan

Jazirat Marawwah
Sir Bani Yas

Khawr Qirqishan

OMAN

Al Yasat

Abu al Jirab

55°

50°

U.A.E.

Tropic of Cancer

SCALE 1:5,000,000
Miller Projection

0   100 kilometers
0   100 statute miles
0   100 nautical miles

10

Qarnayn Island

Tiny Qarnayn Island, just 1.2 square miles (3 km²) in area, is a valuable conservation site for wildlife—seabirds, turtles, fish—in the southern Persian Gulf. Acknowledged as a "Gift to the Earth" by WWF International, the island and its adjacent coral reefs and seagrass meadows have been declared a Marine Protected Area. The island lies 110 miles (180 km) northwest of Abu Dhabi.

The protected waters around Qarnayn Island are a valuable spawning ground for many species of fish. Colorful species such as emperors (above left) and cardinal fish (above right) may be found around the coral reefs.

WESTERN INDIAN OCEAN

From the head of the Arabian Sea to beyond the southern tip of the African continent, the western Indian Ocean covers a vast region. Highly saline water from the Red Sea can be traced to the southern tip of Africa. Fresher water at intermediate depths comes from the Southern Ocean and moves northward. A number of north–south ridges influence the movement of deep and bottom waters. Localized coastal upwelling is found in the Somali, East Madagascar, and Agulhas systems, stimulating higher biological productivity.

Granite shores (left)

Large boulders are common on the shoreline of granitic islands in the Seychelles, where endemic plants and large colonies of seabirds thrive. Human settlement displaced the giant tortoise (*Dipsochelys hololissa*) but it is found on many of the archipelago's coral islands.

SURFACE CURRENTS (below left)

The surface flow along the east coast of Africa is dominated by three currents: the southward Agulhas Current, the northward East African Coastal Current, fed by the South Equatorial Current, and the seasonally reversing Somali Current. The Arabian Sea has clockwise flow in summer, counterclockwise flow in winter.

→ Agulhas Current
--→ Agulhas Return Current
→ Antarctic Circumpolar Current
→ East Madagascar Current
→ South Equatorial Current

NATURAL RESOURCES (right)

- Fishing
- Shellfish
- ✗ Mining
- Oil production
- Tourism

Agulhas Current (below)

The Agulhas Current, which carries water southward along southern Africa, is one of the world's major ocean currents. It extends to a depth of 9,850 feet (3,000 m) and flows swiftly. In this satellite image, clouds are gray, warm Agulhas waters red, and colder water green.

SEAFLOOR TOPOGRAPHY (below)

The islands of Réunion and Mauritius, which lie east of Madagascar, are both volcanic. The volcano on Réunion is quite active. North of Mauritius the shallow Mascarene Plateau forms a formidable barrier to east–west currents such as the South Equatorial Current.

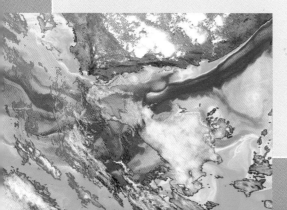

Cargados Carajos Bank
Cargados Carajos Islands
Rodrigues Island
Mauritius
Réunion
Mascarene Islands
Mascarene Plain
Mauritius Trench
Indian Ocean
N

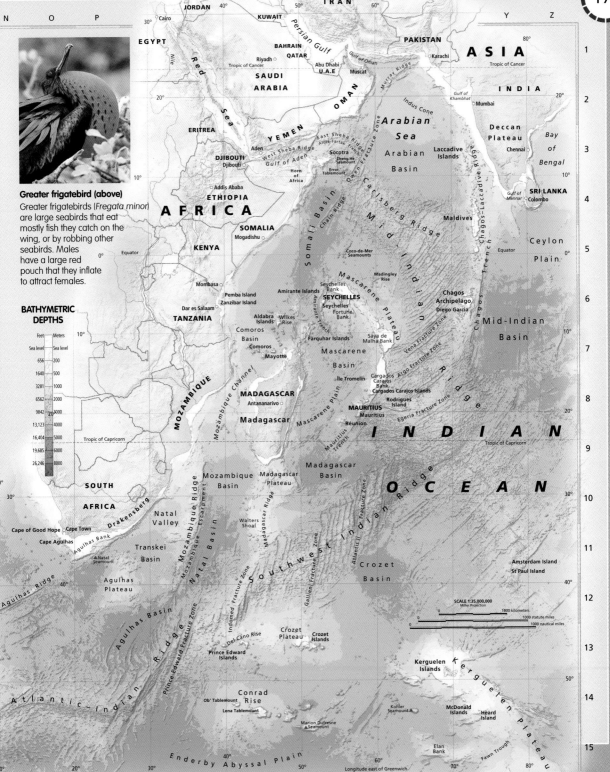

Greater frigatebird (above)

Greater frigatebirds (*Fregata minor*) are large seabirds that eat mostly fish they catch on the wing, or by robbing other seabirds. Males have a large red pouch that they inflate to attract females.

BATHYMETRIC DEPTHS

Feet	Meters
Sea level	Sea level
656	200
1640	500
3281	1000
6562	2000
9842	3000
13,123	4000
16,404	5000
19,685	6000
26,246	8000

SCALE 1:35,000,000
Miller Projection

1800 kilometers
1000 statute miles
1000 nautical miles

MOZAMBIQUE CHANNEL

Lying between the landmass of Africa and the island of Madagascar, the waters and winds of the Mozambique Channel are influenced by both. Eddies are formed at the narrows of the channel and have an influence on the deep-sea ecosystems. Marine birds prefer to feed at their edges. Coral reefs are an important ecological component on the eastern side of the channel. On the western side, major rivers, such as the Zambezi, influence the shelf waters, especially when they intermittently come down in flood, laden with silt.

Coastal fishing (left)
Villagers in Mozambique who rely on fishing have many challenges to contend with. Declining fish stocks, extreme weather events such as tropical cyclones, and regular flooding of low-lying villages by rivers bursting their banks make their trade a hazardous one.

SURFACE CURRENTS (below left)
The flow in the Mozambique Channel is not a continuous north to south current. It consists of a series of eddies, whirlpools of water that drift southward on the western side of the channel. They may draw coastal waters into the deep sea.

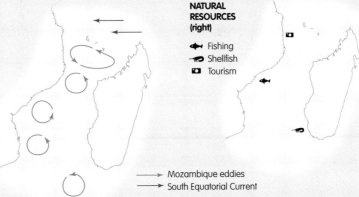

NATURAL RESOURCES (right)

- Fishing
- Shellfish
- Tourism

→ Mozambique eddies
→ South Equatorial Current

Estuary flow (below)
On the northwest coast of Madagascar, seawater penetrates inland to join the freshwater outflow of the Betsiboka River. Numerous islands and sandbars have formed from the sediment in this estuary and have been shaped by the push and pull of tides.

⚡ Coelacanth
Coelacanths (*Latimeria chalumnae*) are highly unusual fish. Long considered to have been extinct for the past 70 million years, they were rediscovered in 1938 and have now been found along much of the east African coast. Weighing 180 pounds (80 kg) and with a length of 6 feet (2 m), individuals may live for 100 years.

Coelacanths are found largely in caves in the continental shelf at depths up to 2,300 feet (700 m).

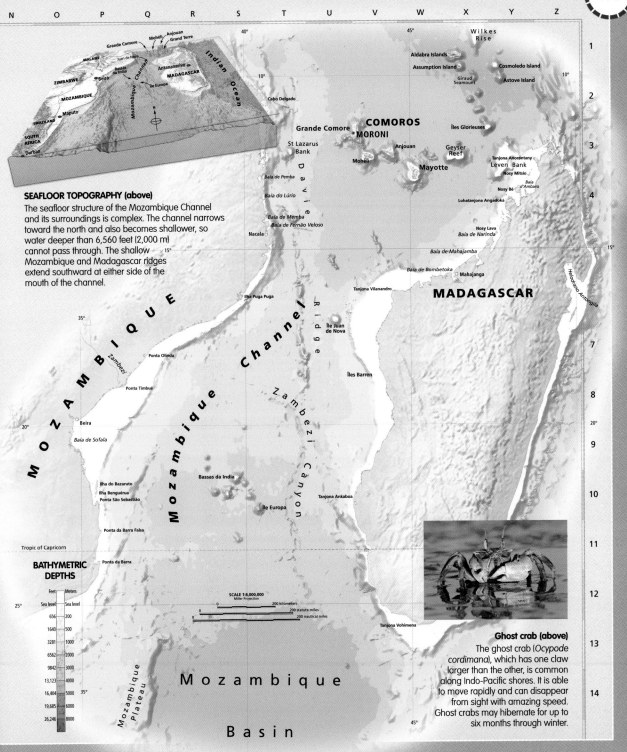

N O P Q R S T U V W X Y Z

40°

45°

Wilkes
Rise

1

Grande Comore Mohéli Anjouan
Grand Terre

MALAWI

Juan de Nova

Indian Ocean

Aldabra Islands
Assumption Island

Cosmoledo Island

2

ZIMBABWE Bassas
da India Antananarivo

MADAGASCAR

Giraud
Seamount

Astove Island

10°

10°

MOZAMBIQUE

Île Europa

Beira

Cabo Delgado

3

SWAZILAND

Maputo

COMOROS
*MORONI

Îles Glorieuses

SOUTH
AFRICA

Durban

Grande Comore

St Lazarus
Bank

Anjouan

Geyser
Reef

Tanjona Anorontany
Leven Bank

Nosy Mitsio

SEAFLOOR TOPOGRAPHY (above)

The seafloor structure of the Mozambique Channel
and its surroundings is complex. The channel narrows
toward the north and also becomes shallower, so
water deeper than 6,560 feet (2,000 m)
cannot pass through. The shallow
Mozambique and Madagascar ridges
extend southward at either side of the
mouth of the channel.

Mohéli

Mayotte

Nosy Bé

Nosy
d'Ambaro

Baía de Pemba

Baía do Lúrio

Lohatanjona Angadoka

4

Baía de Memba
Baía de Fernão Veloso

Nosy Lava
Baía de Narinda

Nacala

Baía de Mahajamba

15°

15°

D a v i e

Baía de Bombetoka

Mahajanga

Heliotrano Antongila

Ilha Puga Puga

Tanjona Vilanandro

MADAGASCAR

R i d g e

Île Juan
de Nova

35°

M

o

Mozambique Channel

7

Zambezi

Ponta Olinda

Îles Barren

z

a

Ponta Timbué

Z

a

m

b

e

z

i

8

20°

m

Beira

20°

Baía de Sofala

C

a

9

b

Ilha do Bazaruto
Ilha Benguérua
Ponta São Sebastião

Bassas da India

n

y

Tanjona Ankaboa

10

i

Île Europa

o

q

Ponta da Barra Falsa

n

Tropic of Capricorn

11

u

Ponta da Barra

BATHYMETRIC
DEPTHS

Feet	Meters
Sea level	Sea level
656	200
1640	500
3281	1000
6562	2000
9842	3000
13,123	4000
16,404	5000
19,685	6000
26,246	8000

25°

SCALE 1:8,000,000
Miller Projection

0   200 kilometers
0   200 statute miles
0   200 nautical miles

Tanjona Vohimena

12

13

Ghost crab (above)

The ghost crab (*Ocypode
cordimana*), which has one claw
larger than the other, is common
along Indo-Pacific shores. It is able
to move rapidly and can disappear
from sight with amazing speed.
Ghost crabs may hibernate for up to
six months through winter.

e

Mozambique Plateau

M o z a m b i q u e

35°

14

45°

B a s i n

EASTERN INDIAN OCEAN

South of the equator, the flow is dominated by the wide South Equatorial Current during the southwest monsoon. The flow of the Southwest Monsoon Current is eastward at the equator. During the northeast monsoon, the westward currents, the North Equatorial Current and the South Equatorial Current, are bisected by an eastward Equatorial Countercurrent. Throughout the year, water flows into the Indian Ocean from the Pacific—the Indonesian Throughflow. The ocean's eastern boundary currents disrupt upwelling and biological productivity, which is therefore underdeveloped.

NATURAL RESOURCES (below)

- Fishing
- Shellfish
- Metallic minerals
- Mining
- Oil production
- Tourism

SURFACE CURRENTS (below)

The region is characterized by currents parallel to the equator, the Leeuwin Current flowing poleward along the west coast of Australia, and leakage of Pacific water through the Indonesian archipelago. Water from the Great Australian Bight also enters the Indian Ocean.

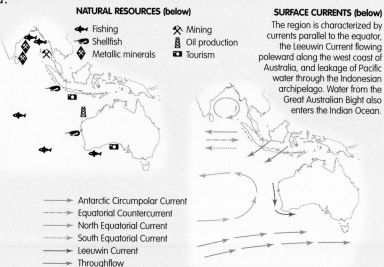

- Antarctic Circumpolar Current
- Equatorial Countercurrent
- North Equatorial Current
- South Equatorial Current
- Leeuwin Current
- Throughflow

Leafy seadragon (above)

Leafy seadragons (*Phycodurus eques*) are marine fish related to the seahorse. Found along the coast of western and southern Australia, their leafy body structures serve as camouflage. Moving slowly through the water they appear to be pieces of floating seaweed.

Ningaloo Reef

Ningaloo Reef, the longest fringing coral reef in the world, stretches for 125 miles (200 km) along the west coast of Australia, 745 miles (1,200 km) north of Perth. The reef is on the migratory route of dolphins, dugongs and humpback whales.

The whale shark (*Rhincodon typus*), a filter feeder, swims with its mouth open to capture plankton. Found at the Ningaloo Reef from March to June, these are the largest living fish species, growing to 40 feet (12 m) in length.

Ningaloo Reef is a declared marine park and its beaches are important breeding grounds for loggerhead, green, and hawksbill turtles.

N O P Q R S T U V W X Y Z

80°
BANGLADESH
Dhaka
Tropic of Cancer
MYANMAR
100°

20°
INDIA
20°
Ganges Cone
Yangon
THAILAND
Bangkok

Bay
of
Bengal
Chennai
Andaman
Islands
Andaman
Sea

10°
Ceylon
Plain
SRI LANKA
Colombo
Gulf of
Mannar
Nicobar
Islands
Andaman
Basin
Gulf
of
Thailand
MALAYSIA
Kuala Lumpur
Singapore
Strait of Malacca

Equator
Afanasy Nikitin
Seamount
Cocos
Basin
Borneo
130°
Equator
0°
140°

Chagos Trench

SEAFLOOR TOPOGRAPHY (above)
The Java Trench is at the border of two major tectonic plates and, as a subduction zone, it is characterized by frequent earthquakes. The trench extends to a depth of 23,376 feet (7,125 m), the deepest point in the Indian Ocean.

Christmas
Island
Sumatra
Jakarta
Java
Java
Sea
Surabaya
Borneo
Bali
Denpasar
Lombok

Indian
Ocean
Java Trench

INDONESIA
Java Sea
Jakarta
Java
Bali
Sunda
Sea
New Guinea
PAPUA NEW GUINEA

5
Mid-Indian
Ocean Basin
Investigator Ridge
Sunda Trench
Sumatra
Java Trench
Sunda Trough
Lesser Sunda Islands
Dili
EAST TIMOR
Arafura
Sea
Port
Moresby
10°

6
Cocos Islands
Christmas
Island
Java Trench
23,376ft (7125m)
Horizon Ridge
North
Australian
Basin
Timor Sea
Arafura
Shelf
Torres Strait
Cape York
Coral
Sea

7
Osborn
Plateau
Gascoyne
Plain
Sahul Shelf
Cape Leveque
Gulf
of
Carpentaria
Darwin

I N D I A N
Wharton
Basin
Exmouth
Plateau
Rowley
Shelf
20°
Tropic of Capricorn
Wallaby
Plateau
Cuvier
Basin
Ningaloo
Reef
Tropic of Capricorn

Batavia
Seamount
Cuvier
Plateau
East Indiaman Ridge
Lost Dutchmen Ridge

O C E A N
Golden Dragon
Seamount
Houtman Ridge
Perth
Basin
AUSTRALIA

30°
Broken
Plateau
Ob' Trench
Perth
30°

Naturaliste
Plateau
Naturaliste Fracture Zone
Diamantina Deep
21,660ft (6602m)
Great Australian Bight
Adelaide

Amsterdam Island
St Paul Island
Diamantina Fracture Zone
South Australian Basin
Melbourne
King Island
Bass Strait
40°

40°
BATHYMETRIC DEPTHS
Tasmania
Hobart
South East Cape
12

Feet | Meters
Sea level | Sea level
S o u t h e a s t   I n d i a n   R i d g e
SCALE 1:35,000,000
Miller Projection
South
Australian
Plain
South
Tasman
Rise

656 | 200
1640 | 500
1000 kilometers
1000 statute miles
1000 nautical miles
13

3281 | 1000
6562 | 2000
9842 | 3000
50°
50°

13,123 | 4000
Kerguelen Plateau
16,404 | 5000
Heard
Island
14

19,685 | 6000
26,246 | 8000
Australian–Antarctic Basin
South Indian
Indian–Antarctic Ridge

Fawn Trough
Banzare
Seamounts
60°
Basin
90°
100°
110°
120°
130°
140°
60°

Longitude east of Greenwich

GREAT AUSTRALIAN BIGHT

The ocean area south of the Australian landmass is the easternmost extension of the Indian Ocean. In its extreme east it adds a cold-water connection to the Pacific Ocean. Bottom water formed at the coast of Antarctica moves north but, where its flow is obstructed by the Australian continental shelf, it moves in an easterly direction into the Indian Ocean. The dry atmosphere over parts of the bight causes excessive evaporation that forms highly saline, dense water, which descends to greater depths.

Nullarbor Coast

The Nullarbor Plain is an extensive, flat, almost treeless region at the southern edge of the Australian continent, adjacent to the Great Australian Bight. This arid, semi-desert region receives only about 7 inches (200 mm) of rainfall per year and is sparsely populated. Thought to have once been part of an ancient seabed, it is the largest limestone area on earth. Its daytime temperatures may reach 120°F (49°C).

The spectacular 213-foot (65-m) high Bunda Cliffs of the Nullarbor coast form part of the northern border of the Great Australian Bight. The cliffs are an excellent vantage point for whale-watching.

Australian sea lion (right)

The Australian sea lion (*Neophoca cinerea*) is found only along the southern coast of Australia. It hunts for fish and squid at sea and comes ashore on rocky islands to breed. Members of the eared seal family, sea lions have small, furled ears. Males can weigh up to 660 pounds (300 kg) at maturity, females 176 pounds (80 kg).

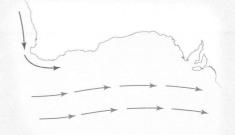

NATURAL RESOURCES

🐟 Fishing
📷 Tourism

→ Antarctic Circumpolar Current
→ Leeuwin Current

SURFACE CURRENTS (above)

South of Australia, at the northern boundary of the Southern Ocean, the powerful Antarctic Circumpolar Current carries water west to east. On Australia's west coast, warm waters from the southward-flowing Leeuwin Current occasionally flow east into the Great Australian Bight and penetrate the cold Antarctic waters.

L   M   115°

30°

Pert
Rottnest Island

Cape Bouvard

Geographe Bay
Cape Naturaliste

Cape Leeuwin
Point D'Entrecasteaux
35°

115°

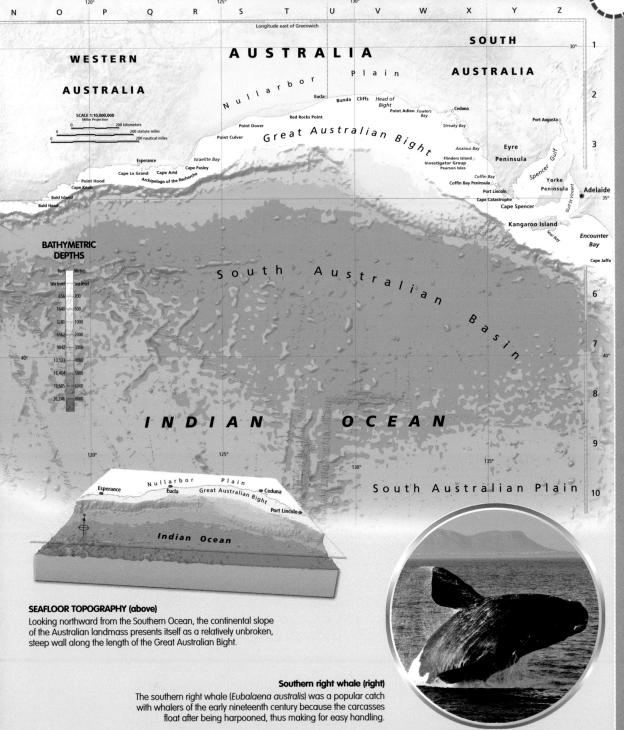

N   O   P   Q   R   S   T   U   V   W   X   Y   Z

120°   125°   130°

Longitude east of Greenwich

SOUTH

AUSTRALIA

WESTERN

AUSTRALIA

AUSTRALIA

30°   1

N u l l a r b o r   P l a i n

Eucla   Bunda   Cliffs   Head of
                        Bight
                Red Rocks Point   Point Adieu   Ceduna
        Point Dover   Fowlers
                                            Bay
                                Streaky Bay

SCALE 1:10,000,000
Miller Projection
                200 kilometers
        0   200 statute miles
        0   200 nautical miles

2

Point Culver

G r e a t   A u s t r a l i a n   B i g h t

Anxious Bay

Eyre
Peninsula

Port Augusta

Esperance   Israelite Bay
        Cape Pasley
Cape Le Grand   Cape Arid
Point Hood   Archipelago of the Recherche
Cape Knob
Bald Island
Bald Head

Flinders Island
Investigator Group
Pearson Isles

Coffin Bay
Coffin Bay Peninsula
Port Lincoln
Cape Catastrophe
Cape Spencer

Spencer Gulf

Yorke
Peninsula

Gulf St Vincent

Adelaide

35°

3

Kangaroo Island

Seal Bay

Encounter
Bay

Cape Jaffa

**BATHYMETRIC
DEPTHS**

Feet	Meters
Sea level	Sea level
656	200
1640	500
3281	1000
6562	2000
9842	3000
13,123	4000
16,404	5000
19,685	6000
26,246	8000

S o u t h   A u s t r a l i a n   B a s i n

6

7

40°   40°

8

I N D I A N   O C E A N

9

120°   125°   130°   135°

S o u t h   A u s t r a l i a n   P l a i n

10

N u l l a r b o r   P l a i n
Esperance
        Eucla   Ceduna
        Great Australian Bight
                Port Lincoln

I n d i a n   O c e a n

SEAFLOOR TOPOGRAPHY (above)
Looking northward from the Southern Ocean, the continental slope
of the Australian landmass presents itself as a relatively unbroken,
steep wall along the length of the Great Australian Bight.

Southern right whale (right)
The southern right whale (*Eubalaena australis*) was a popular catch
with whalers of the early nineteenth century because the carcasses
float after being harpooned, thus making for easy handling.

SOUTHERN INDIAN OCEAN

The southern Indian Ocean extends from the African mainland to the west and south coasts of Australia, with Madagascar as the only interruption. The southern border is the Subtropical Convergence, an oceanic front that separates Indian Ocean waters from the colder, more nutrient-rich waters of the Southern Ocean. The current that flows along this front is known as the Agulhas Return Current on the western side of the basin and as the South Indian Ocean Current to the east.

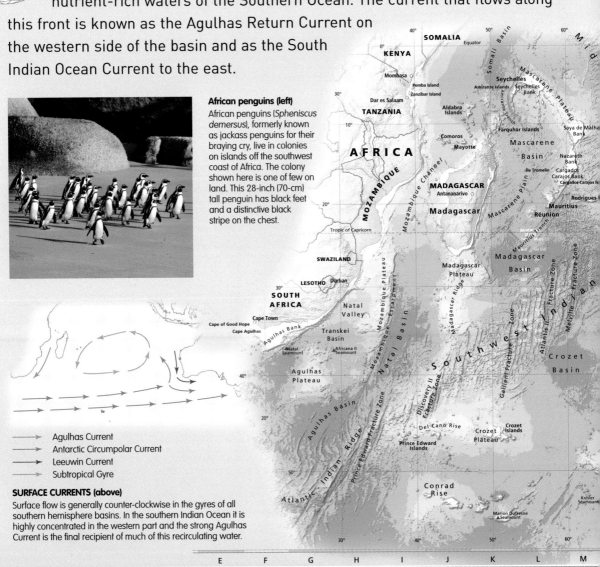

African penguins (left)

African penguins (*Spheniscus demersus*), formerly known as jackass penguins for their braying cry, live in colonies on islands off the southwest coast of Africa. The colony shown here is one of few on land. This 28-inch (70-cm) tall penguin has black feet and a distinctive black stripe on the chest.

→ Agulhas Current
→ Antarctic Circumpolar Current
→ Leeuwin Current
→ Subtropical Gyre

SURFACE CURRENTS (above)

Surface flow is generally counter-clockwise in the gyres of all southern hemisphere basins. In the southern Indian Ocean it is highly concentrated in the western part and the strong Agulhas Current is the final recipient of much of this recirculating water.

SOMALIA
KENYA
Mombasa
Pemba Island
Zanzibar Island
Dar es Salaam
TANZANIA
AFRICA
MOZAMBIQUE
SWAZILAND
LESOTHO   Durban
SOUTH
AFRICA
Cape Town
Cape of Good Hope
Cape Agulhas
Agulhas Bank
Transkei
Basin
Natal
Seamount
Africana II
Seamount
Agulhas
Plateau
Agulhas Basin
Atlantic Indian Ridge
Prince Edward Fracture Zone
Del Cano Rise
Prince Edward
Islands
Conrad
Rise
Marion Dufresne
Seamount
Kohler
Seamount

Equator
Somali Basin
Mascarene Plateau
Mid
Seychelles
Amirante Islands   Seychelles
Bank
Aldabra
Islands
Farquhar Islands
Saya de Malha
Bank
Comoros
Mayotte
Mascarene
Basin
Nazareth
Bank
Île Tromelin   Cargados
Carajos Bank
Cargados Carajos Is
MADAGASCAR
Antananarivo
Madagascar
Mauritius
Réunion
Rodrigues
Mascarene Plain
Madagascar
Plateau
Madagascar
Basin
Madagascar Ridge
Mozambique Channel
Mozambique Escarpment
Mozambique Plateau
Natal
Valley
Natal Basin
Southwest Indian
Discovery II
Fracture Zone
Gallieni Fracture Zone
Atlantis II Fracture Zone
Melville Fracture Zone
Crozet
Basin
Crozet
Islands
Crozet
Plateau

Tropic of Capricorn

E   F   G   H   I   J   K   L   M

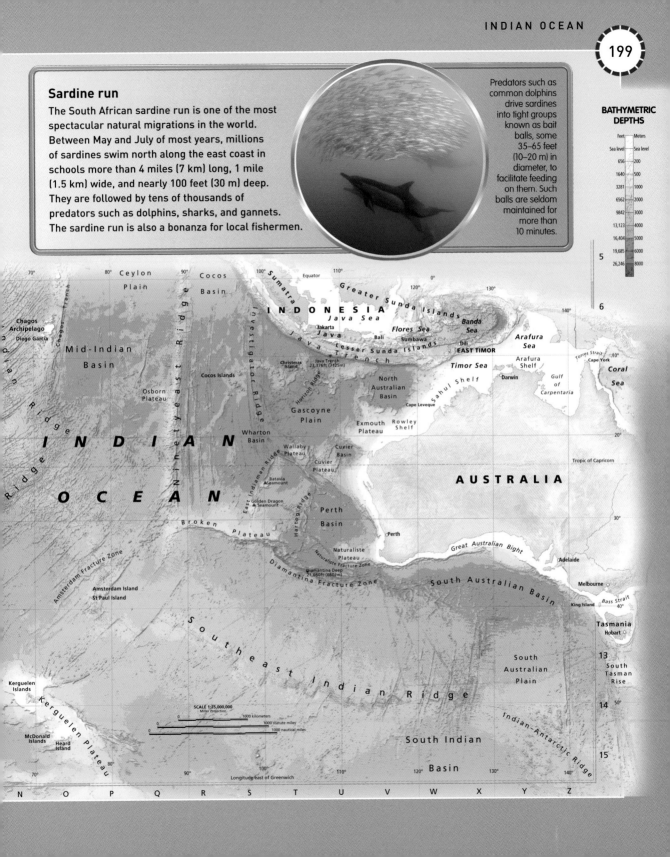

Sardine run

The South African sardine run is one of the most spectacular natural migrations in the world. Between May and July of most years, millions of sardines swim north along the east coast in schools more than 4 miles (7 km) long, 1 mile (1.5 km) wide, and nearly 100 feet (30 m) deep. They are followed by tens of thousands of predators such as dolphins, sharks, and gannets. The sardine run is also a bonanza for local fishermen.

Predators such as common dolphins drive sardines into tight groups known as bait balls, some 35–65 feet (10–20 m) in diameter, to facilitate feeding on them. Such balls are seldom maintained for more than 10 minutes.

BATHYMETRIC DEPTHS

Feet	Meters
Sea level	Sea level
656	200
1640	500
3281	1000
6562	2000
9842	3000
13,123	4000
16,404	5000
19,685	6000
26,246	8000

PACIFIC OCEAN

Humpback whale

A humpback whale (*Megaptera novaeangliae*) breaches in the Pacific Ocean. Humpbacks live in distinct populations in all polar waters during summer and migrate to give birth in subtropical or tropical waters in winter. Males communicate through songs that change from year to year. However, at any one time all North Pacific humpbacks sing the same version. South Pacific humpbacks sing a different song.

PACIFIC OCEAN

The Pacific Ocean is the largest of all oceans. A "Ring of Fire" marked by earthquakes and volcanic eruptions surrounds it and generates powerful tsunamis. Tectonic movement forms some of the world's deepest trenches along its rim. Thousands of seamounts, remnants of submarine volcanoes and homes to highly productive ecosystems, rise from the ocean floor, often to within 1,000 feet (300 m) or less of the surface. The Portuguese explorer Magellan, who sailed across the Pacific in 1521 under its trade winds, named it the "pacific" (peaceful) ocean, but swell from storms of the Roaring Forties always reaches the tropics.

THE FACTS

Area	60.1 million square miles (155.6 million km²)
Average depth	13,127 feet (4,001 m)
Maximum depth	35,826 feet (10,920 m)
Maximum width	11,200 miles (18,000 km)
Maximum length	8,600 miles (13,900 km)

OCEAN SHARE

Pacific Ocean
60.1 million sq miles
(155.6 million km²) 46%

All other oceans

Hubbard Glacier (below)

An iceberg calves from the face of the Hubbard Glacier on the USA–Canada border. Its ice, which formed at an elevation of 11,000 feet (3,350 m), took 400 years to travel the 76 miles (122 km) to the sea.

People of the Pacific (below)

The Pacific Ocean is home to nearly 10 million people. Scattered over thousands of islands, people's lives depend on their navigation skills. This water taxi heads to one of the outlying islands of Fiji.

BATHYMETRIC DEPTHS

Feet	Meters
Sea level	Sea level
656	200
1640	500
3281	1000
6562	2000
9842	3000
13,123	4000
16,404	5000
19,685	6000
26,246	8000

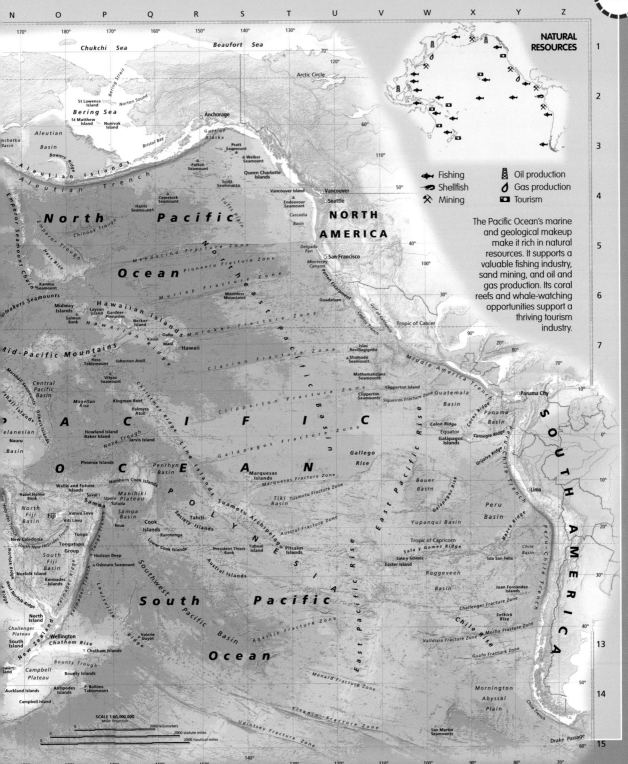

NORTHERN NORTH PACIFIC OCEAN

Two circulation systems dominate the region. The North Equatorial, Philippines, Kuroshio, North Pacific, and California Currents form the clockwise Subtropical Gyre. Water movement at its center is downward, depriving the upper ocean of nutrients, so its waters display the deep blue of the ocean's deserts. Plastic and other garbage accumulates in the gyre, particularly between North America and the Hawaiian Islands. The Alaska Current, Alaskan Stream, Oyashio, and North Pacific Currents form the counterclockwise circulation of the Subpolar Gyre, in which upward movement brings nutrients to the surface, making it a region of high productivity and preferred fishing grounds.

⚡ Steller sea lions

The Steller sea lion (*Eumetopias jubatus*), the largest of all sea lion species, is found from the Kuril Islands and the Sea of Okhotsk to the Gulf of Alaska and central California. Its numbers have been declining and it is on the endangered species list.

NATURAL RESOURCES

- Fishing
- Tourism
- Mining
- Oil production

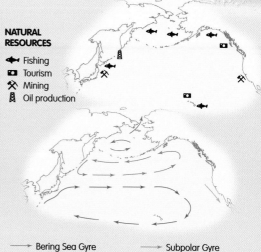

SURFACE CURRENTS (right)

Two basin-wide gyres dominate the North Pacific. South of 40°N the American coastal waters experience upwelling from the California Current. Currents in the deep basin of the Bering Sea move counterclockwise while, over the shelf, northward movement feeds into the Arctic Ocean.

- Bering Sea Gyre
- California Current
- Subpolar Gyre
- Subtropical Gyre

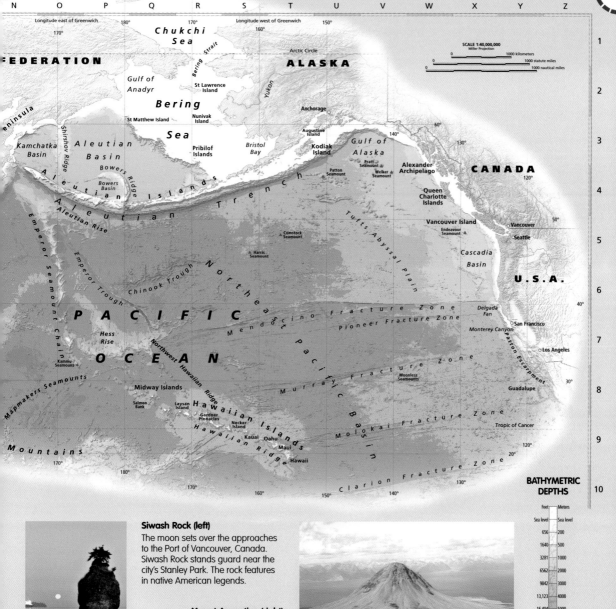

N O P Q R S T U V W X Y Z

Longitude east of Greenwich | Longitude west of Greenwich

Chukchi Sea

Bering Strait

Arctic Circle

ALASKA

SCALE 1:40,000,000
Miller Projection

1000 kilometers
1000 statute miles
1000 nautical miles

FEDERATION

Gulf of Anadyr

St Lawrence Island

Yukon

Anchorage

Bering

Peninsula

St Matthew Island

Nunivak Island

Augustine Island

Sea

Kamchatka Basin

Aleutian Basin

Pribilof Islands

Bristol Bay

Kodiak Island

Gulf of Alaska

Pratt Seamount

Alexander Archipelago

CANADA

Shirshov Ridge

Bowers Ridge

Bowers Basin

Patton Seamount

Welker Seamount

Queen Charlotte Islands

Aleutian Islands

Aleutian Trench

Aleutian Rise

Comstock Seamount

Vancouver Island

Endeavour Seamount

Vancouver

Emperor Seamount

Harris Seamount

Northeast Pacific

Tufts Abyssal Plain

Seattle

Cascadia Basin

U.S.A.

Emperor Trough

Chinook Trough

PACIFIC

Mendocino Fracture Zone

Pioneer Fracture Zone

Delgada Fan

Monterey Canyon

San Francisco

Hess Rise

Northwest Hawaiian Ridge

Murray Fracture Zone

Moonless Seamounts

Patton Escarpment

Los Angeles

Emperor Seamount Chain

OCEAN

Kammu Seamount

Mapmakers Seamounts

Midway Islands

Murray Basin

Guadalupe

Salmon Bank

Laysán Island

Hawaiian Islands

Molokai Fracture Zone

Tropic of Cancer

Mountains

Gardner Pinnacles

Necker Island

Hawaiian Ridge

Kauái

Oahu

Maui

Hawaii

Clarion Fracture Zone

BATHYMETRIC DEPTHS

Feet	Meters
Sea level	Sea level
656	200
1640	500
3281	1000
6562	2000
9842	3000
13,123	4000
16,404	5000
19,685	6000
26,246	8000

Siwash Rock (left)
The moon sets over the approaches to the Port of Vancouver, Canada. Siwash Rock stands guard near the city's Stanley Park. The rock features in native American legends.

Mount Augustine (right)
Augustine volcano on Augustine Island in Cook Inlet, Alaska, 174 miles (280 km) southwest of Anchorage, is one of several active volcanoes of the Ring of Fire. Steam plumes rich in sulfur dioxide disrupted air traffic in 1986, 1994, and 2006, and deposited ash on the city of Anchorage.

BERING SEA

The Bering Sea is the world's third largest marginal sea (after the Arctic Ocean and the Mediterranean Sea). The Aleutian Islands carry several active volcanoes. Bering Strait, the sea's connection with the Arctic Ocean, is only 53 miles (85 km) wide and less than 160 feet (50 m) deep but is important for the global water budget by returning to the Atlantic the fresh water that came as rain across the Isthmus of Panama. Sea ice builds up in November and covers the Siberian–Alaskan Shelf from January. By July the entire region is ice-free. To protect spectacular cold-water "coral gardens," 60 percent of the Aleutian shallow water habitat is closed to bottom trawling.

THE FACTS	
Area	884,900 square miles (2,291,880 km²)
Average depth	5,075 feet (1,547 m)
Maximum depth	15,659 feet (4,773 m)
Maximum width	1,490 miles (2,398 km)
Maximum length	990 miles (1,593 km)

NATURAL RESOURCES

- Fishing
- Shellfish

SURFACE CURRENTS (below)

Two systems make up the currents of the Bering Sea. Counterclockwise circulation in the deep basin supplies some water to the Oyashio through the Kamchatka Current, while water from the Alaskan Stream crosses the shallow eastern region to join the Anadyr Current toward Bering Strait.

- Alaskan Stream
- Aleutian North Slope Current
- Anadyr Current
- Kamchatka Current

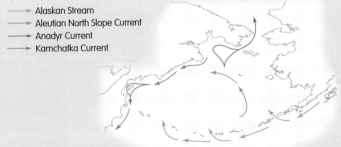

Beluga (above)

The beluga or white whale (*Delphinapterus leucas*), a whale species of the Arctic and subarctic oceans, grows to 15 feet (5 m) in length. It spends the summers in bays, estuaries, and shallow inlets and follows the progressing ice edge into open water in winter.

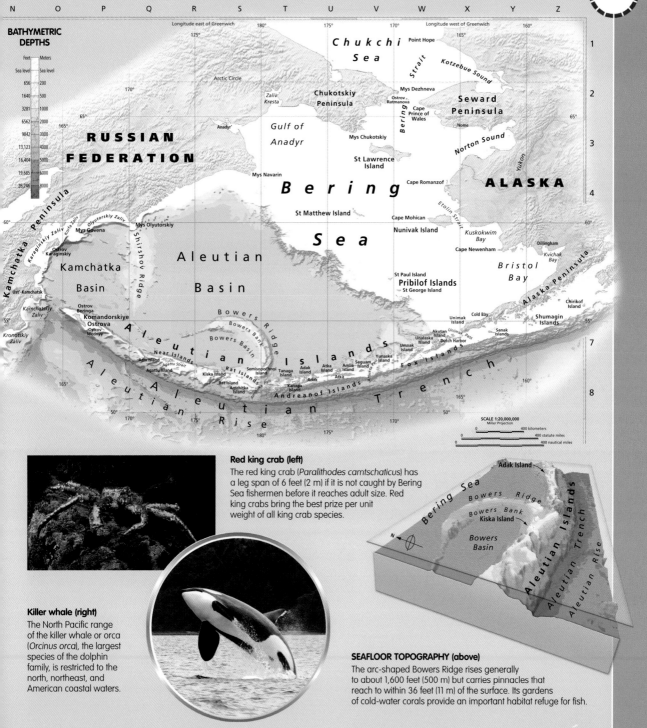

N O P Q R S T U V W X Y Z

BATHYMETRIC DEPTHS

Feet	Meters
Sea level	Sea level
656	200
1640	500
3281	1000
6562	2000
9842	3000
13,123	4000
16,404	5000
19,685	6000
26,246	8000

Longitude east of Greenwich

Longitude west of Greenwich

Chukchi Sea

Point Hope

Kotzebue Sound

Arctic Circle

Mys Dezhneva

Zaliv Kresta

Chukotskiy Peninsula

Ostrov Ratmanova

Cape Prince of Wales

Bering Strait

Seward Peninsula

Nome

Anadyr'

Gulf of Anadyr

Mys Chukotskiy

Norton Sound

RUSSIAN FEDERATION

St Lawrence Island

Yukon

ALASKA

Mys Navarin

Cape Romanzof

B e r i n g

St Matthew Island

Cape Mohican

Nunivak Island

Kuskokwim Bay

S e a

Cape Newenham

Dillingham

Kvichak Bay

Kamchatka Peninsula

Mys Govena

Mys Olyutorskiy

A l e u t i a n

Bristol Bay

St Paul Island

Pribilof Islands

St George Island

Alaska Peninsula

Chirikof Island

Karaginskiy Zaliv

Olyutorskiy Zaliv

Korfa Zaliv

Ostrov Karaginskiy

Shirshov Ridge

B a s i n

Kamchatka Basin

Kamchatka Basin

Ostrov Beringa

Komandorskiye Ostrova

Ostrov Mednyy

Cold Bay

Shumagin Islands

Ust'-Kamchatsk

Kamchatskiy Zaliv

A l e u t i a n

Bowers Ridge

Bowers Bank

Unimak Island

Akutan Island

Unimak Pass

Sanak Islands

Kronotskiy Zaliv

Bowers Basin

Unalaska Island

Dutch Harbor

Umnak Island

I s l a n d s

Fox Islands

A l e u t i a n

Near Islands

Attu Island

Agattu Strait

Agattu Island

Rat Islands

Kiska Island

Semisopochnoi Island

Tanaga Island

Adak Island

Atka Island

Seguam Island

Amlia Island

Yunaska Island

Rat Island

Andreanof Islands

Kanaga Island

Adak

Atka

Antichka Island

A l e u t i a n   T r e n c h

A l e u t i a n   R i s e

SCALE 1:20,000,000
Miller Projection

0   400 kilometers
0   400 statute miles
0   400 nautical miles

Red king crab (left)

The red king crab (*Paralithodes camtschaticus*) has a leg span of 6 feet (2 m) if it is not caught by Bering Sea fishermen before it reaches adult size. Red king crabs bring the best prize per unit weight of all king crab species.

Adak Island

Bering Sea

Bowers Ridge

Bowers Bank

Kiska Island

Aleutian Islands

Bowers Basin

N

Aleutian Trench

Aleutian Rise

Killer whale (right)

The North Pacific range of the killer whale or orca (*Orcinus orca*), the largest species of the dolphin family, is restricted to the north, northeast, and American coastal waters.

SEAFLOOR TOPOGRAPHY (above)

The arc-shaped Bowers Ridge rises generally to about 1,600 feet (500 m) but carries pinnacles that reach to within 36 feet (11 m) of the surface. Its gardens of cold-water corals provide an important habitat refuge for fish.

GULF OF ALASKA

The Inside Passage between the Alexander Archipelago and the mainland allows ships to avoid storms in the open Gulf of Alaska. The gulf is also exposed to tsunamis generated by earthquakes in the Queen Charlotte–Fairweather Fault System; the largest tsunami ever observed was triggered by a rockfall in Lituya Bay. A hot spot near Queen Charlotte Islands created the now-extinct volcanoes of the Kodiak–Bowie Seamount Chain. Cold-water corals are found near Kodiak and Queen Charlotte Islands.

K   L   M

Bristol Bay

60°

165°

Unimak Island

55°

Shumagin Islands

Aleutian

165°   Seamap   Channel

Sirius Seamount
9268ft (2825m)

50°

THE FACTS	
Area	592,000 square miles (1,533,273 km²)
Average depth	7,976 feet (2,431 m)
Maximum depth	16,500 feet (5,029 m)
Maximum width	1,400 miles (2,240 km)
Maximum length	1,200 miles (2,000 km)

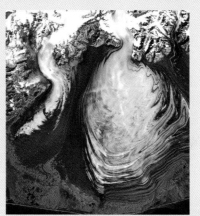

Malaspina Glacier (left)
Where several valley glaciers spill onto the Alaskan coastal plain they form the Malaspina Glacier, seen here in a false-color satellite image. As a typical "piedmont glacier" the Malaspina Glacier does not reach the gulf but supplies its meltwater through streams from two lakes.

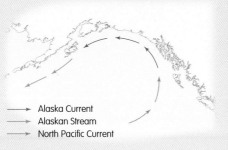

→ Alaska Current
→ Alaskan Stream
→ North Pacific Current

SURFACE CURRENTS (above)
Water transport in the Alaska Current, also known as the Alaska Coastal Current, increases along its way due to freshwater input from meltwater and rivers. Its temperature, however, remains high, above 39°F (4°C), due to the supply of warm water from the North Pacific Current.

Prince William Sound (right)
The "tidewater glaciers" that enter the many fjords of Prince William Sound are a favorite destination of tourist vessels. Tidewater glaciers supply meltwater through the calving of icebergs, which can create a huge wave. Cruise ships are well advised to keep their distance.

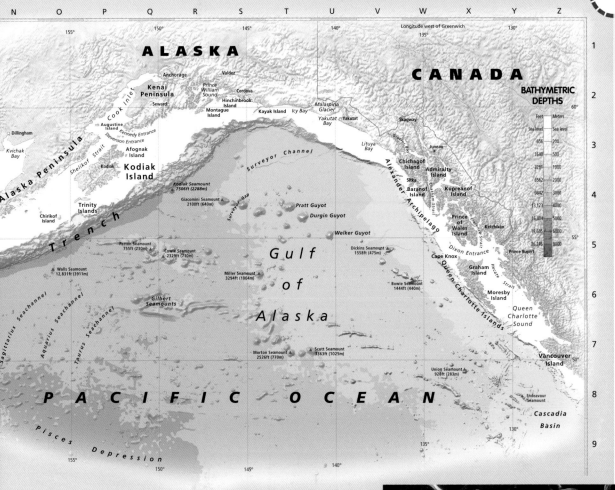

ALASKA

CANADA

N O P Q R S T U V W X Y Z

155° 150° 145° 140° 135° Longitude west of Greenwich 130°

1

Anchorage
Valdez
Kenai
Peninsula
Prince
William
Sound
Cordova
Seward
Cook Inlet
Hinchinbrook
Island
Kayak Island
Icy Bay
Malaspina
Glacier
Montague
Island
Yakutat
Bay
Yakutat
Skagway

BATHYMETRIC
DEPTHS

60°

2

Dillingham

Kvichak
Bay

Augustine
Island
Kennedy Entrance
Stevenson Entrance
Afognak
Island
Kodiak
Kodiak
Island

Lituya
Bay
Chichagof
Island
Sitka
Admiralty
Island
Juneau

Feet   Meters
Sea level   Sea level
656   200
1640   500
3281   1000
6562   2000
9842   3000
13,123   4000
16,404   5000
19,685   6000
26,246   8000

55°

3

Alaska Peninsula

Chirikof
Island

Trinity
Islands

Shelikof Strait

Surveyor Channel

Kodiak Seamount
7506ft (2288m)

Giacomini Seamount
2100ft (640m)

Surveyor Gap

Pratt Guyot
Durgin Guyot

Baranof
Island
Kupreanof
Island
Prince
of
Wales
Island
Ketchikan

Alexander Archipelago

Welker Guyot

Dixon Entrance

Cape Knox

Prince Rupert

Graham
Island

Hecate Strait

4

T r e n c h

Patton Seamount
755ft (230m)

Cowie Seamount
2329ft (710m)

Miller Seamount
3294ft (1004m)

Dickins Seamount
1558ft (475m)

Bowie Seamount
1444ft (440m)

Queen Charlotte Islands

Moresby
Island

5

Walls Seamount
12,831ft (3911m)

Gilbert
Seamounts

Gulf

of

Alaska

Queen
Charlotte
Sound

6

Sagittarius Seachannel

Aquarius Seachannel

Taurus Seachannel

Morton Seamount
2526ft (770m)

Scott Seamount
3363ft (1025m)

Union Seamount
928ft (283m)

Vancouver
Island

50°

7

P A C I F I C   O C E A N

Endeavour
Seamount

Cascadia
Basin

130°

8

Pisces   Depression

155°   150°   145°   140°   135°

9

SCALE 1:20,000,000
Miller Projection

0   400 kilometers
0   400 statute miles
0   400 nautical miles

NATURAL RESOURCES

Fishing
Tourism

Sockeye salmon

Sockeye salmon (*Oncorhynchus nerka*) are found in cold waters from northern Japan in the west to Canada in the east. They spawn in streams and lakes, where the young fish spend up to four years before they migrate to the ocean. After another one to four years they change from bluish-green to red, and return to the rivers to spawn.

HAWAIIAN ISLANDS

Formed over a hot spot to their southeast, the Hawaiian Islands are a chain of 137 islands and atolls, many smaller islands, and seamounts that stretch northwestward to Midway and Kure atolls. Mauna Loa and Kilauea on Hawaii, the largest of the nine major islands and the closest to the hot spot, are the only active island volcanoes. Loihi, a submerged volcano closer to the hot spot, is 3,200 feet (975 m) below the surface but is growing and active. The islands form an obstacle to the North Equatorial Current and the trade winds, and create a wake effect some 1,900 miles (3,000 km) long in the atmosphere.

Longitude west of Greenwich

PACIFIC

Mercury Seamount 640ft (195m)

Woollard Seamount 329ft (100m)
Turnip Seamount 124ft (38m)
Wentworth Seamount 329ft (100m)
Loudoun Seamount 2926ft (892m)

Zapadnaya Seamount 159ft (48m)

Ladd Seamount 64ft (210m)

Academician Berg Seamount 183ft (56m)

Kure Atoll (Ocean Island)

Midway islands

North Island
Pearl and Hermes Atoll
Southeast Island

Nero Seamount 68ft (21m)

Kittery Island

Salmon Bank

Pioneer Tablemount 26ft (8m)

Lisianski Island

Don Quixote Seamount 1317ft (401m)
Euphemia Seamount 1916ft (584m)
Tamana Seamount 989ft (301m)

Tropic of Cancer

Volcanoes

Five volcanoes make up Hawaii's Big Island: Mauna Loa and Kilauea are active, Kohala is extinct, Mauna Kea and Hualalai are dormant. They are "shield volcanoes," built by the supply of low-viscosity lava that can flow over great distances.

Kilauea (left) and Mauna Loa add new layers of lava to the island, occasionally forcing the relocation of houses. Here lava from Kilauea reaches the ocean.

Mauna Kea (right) rises to 13,803 feet (4,207 m) above the sea and 33,476 feet (10,203 m) above its base on the ocean floor.

This false-color composite image of the Big Island (processed to simulate true color) shows the spreading range of Mauna Loa to the south, with Mauna Kea's crater to the north. Kilauea is in the east, Kohala in the northwest.

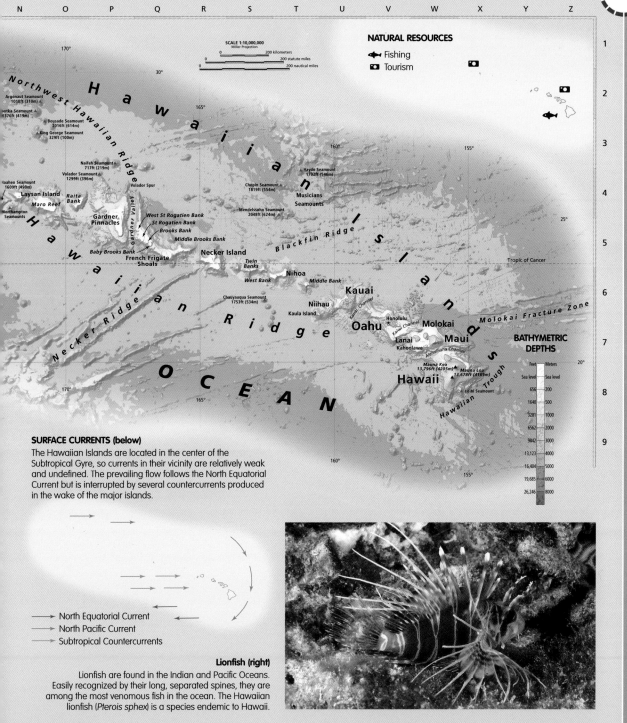

N O P Q R S T U V W X Y Z

170°

30°

165°

160°

155°

25°

Tropic of Cancer

20°

170°

165°

160°

155°

SCALE 1:10,000,000
Miller Projection

0 — 200 kilometers
0 — 200 statute miles
0 — 200 nautical miles

NATURAL RESOURCES

Fishing

Tourism

Northwest Hawaiian Ridge

Argonaut Seamount
1018ft (310m)
otka Seamount
1376ft (419m)

Bousade Seamount
2016ft (614m)

King George Seamount
329ft (100m)

Naifeh Seamount
717ft (219m)

Volador Seamount
1299ft (396m)

Volador Spur

laaheo Seamount
1609ft (490m)

Northampton
Seamounts

Laysan Island

Raita Bank

Maro Reef

Gardner Pinnacles

Gardner Valley

West St Rogatien Bank
St Rogatien Bank
Brooks Bank
Middle Brooks Bank

Baby Brooks Bank

French Frigate Shoals

Necker Island

Twin Banks

West Bank

Nihoa

Middle Bank

Chopin Seamount
1819ft (554m)

Mendelssohn Seamount
2048ft (624m)

Haydn Seamount
1792ft (546m)

Musicians Seamounts

Blackfin Ridge

Hawaiian Islands

Necker Ridge

Hawaiian Ridge

Chauyauqua Seamount
1753ft (534m)

Niihau

Kaula Island

Kauai

Kauai Channel

Oahu

Honolulu

Kaiwi Channel

Molokai

Lanai

Kahoolawe

Maui

Alenuihaha Channel

Molokai Fracture Zone

Mauna Kea
13,796ft (4205m)

Mauna Loa
13,678ft (4169m)

Hawaii

Loihi Seamount

Hawaiian Trough

O C E A N

BATHYMETRIC DEPTHS

Feet	Meters
Sea level	Sea level
656	200
1640	500
3281	1000
6562	2000
9842	3000
13,123	4000
16,404	5000
19,685	6000
26,246	8000

SURFACE CURRENTS (below)

The Hawaiian Islands are located in the center of the Subtropical Gyre, so currents in their vicinity are relatively weak and undefined. The prevailing flow follows the North Equatorial Current but is interrupted by several countercurrents produced in the wake of the major islands.

→ North Equatorial Current
→ North Pacific Current
→ Subtropical Countercurrents

Lionfish (right)

Lionfish are found in the Indian and Pacific Oceans. Easily recognized by their long, separated spines, they are among the most venomous fish in the ocean. The Hawaiian lionfish (*Pterois sphex*) is a species endemic to Hawaii.

SEA OF OKHOTSK

The Sea of Okhotsk is between the Siberian coast, the Kamchatka Peninsula, and the volcanically active Kuril Islands. It falls off from a wide shelf in the north to a deep basin in the south. Numerous deep passages between the Kuril Islands connect it with the main Pacific basins; straits east and west of Sakhalin Island provide connections to the Sea of Japan. During the winter (October–April) the sea is covered with drift ice, but storm winds from Siberia can still cause waves to rise up to 30 feet (10 m).

THE FACTS	
Area	611,000 square miles (1,582,483 km²)
Average depth	2,818 feet (859 m)
Maximum depth	11,063 feet (3,742 m)
Maximum width	932 miles (1,500 km)
Maximum length	1,530 miles (2,463 km)

Kuril Islands (right)
Snow covers the peaks of the 56 Kuril Islands that stretch for 700 miles (1,300 km) from Hokkaido, Japan, to Kamchatka, Russia. Different water coloration indicates patches of high productivity where the Soya Warm Current, from the Sea of Japan, and the Kamchatka Current meet.

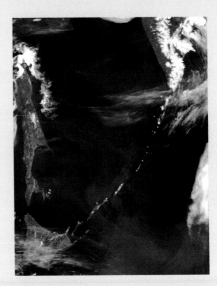

Ice floes

Salt lowers the freezing point of water, so the first ice to form is from fresh water in rivers. When the temperature drops to 28.8°F (-1.8°C), ice begins to form on the sea. Wind and waves break it up into pancake ice. Compacted pancake ice builds up to ice floes that drift with the current and can be piled up into pack ice.

A low winter sun shines on a thin sheet of new ice that forms in a river mouth. In the background the current carries parcels of older ice toward the sea.

NATURAL RESOURCES (right)
🐟 Fishing
🛢 Oil Production

SURFACE CURRENTS (right)
Currents in the Sea of Okhotsk mostly follow the coast. In the interior they are weaker and irregular. Limited observations indicate a closed gyre at the center of the Sea of Okhotsk.

→ Kamchatka Current
→ Soya Warm Current
→ Prevailing flow

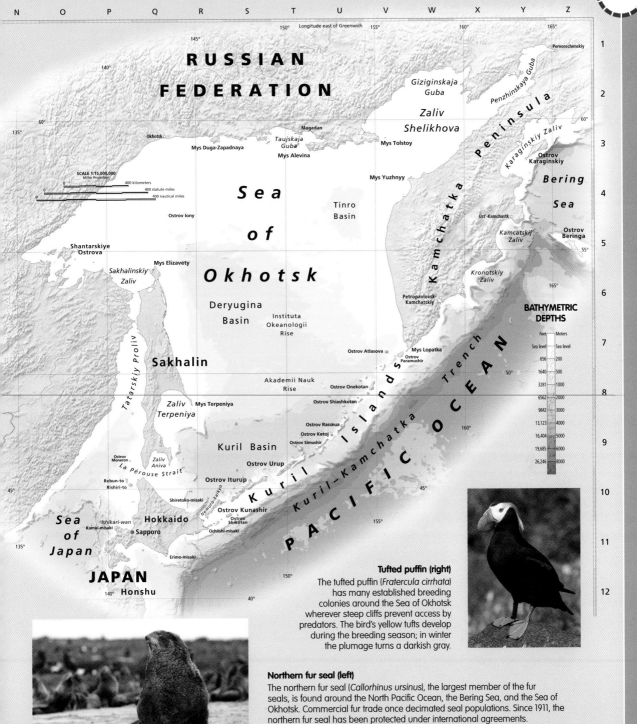

N O P Q R S T U V W X Y Z

RUSSIAN FEDERATION

Longitude east of Greenwich

150° 155° 165°

145°

140°

Pervorechenskiy

1

135°

60°

Giziginskaja Guba

Zaliv Shelikhova

Penzhinskaya Guba

2

Magadan

Okhotsk.

Taujskaja Guba

Mys Tolstoy

Karaginskiy Zaliv

60°

3

Mys Duga-Zapadnaya

Mys Alevina

Ostrov Karaginskiy

SCALE 1:15,000,000
Miller Projection

400 kilometers

400 statute miles

400 nautical miles

Mys Yuzhnyy

Bering

Sea

4

S e a

Tinro Basin

Ostrov Iony

Ust'-Kamchastk

Ostrov Beringa

Kamcatskij Zaliv

55°

5

Shantarskiye Ostrova

o f

Mys Elizavety

Sakhalinskiy Zaliv

O k h o t s k

Kronotskiy Zaliv

165°

6

Deryugina Basin

Instituta Okeanologii Rise

Petropavlovsk-Kamchatskiy

BATHYMETRIC DEPTHS

Feet	Meters
Sea level	Sea level
656	200
1640	500
3281	1000
6562	2000
9842	3000
13,123	4000
16,404	5000
19,685	6000
26,246	8000

7

Ostrov Atlasova

Mys Lopatka

Ostrov Paramushir

50°

Tatarskiy Proliv

Sakhalin

Akademii Nauk Rise

Ostrov Onekotan

8

Zaliv Terpeniya

Mys Terpeniya

Ostrov Shiashkotan

160°

45°

Ostrov Rasœua

Ostrov Ketoj

Ostrov Simushir

Kuril Basin

Ostrov Urup

9

Ostrov Moneron

Zaliv Aniva

La Pérouse Strait

Ostrov Iturup

155°

45°

Rebun-to
Rishiri-to

Shiretoko-misaki

Nemuro-kaikyo

Ostrov Kunashir

Ostrov Shikotan

10

Sea of Japan

Ishikari-wan

Kamui-misaki

Hokkaido

Sapporo

Ochiishi-misaki

135°

11

Erimo-misaki

150°

12

JAPAN

140° Honshu

40°

Tufted puffin (right)
The tufted puffin (*Fratercula cirrhata*) has many established breeding colonies around the Sea of Okhotsk wherever steep cliffs prevent access by predators. The bird's yellow tufts develop during the breeding season; in winter the plumage turns a darkish gray.

Northern fur seal (left)
The northern fur seal (*Callorhinus ursinus*), the largest member of the fur seals, is found around the North Pacific Ocean, the Bering Sea, and the Sea of Okhotsk. Commercial fur trade once decimated seal populations. Since 1911, the northern fur seal has been protected under international agreements.

SEA OF JAPAN (EAST SEA)

The Sea of Japan consists of isolated deep basins separated by a shallow ridge on which the Yamato Bank comes up to a depth of 177 feet (285 m). It connects with the Yellow Sea through Korea Strait, with the Sea of Okhotsk through La Perouse Strait and Tartar Strait, and with the main Pacific basins through Tsugaru Strait and Kanmon Straits. All of these straits are less than 120 feet (200 m) deep, so water in the basins is renewed through the sinking of cold surface water during winter.

THE FACTS	
Area	377,600 square miles (977,979 km²)
Average depth	5,748 feet (1,751 m)
Maximum depth	12,276 feet (3,742 m)

Pinecone fish (left)
The pinecone fish (*Monocentris japonica*) lives in rocky and coral reefs in the tropical Indo-Pacific. It rests in crevices during the day and is a nocturnal predator. This is a juvenile.

Spider crab

The Japanese spider crab (*Macrocheira kaempferi*) is the largest crab of the world's oceans. With a body of around 15 inches (40 cm), its legs reach a span of more than 10 feet (3 m). It lives around the islands of Japan at depths below 100 feet (300 m), where it feeds on dead animals and shellfish. At maturity it may weigh about 44 pounds (20 kg) and is believed to be very long-lived.

SURFACE CURRENTS (right)
The outstanding feature of the circulation in the region is the temperature contrast between southward-setting cold currents and northward-setting warm currents. Movement of cold water across the central Sea of Japan is known as the Mid-Japan Sea or Maritime Province Cold Current.

⟶ Liman Current
⟶ North Korea Cold Current
⟶ Tsushima Current
⟶ Prevailing flow
----- Polar Front

Sea of Okhotsk

145°

50°

Sakhalin

Zaliv Terpeniya

Mys Terpeniya

Kuril Basin

Tatarskiy Proliv (Tartar Strait)

135°

RUSSIAN FEDERATION

Ostrov Moneron

Zaliv Aniva

Mys Aniva

Mys Kril'on

Soya-wan

La Pérouse Strait

Soya-misaki

Rebun-to

Rishiri-to

Yagishiri-to

Teuri-to

Shiretoko-misaki

Hokkaido

Nemuro-kaikyo

Ostrov Kunashir

Nemuro-wan

Shakotan-misaki

Ishikari-wan

Kushiro

Sapporo

Akkeshi-wan

130°

45°

Vladivostok

Motsuta-misaki

Uchiura-wan

Okushiri-to

Hakodate

Esan-misaki

Erimo-misaki

C H I N A

125°

Ch'ongjin

O-shima

Ko-jima

Tsugaru-kaikyo

Shiriya-zaki

Mutsu-wan

145°

SEAFLOOR TOPOGRAPHY (above)
Tsushima Island divides Korea Strait into two shallow passages, the Western and Eastern Channels. The Tsushima Current enters through the strait, mostly passing through the Western Channel before turning toward the coast of Japan.

Japan Basin

S e a   o f   J a p a n (East Sea)

Henashi-zaki

Aomori

Nyudo-zaki

40°

9

NORTH KOREA

Yamato Bank

Akita

Kesennuma

Kinka-san

JAPAN

10

● P'YONGYANG

Yamato Basin

Awa-shima

Hajiki-zaki

Sado-shima

Niigata

Sendai ●

Sendai-wan

Japan Trench

Japan Rise

11

■ SEOUL

Ullung-do

Sawasaki-bana

Rokko-zaki

Noto-hanto

Toyama-wan

Shioya-zaki

SOUTH KOREA

Oki-shoto

Dogo

Dozen

Nakano-shima

Chiburi-jima

Kyoga-misaki

Wakasa-wan

Jizo-zaki

Kashima-nada

H o n s h u

12

BATHYMETRIC DEPTHS

Yellow Sea

Pusan

Koje-do

Mi-shima

Strait

Tsushima

Kanmon Kaikyo

Iki

Iki-suido

Uku-jima

Ojika-jima

Nakadori-shima

Goto-retto

Fukue-jima

Amakusa-Shimo-shima

Kami-Koshiki-jima

Koshikijima-retto

Shimo-Koshiki-jima

Amakusa-nada

Noma-misaki

Kyushu

Sata-misaki

Tanega-shima

Yaku-shima

35°

Cheju-do

Kobe

Osaka

Seto-naikai

Awaji-shima

Osaka-wan

Shikoku

Kii-suido

Tosa-wan

Muroto-zaki

Ashizuri-misaki

Okino-shima

Shiono-misaki

Nagoya

TOKYO

Tokyo-wan

Suruga-wan

Sagami-nada

O-shima

Iro-zaki

Inubo-zaki

Nojima-zaki

To-shima

Nii-jima

Daio-zaki

Enshu-nada

Kozu-shima

Miyake-jima

Mikura-jima

Izu-shoto

Hachijo-jima

140°

35°

Hiroshima

Nagasaki

Fukuoka

Bungo-suido

East China Sea

Nankai Trough

Feet	Meters
Sea level	Sea level
656	200
1640	500
3281	1000
6562	2000
9842	3000
13,123	4000
16,404	5000
19,685	6000
26,246	8000

SCALE 1:10,000,000
Miller Projection

0   200 kilometers

0   200 statute miles

0   200 nautical miles

Longitude east of Greenwich

130°

135°

N   O   S   T   U   V   W   X   Y   Z

Inset (upper left):

JAPAN

Shikoku

Kyushu

Tsushima

Cheju-do

Nagoya

Honshu

Osaka

Hiroshima

Pusan

SOUTH KOREA

Yellow Sea

Seoul

NORTH KOREA

Sea of Japan

EAST CHINA SEA AND YELLOW SEA

The vast shelf region between Taiwan and Korea comprises two interconnected seas. The region south of a line between Kyushu and Shanghai is known as the East China Sea. The deep, fast-flowing, Kuroshio Current carries warm, saline water along its eastern perimeter. Dilution from the Yangtze River lowers salinity in the west. Sediment brought from China's loess plateau by the Yellow River (Hwang Ho), which enters the region through the Bo Hai Gulf, gives the Yellow Sea its name. Its wide intertidal mudflats are an important resting place for millions of wading birds during their migration from Siberia and Alaska to the southern hemisphere.

Sediment flow (below)
A true-color satellite image reveals the effect of sediment carried by the Yellow River plume far out into the Bo Hai Sea. Some coastal waters are turbid from tidal current action. Farther south the coastal region is affected by the discharge of the Yangtze River.

NATURAL RESOURCES (right)

- Fishing
- Shellfish
- Tourism

→ China Coastal Current
→ Korea Coastal Current
→ Kuroshio
→ Yellow Sea Warm Current

SURFACE CURRENTS (above)
The circulation in the East China Sea and Yellow Sea is counterclockwise and follows the coast. A warm current branches off from the Kuroshio and flows into the center of the region.

Gray whale (left)
The endangered Asian population of gray whales (*Eschrichtius robustus*), which consists of fewer than 300 animals, migrates between the Sea of Okhotsk and Korea. Gray whales once also lived in the North Atlantic. Some 21,000 gray whales still migrate in the eastern Pacific between Alaska and California.

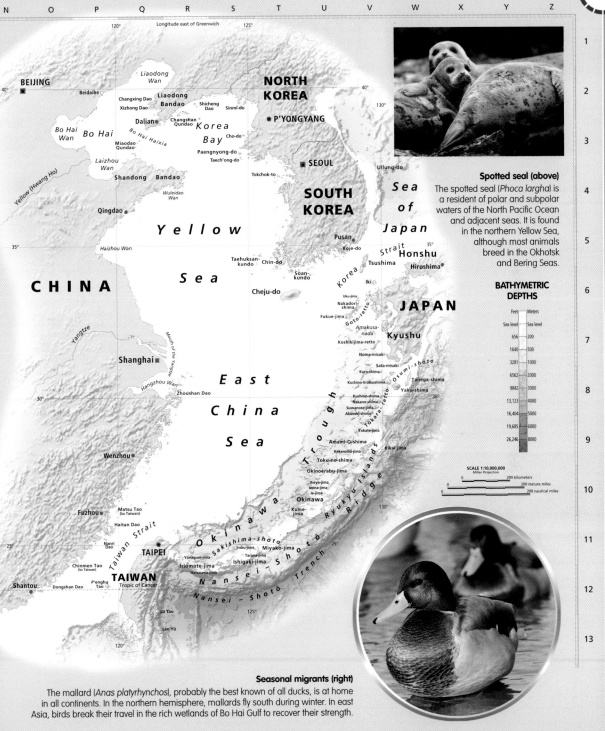

Spotted seal (above)
The spotted seal (*Phoca largha*) is a resident of polar and subpolar waters of the North Pacific Ocean and adjacent seas. It is found in the northern Yellow Sea, although most animals breed in the Okhotsk and Bering Seas.

BATHYMETRIC DEPTHS

Feet	Meters
Sea level	Sea level
656	200
1640	500
3281	1000
6562	2000
9842	3000
13,123	4000
16,404	5000
19,685	6000
26,246	8000

SCALE 1:10,000,000
Miller Projection

0   200 kilometers
0   200 statute miles
0   200 nautical miles

Seasonal migrants (right)
The mallard (*Anas platyrhynchos*), probably the best known of all ducks, is at home in all continents. In the northern hemisphere, mallards fly south during winter. In east Asia, birds break their travel in the rich wetlands of Bo Hai Gulf to recover their strength.

Map labels:

N O P Q R S T U V W X Y Z
1 2 3 4 5 6 7 8 9 10 11 12 13

BEIJING
Beidaihe
Longitude east of Greenwich
120° 125° 130°
40°

Liaodong Wan
NORTH KOREA
Changxing Dao
Liaodong Bandao
Xizhong Dao
Shicheng Dao
Sinmi-do
Dalian
Changshan Qundao
Korea Bay
P'YONGYANG
Cho-do
Bo Hai Wan
Bo Hai
Miaodao Qundao
Bo Hai Haixia
Paengnyong-do
Taech'ong-do
Laizhou Wan
Shandong Bandao
Tokchok-to
SEOUL
Ullung-do
Yellow (Hwang Ho)
Qingdao
Wuleidao Wan
SOUTH KOREA
Sea of Japan
35°
Haizhou Wan
Pusan
Koje-do
Honshu
Taehuksan-kundo
Chin-do
Korea Strait
Tsushima
Hiroshima
Yellow
Soan-kundo
Uku-jima
Iki
CHINA
Sea
Cheju-do
Nakadori-shima
Fukue-jima
Goto-retto
JAPAN
Yangtze
Amakusa-nada
Kyushu
Koshikijima-retto
Noma-misaki
Sata-misaki
Osumi-shoto
Shanghai
Mouth of the Yangtze
Kuro-shima
Kuchino-Erabushima
Tanega-shima
Yaku-shima
Hangzhou Wan
Zhoushan Dao
Kuchino-shima
Nakano-shima
Suwanose-jima
Akuseki-shima
Yokate-jima
East
China
Sea
Amami-O-shima
Kekeroma-jima
Toku-no-shima
Kikai-jima
Wenzhou
Okinoerabu-jima
Iheya-jima
Izena-jima
Ie-jima
Okinawa
Kume-jima
Okinawa Trough
Tokara-retto
Nansei-Shoto Trench
Ryukyu Islands
Ryukyu Ridge
Fuzhou
Matsu Tao (to Taiwan)
Haitan Dao
Sakishima-shoto
Miyako-jima
Nanri Dao
Taiwan Strait
TAIPEI
Yonaguni-jima
Irabu-jima
Tarama-jima
Ishigaki-jima
Iriomote-jima
Hateruma-jima
Chinmen Tao (to Taiwan)
TAIWAN
Tropic of Cancer
Shantou
Dongshan Dao
P'enghu Tao
Lü Tao
Lan Yü
Nansei-Shoto Trench
125°
120°
30°
25°

WESTERN TROPICAL PACIFIC OCEAN

Deep trenches, isolated deep basins, myriad seamounts, and Micronesia's many hundred islands characterize the western tropical Pacific. The heavily populated regions in its west, where fishing has been supplemented by aquaculture for centuries, contrast with the pristine conditions of the islands in the east and south. The high water temperatures of the "West Pacific Warm Pool" are the source of cyclones and play a role in the El Niño–Southern Oscillation.

Outrigger (left)

Pacific islanders navigated their vast ocean space in outrigger canoes for centuries, using star constellations, swell patterns, and bird flight to guide them. This Melanesian is on a less challenging voyage: he heads for a nearby village to participate in a village festivity.

Sea fan (below)

A yellow sea fan (*Gorgonia ventalina*) reaches out into the current that sweeps along a reef front in the Solomon Islands. Sea fans do not contribute to reef building: they are soft corals inhabited by small polyps whose tentacles intercept passing plankton.

SURFACE CURRENTS (below)

The western tropical Pacific plays a key role in global oceanic circulation. It is the main region of the Pacific where currents transfer water between the two hemispheres, and it provides an opening into the Indonesian seas for water movement from the Pacific to the Indian Ocean.

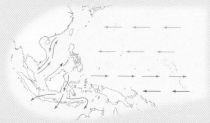

→ North Equatorial Countercurrent
→ South Equatorial Current
→ North Equatorial Current
→ Seasonally variable
→ Throughflow
·······➤ Prevailing flow

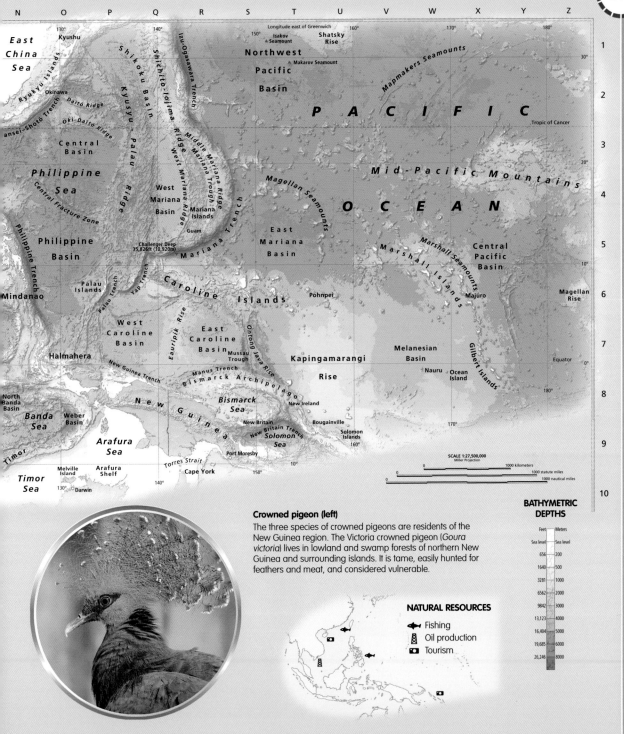

N O P Q R S T U V W X Y Z

East China Sea
Kyushu
Ryukyu Islands
Okinawa
ansei-Shotō Trench
Daitō Ridge
Oki-Daitō Ridge
Central Basin
Philippine Sea
Central Fracture Zone
Philippine Basin
Philippine Trench
Mindanao
Halmahera
Shikoku Basin
Shichito-Iojima Ridge
Izu-Ogasawara Trench
Kyushu Palau Ridge
Palau Ridge
Middle Mariana Ridge
West Mariana Ridge
West Mariana Basin
Mariana Islands
Guam
Challenger Deep 35,826ft (10,920m)
Mariana Trench
Yap Trench
Palau Trench
Palau Islands
West Caroline Basin
Eauripik Rise
East Caroline Basin
Caroline Islands
Mussau Trough
Ontong Java Rise
Manus Trench
New Guinea Trench
Bismarck Archipelago

Longitude east of Greenwich
Isakov Seamount
Shatsky Rise
Makarov Seamount
Northwest Pacific Basin
Mapmakers Seamounts

P A C I F I C
Tropic of Cancer

Mid-Pacific Mountains

O C E A N

Magellan Seamounts
East Mariana Basin

Marshall Seamounts
Marshall Islands
Majuro
Central Pacific Basin
Magellan Rise

Pohnpei
Kapingamarangi Rise
Melanesian Basin
Nauru
Ocean Island
Gilbert Islands
Equator

North Banda Basin
Banda Sea
Weber Basin
Timor
Arafura Sea
New Guinea
Bismarck Sea
New Ireland
New Britain
New Britain Trench
Bougainville
Solomon Islands
Solomon Sea
Port Moresby
Torres Strait
Cape York
Melville Island
Arafura Shelf
Timor Sea
Darwin

SCALE 1:27,500,000
Miller Projection

0   1000 kilometers
0   1000 statute miles
0   1000 nautical miles

Crowned pigeon (left)

The three species of crowned pigeons are residents of the New Guinea region. The Victoria crowned pigeon (*Goura victoria*) lives in lowland and swamp forests of northern New Guinea and surrounding islands. It is tame, easily hunted for feathers and meat, and considered vulnerable.

NATURAL RESOURCES

- Fishing
- Oil production
- Tourism

BATHYMETRIC DEPTHS

Feet	Meters
Sea level	Sea level
656	200
1640	500
3281	1000
6562	2000
9842	3000
13,123	4000
16,404	5000
19,685	6000
26,246	8000

SOUTH CHINA SEA

The South China Sea reaches from Taiwan in the north to Singapore in the south. Numerous tiny islands, most of them uninhabited and without much vegetation, along with hundreds of coral reefs, are the object of dispute between coastal states. The South China Sea connects with the Indian Ocean through the Strait of Malacca, one of the most important shipping lanes in the world. The strait has a minimum depth of 82 feet (25 m) and is dominated by large tidal currents that produce shifting sandbars 13–23 feet (4–7 m) high on its floor.

THE FACTS

Area	895,400 square miles (2,319,075 km²)
Average depth	5,419 feet (1,652 m)
Maximum depth	16,456 feet (5,015 m)
Maximum width	840 miles (1,352 km)
Maximum length	1,182 miles (1,902 km)

Ha Long Bay (right)
The 1,969 limestone islands of Ha Long Bay in northern Vietnam are a UNESCO World Heritage site and a popular tourist destination. The islands' terrain is too steep for settlements, but the quiet waters between some islands support floating villages.

SURFACE CURRENTS (below)
Currents in the South China Sea are determined by the monsoon. During summer the southwest monsoon pushes water from the Sunda Shelf northward. During winter the northeast monsoon causes southward movement along the Vietnamese coast, but currents along Borneo continue to flow northward.

NATURAL RESOURCES (right)

🐟 Fishing
🦐 Shellfish
📷 Tourism

→ Seasonally variable
⋯→ Prevailing flow

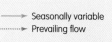

Fairy terns (right)
The fairy or white tern (Gygis alba) lives in the tropical regions of all oceans. It nests in trees on coral islands and lays its single egg on a fork between thin branches without a nest. It is not shy, and is even inquisitive. It sometimes uses man-made structures for nesting.

SCALE 1:12,500,000
Miller Projection

0   200 kilometers
0   200 statute miles
0   200 nautical miles

BATHYMETRIC DEPTHS

Feet	Meters
Sea level	Sea level
656	200
1640	500
3281	1000
6562	2000
9842	3000
13,123	4000
16,404	5000
19,685	6000
26,246	8000

CHINA

Longitude east of Greenwich

Tropic of Cancer

Shantou

Taiwan Banks

Hong Kong

HANOI
Zhanjiang
Weizhou Dao
Donghai Dao
Shangchuan Dao

Vereker Banks

Luzon Strait
North Island
Siayan
Batan Islands
Batan
Sabtang
Ballintang Channel
Calayan
Dalupiri
Fuga
Babuyan Channel
Babuyan Islands
Camiguin
Escarpada Point

Bashi Channel

Pratas Island

Hạ Long Bay
Dao Cat Ba

Gulf
of
Tongking
Hainan
Qizhou Liedao
Hainan Strait

VIENTIANE

Dao Con Co

Palanan Point

Luzon

Baler Bay

Paracel Islands
Macclesfield Bank

South
China

Da Nang
Cu Lao Cham
Cu Lao Re

THAILAND

MANILA

Catanduanes

CAMBODIA

South China Basin

Sea

Polillo Islands
Lamon Bay

PHNOM PENH

Cam Ranh

Cape Calavite

Marinduque

Mindoro Strait

Busuanga
Culion

Burias
Tablas
Sibuyan

Masbate
Samar

Semirara Islands
Linapacan

Hồ Chí Minh

Cu Lao Thu

Kitty Hawk Seamount
2,877ft (3625m)

Loaita Bank

Reed Bank

Southern Reefs

Mouths of the Mekong

Cochin

Gulf
of
Thailand

Côn Son

Hon Khoai

Palawan Passage
Palawan Trough

Cuyo Islands
Cuyo

Dumaran

Panay
Guimaras

Leyte

Cebu

Leyte Gulf

Dinagat

Siargao

Palawan

Dondonay

Panay Gulf

Negros

Bohol

Camiguin

PHILIPPINES

Siquijor

Mindanao
Davao

Davao Gulf

Vanguard Bank

Rifleman Bank

Ardasier Reefs

Cape Buliluyan
Pandanan

Balabac Strait

Banggi

Bulubangan

Cape Bulubuyan

Sulu Basin

Sulu Sea

Mapin

Zamboanga

Moro Gulf

Basilan

Cape San Agustin

Sunda
Shelf

South Luconia Shoals

Sandakan

Pangutaran
Tongquil

Sulu Archipelago

Siasi
Tawitawi

Jolo

Sarangani Islands

Miangas

Kota Bharu

Kepulauan Nanusa

BANDAR SERI BEGAWAN
BRUNEI

Brunei Bay

MALAYSIA

Sibutu Group

Matutuang

Arjaga

Karakelong

Kepulauan Talaud

Kaburuang

Celebes Sea

MALAYSIA

KUALA LUMPUR

Laut

Natuna Besar

Siantan
Matak
Bajau
Air
Kepulauan Anambas

Subi Besar

Tanjung Sirik

Selat Serasan

Celebes Basin

Kepulauan Sangir

Tioman
Jemaja
Midai

Teluk Datu

Salibabu
Sangir

Aur

Tanjung Mungguresak

Kuching

Tanjung Kandi

Kepulauan Sangir

Siau
Tahulandang
Biaro
Bangka

SINGAPORE

Kepulauan Tambelan

Tambelan Besar

Manado

Mayu

Batam
Bintan

Benua

Tifore

Molucca

Kundur

Lingga
Kepulauan Lingga
Singkep

Equator

Pejantan

Borneo

Unauna
Kepulauan Togian
Togian
Batudaka
Waleabahi

Gorontalo Basin

Sea

Teluk Tomini

Selat Walea

Padangtikar

Peleng

Natuna
Sea

Maya

Teluk Sukadana

Makassar Basin

Palu
Teluk Poso

Banggai
Kepulauan Banggai

Sulabesi
Tanjung Waka

Bangka

Mangole

Selat Berhala

Selat Karimata

Karimata

INDONESIA

Taliabu

Bangka

Bawal

Tanjung Palpetu

Belitung

Tanjung Lumpur

Tanjung Sambar

Teluk Kumai

Teluk Sampit

Sebuku

Sulawesi

Manui

North Banda Basin

Buru

Sumatra

Java

Sea

Tanjung Puting

Tanjung Selatan

Selat Laut

Laut
Laut Kecil

Teluk Bone

Wowoni

Muna

Buton

Wangiwangi
Kaledupa
Tomea
Binongko

Kepulauan Tukangbesi

Karamian

South Makassar Basin

Doangdoangan Kecil

Ujung Pandang

Kabaena

Moromaho

Tanjung Cina

Masalembu Kecil
Masalembu Besar

Bawean

Selayar

Bone Basin

South Banda Basin

Panaitan

Tanjung Bugel

Sapudi
Raas

Kepulauan Kangean

Selayar
Kepulauan Sabalana

Kepulauan Taka Bonerate

Kakabia
Kalaotoa

Tanjung Guhakolak

JAKARTA

Surabaya

Madura

Kepulauan Karimunjawa

Kepulauan Tengah

Kepulauan Bonerate
Bonerate

Saubi

Kalao

Flores Sea

Kepulauan Solor
Adonara
Pantar
Lomblen

Java

Selat Bali

Bali
Sea

Bali Basin

Moyo

Sangeang
Komodo

Palu

Flores Basin

Flores

Bali
Lombok
Sumbawa

Strait of Malacca

N   O   P   Q   R   S   T   U   V   W   X   Y   Z

Manila Trench

Gaffney Ridge

Spratly Islands

Selat Peleng

Makassar Strait

Ujong

GULF OF THAILAND

The Gulf of Thailand is relatively shallow. Rainfall exceeds evaporation here and creates a two-layered system, with low-salinity water leaving the gulf at the surface and water of oceanic salinity entering across the sill, 190 feet (58 m) deep, that separates the gulf from the South China Sea. Turbid water and sediment from rivers support mangrove forests. The gulf also supports important artisanal and commercial fisheries. Oil and gas reserves are developed jointly between Malaysia, Thailand, and Vietnam.

THE FACTS	
Area	123,553 square miles (320,000 km²)
Average depth	148 feet (45 m)
Maximum depth	262 feet (80 m)
Maximum width	350 miles (563 km)
Maximum length	450 miles (724 km)

Lyretail anthias (below left)

The lyretail anthias (*Pseudanthias squamipinnis*) is one of the many anthias species. In the wild, anthias congregate in swarms of thousands of fish. Within the swarm, males defend small "harems" of females against others. Anthias are born female; if a dominant male dies, a female changes into a male to take its place.

Magnificent anemone (left)

A clownfish hides in a magnificent anemone (*Heteractis magnifica*). In locations with good light and a strong, turbulent current, such as the wave zone on a reef front, giant anemones can grow to 3 feet (1 m) in diameter. They feed on vertebrates and invertebrates, including fish and crustaceans.

Yellow scroll coral (above)

Yellow scroll coral, also known as lettuce coral (*Turbinaria reniformis*), is a stony coral species. Colonies are either male or female. Breeding, when all colonies release their gametes into the sea, takes place a week after the full moon in November.

Mu Ko Ang Thong Marine Park (left)

Thailand's Mu Ko Ang Thong Marine Park provides food and shelter for more than 50 species of waterbirds, as well as parrotfish, angelfish, butterflyfish, and many other reef fish species.

N O P Q R S T U V W X Y Z

1

THAILAND

■ BANGKOK

100°

2

SURFACE CURRENTS (below)
Currents in the Gulf of Thailand are driven by the monsoon. The southwest monsoon drives a clockwise circulation during summer; the northeast monsoon causes counterclockwise circulation during winter.

→ Summer
→ Winter

C A M B O D I A

Bight of Bangkok

Ko Khram

Mali Kyun

Kadan Kyun

Saganthif Kyun

Kanmaw Kyun

Kau-ye Kyun

Campbell Island

Bada

Ko Samet

Ko Chang

Ko Kut

Kaôh Kong

● PHNOM
PENH

105°

M Y A N M A R

Isthmus of Kra

Ao Sawi

Ko Tao

Ko Ang Thong

Ao Ban Don

Ko Phangan

Ko Samui

Surat Thani ○

Sayer Island

Ko Phra Thong

Ko Phuket

Ko Yao Yai

Ko Lanta

Ko Libong

Terutao

Butang Group

Langkawi

Perak

Pinang ● George Town

MALAYSIA

Chăk Sihanoukville

Kaôh Rung

Dao Phu Quôc

Dao Vãy

Vĩnh Rạch Gia

Quân Dao Nam Du

Hon Rai

VIETNAM

Dao Thô Chur

Cua Song-bay-hap
Mui Ca Mau

Hon Khoai

Côn Son

Gulf

of

Thailand

S u n d a

S h e l f

Kota Bharu

Perhentian Besar

Redang

Tenggul

100°

105°

10°

5°

5°

3

4

5

6

7

8

9

10

11

12

BATHYMETRIC DEPTHS

Feet	Meters
Sea level	Sea level
656	200
1640	500
3281	1000
6562	2000
9842	3000
13,123	4000
16,404	5000
19,685	6000
26,246	8000

SCALE 1:5,000,000
Miller Projection
0 _____ 100 kilometers
0 _____ 100 statute miles
0 _____ 100 nautical miles

Fishing fleet (below)
Thai fishing boats anchor at Ko Samui. Although tourism has shaped the face of the island, fishing vessels built from local teak still bring in a fresh catch in the morning.

BANDA SEA, CELEBES SEA, AND ADJACENT SEAS

The seas between Indonesia and the Philippines display the most complicated bathymetry of the world's oceans. Shallow sills divide the region into several deep basins. Water from the Pacific is transported through the various seas to the Indian Ocean, giving the region an important role in the global ocean conveyor belt. Annual rainfall exceeds evaporation by 6.5 feet (2 m), so Pacific water is strongly diluted during its passage and reaches the Indian Ocean with much reduced salinity.

SEAFLOOR TOPOGRAPHY (below)
The Lesser Sunda Islands form part of the Pacific Ring of Fire and, in 1815, experienced the most violent volcanic eruptions in recent history.

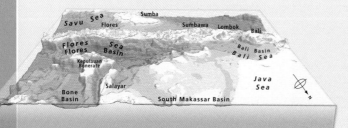

Komodo dragon (below)
The largest living lizard, the Komodo dragon (*Varanus komodoensis*), lives on a few small, arid volcanic islands, including Flores and Komodo. It feeds on carrion and hunts for invertebrates, birds, and mammals as large as pigs and buffalo.

Makassar Strait

Makassar Strait is a busy shipping route. Vessels that are too large to go through the Strait of Malacca, between mainland Malaysia and Sumatra, have to pass through this strait and continue through the Lesser Sunda Islands. The strait is shallow on the western side but deeper than 6,500 feet (2,000 m) in the east, where it is connected with the Celebes Sea.

→ New Guinea Costal Current
→ Prevailing flow
→ Throughflow

Most of the Indonesian Throughflow passes from the Pacific to the Indian Ocean via Makassar Strait, thus giving this waterway between Borneo and Sulawesi an important role in global ocean circulation.

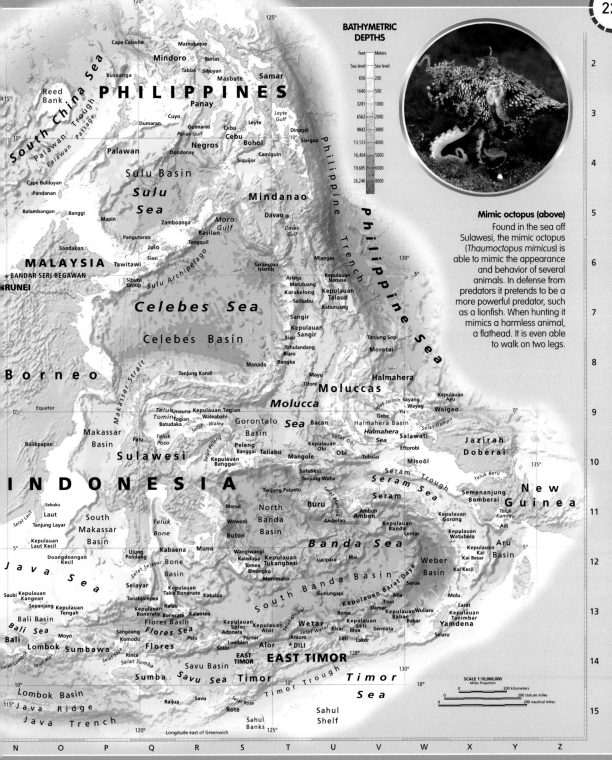

BATHYMETRIC DEPTHS

Feet	Meters
Sea level	Sea level
656	200
1640	500
3281	1000
6562	2000
9842	3000
13,123	4000
16,404	5000
19,685	6000
26,246	8000

Mimic octopus (above)
Found in the sea off Sulawesi, the mimic octopus (*Thaumoctopus mimicus*) is able to mimic the appearance and behavior of several animals. In defense from predators it pretends to be a more powerful predator, such as a lionfish. When hunting it mimics a harmless animal, a flathead. It is even able to walk on two legs.

South China Sea
Reed Bank
Cape Calavite
Marinduque
Mindoro
Burias
Busuanga
Tablas
Sibuyan
Masbate
Samar
PHILIPPINES
Panay
Palawan Trough
Palawan Passage
Cuyo
Guimaras
Leyte
Gulf
Dumaran
Panay Gulf
Cebu
Cebu
Dinagat
Negros
Bohol
Siargao
Cape Buliluyan
Dondonay
Camiguin
Pandanan
Siquijor
Sulu Basin
Mindanao
Balambangan
Mapin
Davao
Banggi
Zamboanga
Moro
Gulf
Davao
Gulf
Sulu
Sea
Basilan
Pangutaran
Jolo
Tongquil
MALAYSIA
Sandakan
Siasi
Miangas
BANDAR SERI BEGAWAN
Sibutu
Group
Sarangani
Islands
BRUNEI
Tawitawi
Sulu Archipelago
Ariaga
Kepulauan
Nanusa
Matutuang
Celebes Sea
Karakelong
Kepulauan
Talaud
Salibabu
Philippine Trench
Celebes Basin
Sangir
Kaburuang
Kepulauan
Sangir
Tanjung Sopi
Siau
Morotai
Tahulandang
Biaro
Makassar Strait
Tanjung Kandi
Bangka
Manado
Mayu
Halmahera
Borneo
Tifore
Moluccas
Selat Jailolo
Sayang
Kepulauan
Wayag
Ayu
Molucca
Sea
Gebe
Yu
Waigeo
Equator
Teluk
Inauna
Kepulauan Togian
Bacan
Halmahera Basin
Salawati
Tomini
Togian
Waleabahi
Gorontalo
Halmahera
Jazirah
Batudaka
Selat Walea
Basin
Sea
Doberai
Makassar
Teluk
Peleng
Kepulauan
Selat Dampir
Basin
Poso
Banggai
Taliabu
Obi
Obi
Eftorobi
Balikpapan
Palu
Kepulauan
Mangole
Tubalai
Misool
Teluk Beru
Banggai
Sulawesi
Seram Trough
Semenanjung
Sulawesi
Tanjung Waka
Seram Sea
Bomberai
New
INDONESIA
Tanjung Palpetu
Seram
Teluk
Guinea
Manui
North
Buru
Kamrau
Sebuku
Banda
Ambon
Kepulauan
Adi
Laut
Wowoni
Basin
Ambon
Gorong
Tanjung Layar
Buton
Ambelau
Kepulauan
Kepulauan
South
Banda
Watubela
Kepulauan
Makassar
Lontar
Aru
Laut Kecil
Basin
Banda Sea
Kepulauan
Basin
Teluk
Kabaena
Kai
Doangdoangan
Bone
Muna
Wangiwangi
Mai
Besar
Kecil
Java
Ujung
Kaledupa
Kepulauan
Lucipara
Weber
Kai Kecil
Sea
Pandang
Selat Selayar
Bone
Tomea
Tukangbesi
Basin
Molu
Selayar
Basin
Binongko
Serua
Saubi
Kepulauan
Kepulauan
Moromaho
Gunungapi
Larat
Kangean
Taka Bonerate
Kakabia
Nila
Kepulauan
Sepanjang
Kepulauan
Kalao
South Banda Basin
Roma
Toun
Wuliaru
Tanimbar
Tengah
Bonerate
Kalaotoa
Damar
Kepulauan
Bali Basin
Tanahjampea
Kepulauan
Roma
Kepulauan
Yamdena
Sangeang
Bonerate
Solor
Kepulauan
Leti
Babar
Bali Sea
Komodo
Palu
Adonara
Alor
Wetar
Leti
Sermata
Selaru
Bali
Moyo
Flores Basin
Pantar
Atauro
Kisar
Lakor
Lombok
Sumbawa
Rinca
Lomblen
Selat Wetar
Moa
Flores
Solor
Alor
DILI
Selat Lombok
Selat Sape
EAST
EAST TIMOR
Selat Alas
Selat Sumba
Savu Basin
TIMOR
Timor
Sumba
Savu Sea
Timor
Lombok Basin
Raijua
Savu
Sea
Java Ridge
Selat Rote
Sahul
Java Trench
Rote
Shelf
Sahul
Banks
Longitude east of Greenwich

SCALE 1:10,000,000
Miller Projection
0   200 kilometers
0   200 statute miles
0   200 nautical miles

PHILIPPINE SEA

The Philippine Sea is an isolated deep ocean region that contains some of the world's deepest trenches. The Mariana Trench, the deepest depression in the ocean floor, lies east of the Mariana Islands—just outside the Philippine Sea—where the Pacific Plate subducts under the Philippine Plate. In the west of the region is the Philippine Trench, the second deepest trench, formed by subduction of the Philippine Plate under the Eurasian Plate.

Typhoon winds (right)

This satellite image shows Typhoon Nesat of June 2005. Color indicates wind speed, dark purple and light pink showing the strongest winds. White arrows near the center of the typhoon indicate heavy rain.

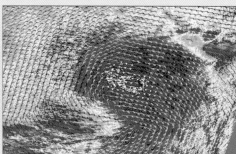

Typhoon origins (right)

The warm waters of the Philippine Sea present ideal conditions for the formation of tropical cyclones, known in the region as typhoons. A large pressure difference between the cyclone center and the surrounding ocean produces gale-force winds and torrential rain.

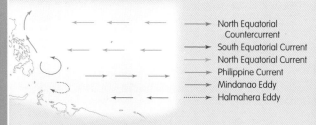

→ North Equatorial Countercurrent
→ South Equatorial Current
→ North Equatorial Current
→ Philippine Current
→ Mindanao Eddy
⋯→ Halmahera Eddy

SURFACE CURRENTS (above)

Most of the Philippine Sea experiences westward flow from the North Equatorial Current. The North Equatorial Countercurrent originates in the region and flows eastward near 5°N.

N O P Q R S T U V W X Y Z

130° 135° Longitude east of Greenwich 140° 145° 150° 155° 160°

Central Fracture Zone

Palau Ridge

West Mariana Ridge

Middle Mariana Ridge

Mariana Islands

Mariana Trench

P A C I F I C

20°

Farallon de
Pajaros
Maug
Islands
Asuncion

Agrihan

Pagan

Alamagan
Guguan

**NORTHERN
MARIANA ISLANDS**

West
Mariana
Basin

Mariana Trough

West Mariana Ridge

Sarigan
Anatahan
Farallon de
Medinilla

Saipan
SAIPAN
Tinian

HAGÅTÑA
GUAM

Rota

Guam

O C E A N

East
Mariana
Basin

Magellan Seamounts

15°

Philippine

Basin

Philippine

Sea

Yap

Ngulu

Palau Islands
Ngajangel
KOROR
PALAU

Palau Trench

Yap Trench

Challenger Deep
35,826ft (10,920m)

Mariana Trench

Ulithi

Sorol

Gaferut

Faraulep

Wofeai
Ifalik
Eauripik

Elato

West Fayu

Pulap
Pulawat
Pulusuk

Namoluk

C a r o l i n e   I s l a n d s

Namonuito

Hall
Islands
Murilo Atoll
Fayu Nomwin

Ulul

**Chuuk
Islands**
Losap

Oroluk

PALIKIR
Pohnpei

Mwokil

Ngetik Atoll

Pingelap

C a r o l i n e   S e a m o u n t s

Sonsorol Islands

Pulo Anna
Merir

Morotai
Moluccas
SIA
Halmahera
Sayang

Kepulauan Asia

Kepulauan Ayu
Waigeo
Selat Dampi

Equator

130° 135°

Manim

Teluk
Cenderawasih
135°

Biak
Yapen

N e w
G u i n e a

140°

West
Caroline
Basin

Eauripik Rise

Aua Island
Wuvulu Island

Ninigo
Group
Hermit
Islands

Admiralty Islands
Manus Island
Bismarck Archipelago

New Guinea Basin

145°

East
Caroline
Basin

Mortlock
Islands

FEDERATED STATES
OF MICRONESIA

Manus Trench

St Matthias Group

Manus Trough
Mussau Island
Emirau Island
Isabel Channel
New Hanover

Manus Basin

Tabar Islands

New
Ireland

Lihir Group

Nukuoro

S o l o m o n

R i s e

5°

Equator 0°

160°

155°

9

150°

20°

1

2

15°

3

4

10°

5

6

5°

7

8

0°

9

10

**BATHYMETRIC
DEPTHS**

Feet	Meters
Sea level	Sea level
656	200
1640	500
3281	1000
6562	2000
9842	3000
13,123	4000
16,404	5000
19,685	6000
26,246	8000

SEAFLOOR TOPOGRAPHY (right)

The Mariana Trench is the deepest location on the surface of Earth.
Its maximum depth of 35,826 feet (10,920 m) is in the Challenger
Deep. It contains hydrothermal vents where acidic
hot water of up to 570°F (330°C), laden with
hydrogen sulfide, enters the ocean.

Mariana Trench

Mariana Islands

Guam

Challenger Deep
35,826ft (10,920m)

West
Mariana
Basin

P a c i f i c

O c e a n

Yap Trench

Palau Trench

Palau

Sea urchin (above)

Sea urchins (*Echinoidea sp.*) are found in all oceans; more than 80 different
species occur in the Philippine Sea. This species is known as the slate pencil urchin
(*Heterocentrotus mamillatus*). Many species are harvested for their roe, an important
sushi ingredient in Japan, and rising demand has led to severe overfishing. Moves are
now under way to control the fishery and to develop cultivation in sea-urchin farms.

SOUTHWESTERN PACIFIC OCEAN

Coral islands, extensive plateaus, and deep basins characterize the southwestern Pacific. Where the Pacific Plate subducts under the Australian Plate, the ocean floor is folded into island chains beside deep trenches. The region's hydrography is determined by the western part of the Subtropical Gyre of the southern hemisphere.

Fiji (above)

Fiji's 322 islands hold nearly 4,000 square miles (10,000 km²) of reef. In 2000, a crown-of-thorns starfish invasion posed a serious threat. Warm water temperatures in the following years led to extensive bleaching, and the reef area is declining.

Manta ray (above)

Despite its size—its wingspan can reach 25 feet (7.5 m)—the manta ray (*Manta birostris*) is a graceful creature. It glides majestically through the waters of all tropical oceans, filtering water through its gills for plankton. Coral reefs are its favored habitat.

SURFACE CURRENTS (below)

South of 45°S, the Antarctic Circumpolar Current flows eastward. It has moderate speed but is deep-reaching and carries the largest transport of all currents. The western part of the Subtropical Gyre determines the circulation to the north. At its center, currents are mostly weak and variable.

→ Antarctic Circumpolar Current
→ East Auckland Current
→ East Australian Current
→ South Equatorial Current
→ South Pacific Current

NATURAL RESOURCES

🐟 Fishing
🐋 Whales
⛏ Oil production
⬧ Gas production
⬛ Tourism

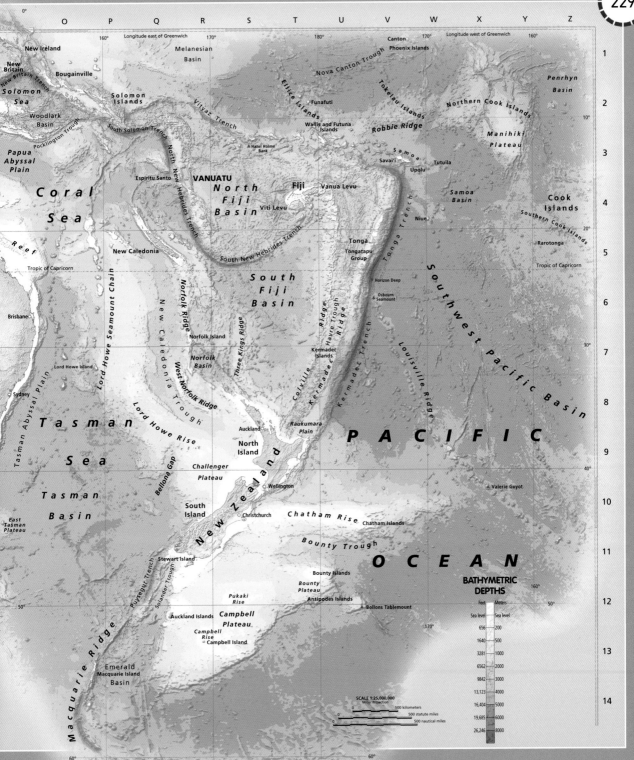

O P Q R S T U V W X Y Z

Longitude east of Greenwich 160° 170° 180° Canton 170° Longitude west of Greenwich 160°

New Ireland

New Britain

Melanesian Basin

Bougainville

Solomon Sea

Woodlark Basin

Solomon Islands

Pocklington Trough

South Solomon Trench

Vityaz Trench

North New Hebrides Trench

Papua Abyssal Plain

Coral Sea

Espiritu Santo

VANUATU

South New Hebrides Trench

North Fiji Basin

Fiji

Viti Levu

Vanua Levu

Hazel Holme Bank

New Caledonia

Reef

Brisbane

Lord Howe Seamount Chain

New Caledonia Trough

Norfolk Ridge

South Fiji Basin

Norfolk Island

Three Kings Ridge

West Norfolk Ridge

Norfolk Basin

Lord Howe Rise

Lord Howe Island

Sydney

Tasman Abyssal Plain

Tasman Sea

Bellona Gap

Tasman Basin

Auckland

North Island

Challenger Plateau

Wellington

Raukumara Plain

Colville Ridge

Kermadec Islands

Havre Trough

Kermadec Ridge

Kermadec Trench

Tonga

Tongatapu Group

Tonga Trench

Horizon Deep

Osbourn Seamount

Louisville Ridge

Southwest Pacific Basin

PACIFIC

Nova Canton Trough

Phoenix Islands

Ellice Islands

Funafuti

Wallis and Futuna Islands

Tokelau Islands

Robbie Ridge

Samoa

Savai'i

Upolu

Tutuila

Niue

Samoa Basin

Penrhyn Basin

Northern Cook Islands

Manihiki Plateau

Cook Islands

Southern Cook Islands

Rarotonga

Tropic of Capricorn

Valerie Guyot

East Tasman Plateau

Tasman Basin

South Island

New Zealand

Christchurch

Chatham Rise

Chatham Islands

Bounty Trough

OCEAN

Puysegur Trench

Stewart Island

Solander Trough

Pukaki Rise

Bounty Islands

Bounty Plateau

Antipodes Islands

Bollons Tablemount

BATHYMETRIC DEPTHS

Macquarie Ridge

Auckland Islands

Campbell Plateau

Campbell Rise

Campbell Island

Emerald Basin

Macquarie Island

Feet	Meters
Sea level	Sea level
656	200
1640	500
3281	1000
6562	2000
9842	3000
13,123	4000
16,404	5000
19,685	6000
26,246	8000

SCALE 1:25,000,000
Miller Projection

500 kilometers

500 statute miles

500 nautical miles

0° 10° 20° Tropic of Capricorn 30° 40° 50° 60°

1 2 3 4 5 6 7 8 9 10 11 12 13 14

ARAFURA SEA AND GULF OF CARPENTARIA

During the last ice age, the Arafura Sea and the Gulf of Carpentaria formed a land bridge between Australia and New Guinea. Today they are shelf seas 150–250 feet (45–80 m) deep. The Arafura Sea adjoins the Indian Ocean where it meets the Timor Sea. In the east it connects with the Coral Sea through Torres Strait, which has a maximum depth of only 36 feet (11 m); large ships following the busy sea lane through the Arafura Sea have to wait for high tide before passing through the strait. The region is rich in marine life. Sea cucumbers are prized by Indonesian fishermen and shrimp fishing is a key industry in the Gulf of Carpentaria.

THE FACTS (ARAFURA SEA)	
Area	250,990 square miles (650,000 km²)
Average depth	230 feet (70 m)
Maximum depth	12,000 feet (3,660 m)
Maximum width	435 miles (700 km)
Maximum length	620 miles (1,000 km)

Cobourg Peninsula (below)
Separated from Melville Island by Dundas Strait, the Cobourg Peninsula forms part of the northern boundary of Van Diemen Gulf in Australia's far northwest. It is nearly entirely Aboriginal land and has been declared a national park. It comprises coral reefs, wetlands, and rain forest and protects six species of sea turtles.

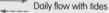
Daily flow with tides

SURFACE CURRENTS (left)
The prevailing currents in the Arafura Sea and Gulf of Carpentaria are tidal, changing direction twice a day. The wind-driven currents are weak and usually of secondary importance. From November to April this pattern can be disturbed by cyclones and their associated strong currents.

NATURAL RESOURCES (above)
- Fishing
- Shellfish
- Metallic minerals

Blue starfish (left)
Sea stars or starfish generally have five arms, which they can regenerate as long as at least one arm is still attached to the central disk. This species is known as the blue starfish (Linckia laevigata).

BATHYMETRIC DEPTHS

Feet	Meters
Sea level	Sea level
656	200
1640	500
3281	1000
6562	2000
9842	3000
13,123	4000
16,404	5000
19,685	6000
26,246	8000

Sea squirts (right)
A group of green sea squirts (*Didemnum molle*), also known as tunicates, extracts small plankton from the current. Surprisingly, sea squirts are genetically related to humans. Their capacity for correcting abnormalities over a few generations is of great interest to science.

SCALE 1:7,500,000
Miller Projection

200 kilometers
200 statute miles
200 nautical miles

Teluk Kamrau
Adi
Irian Jaya
Aru Basin
Kepulauan Barat Daya
Weber Basin
Kepulauan Kai
Kai Besar
Kai Kecil
Serua
Nila
Tuen
Damar
Molu
Kai Besar
Wokam
Kepulauan Aru
Kobroör
Trangan
Workai
Kepulauan Babar
Wuliaru
Yamdena
Kepulauan Tanimbar
Babar
Larat
Selaru
Sermata
Selaru

INDONESIA

Pulau Dolak
Tanjung Vals
Merauke

PAPUA NEW GUINEA
Gulf of Papua

Arafura Sea
Arafura Shelf

Timor Sea

Torres Strait
Badu Island
Moa Island
Thursday Island
Horn Island
Prince of Wales Island
Cape York
Bamaga

Melville Island
Bathurst Island
Cobourg Peninsula
Dundas Strait
Van Diemen Gulf
Beagle Gulf
Darwin

Goulburn Islands
Cape Wessel
Wessel Islands

Cape Arnhem
Nhulunbuy

Cape Grenville

Duyfken Point
Weipa
Albatross Bay
Cape Melville

Arnhem Land
Cape Shield
Cape Ford

Groote Eylandt

Gulf of Carpentaria

Cape York Peninsula
Princess Charlotte Bay
Cape Flattery

Joseph Bonaparte Gulf

NORTHERN

Limmen Bight

Sir Edward Pellew Group
Vanderlin Island

TERRITORY

Mornington Island
Wellesley Islands

Bentinck Island

QUEENSLAND

Karumba

AUSTRALIA

Longitude east of Greenwich

N O P Q R S T U V W X Y Z

CORAL SEA

Located between tropical Australia and the island arc formed by the Solomon Islands, Vanuatu, New Caledonia, and Norfolk Island in the south, the Coral Sea contains deep trenches in the east, deep basins in the north, part of the Lord Howe Rise in the south, and myriad coral reefs in the north and west. January to April is the cyclone season, when palm trunks and other debris from devastation on land can be found drifting across the Coral Sea. Many marine life species that are endangered elsewhere are still found in healthy numbers in this sea, including reef and hammerhead sharks, manta rays, maori wrasse, and five of the seven species of sea turtles.

THE FACTS

Area	1,849,000 square miles (4,788,888 km²)
Average depth	7,870 feet (2,398 m)
Maximum depth	25,134 feet (7,661 m)
Maximum width	1,500 miles (2,414 km)
Maximum length	1,400 miles (2,253 km)

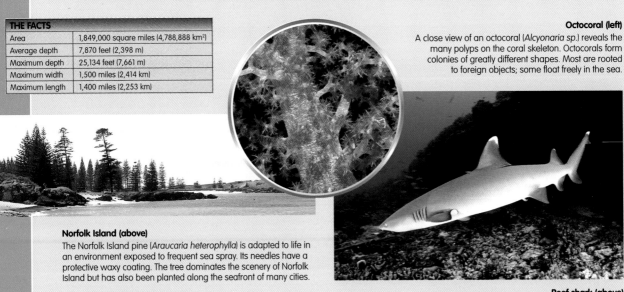

Octocoral (left)

A close view of an octocoral (*Alcyonaria sp.*) reveals the many polyps on the coral skeleton. Octocorals form colonies of greatly different shapes. Most are rooted to foreign objects; some float freely in the sea.

Norfolk Island (above)

The Norfolk Island pine (*Araucaria heterophylla*) is adapted to life in an environment exposed to frequent sea spray. Its needles have a protective waxy coating. The tree dominates the scenery of Norfolk Island but has also been planted along the seafront of many cities.

SURFACE CURRENTS (right)

As the westward-flowing South Equatorial Current approaches the Great Barrier Reef, its flow is mainly directed northward and southward. Water exchange between the Coral Sea and the reef's lagoon is achieved by strong tidal currents that sweep through the narrow channels between individual reefs.

→ East Australian Current
→ New Guinea Coastal Current
→ South Equatorial Current

Reef shark (above)

The non-aggressive whitetip reef shark (*Triaenodon obesus*) is a common shark found around coral reefs in the Indo-Pacific. It is nocturnal in habit; snorkelers often see it resting on the bottom during the day.

NATURAL RESOURCES

🐟 Fishing
🐋 Whales
📷 Tourism

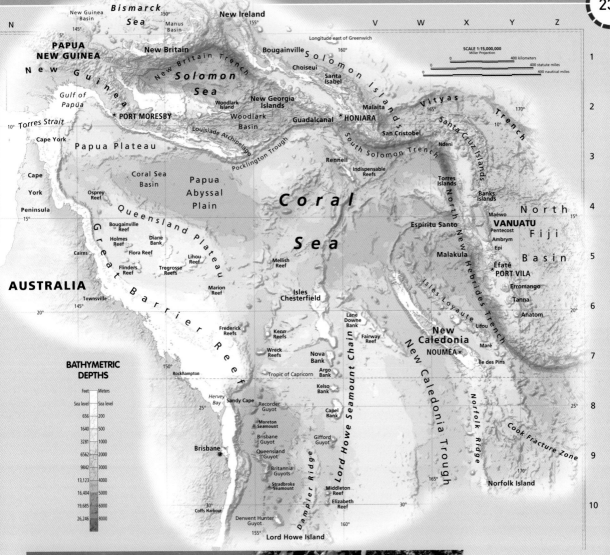

N | 145° | 150° | 155° | **V** | **W** | **X** | **Y** | **Z**

New Guinea
Basin

**Bismarck
Sea**

New Ireland

Longitude east of Greenwich

SCALE 1:15,000,000
Miller Projection

400 kilometers
400 statute miles
400 nautical miles

1

**PAPUA
NEW GUINEA**

Manus
Basin

New Britain

Bougainville

Choiseul

Santa
Isabel

Solomon Islands

Vityas

Trench

10°

2

New Guinea

New Britain Trench

**Solomon
Sea**

Woodlark
Island

New Georgia
Islands

Malaita

Santa Cruz Islands

Gulf of
Papua

* PORT MORESBY

Woodlark
Basin

Guadalcanal

* HONIARA

San Cristobel

170°

Torres Strait

Louisiade Archipelago

Ndeni

3

Papua Plateau

Pocklington Trough

South Solomon Trench

Rennell

Torres
Islands

Cape
York

Indispensable
Reefs

North

Banks
Islands

4

Cape

York

Peninsula

Coral Sea
Basin

**Papua
Abyssal
Plain**

C o r a l

Espíritu Santo

Maéwo

VANUATU

Pentecost

15°

Fiji

Osprey
Reef

Queensland Plateau

Bougainville
Reef

Holmes
Reef

Diane
Bank

S e a

Malakula

Ambrym

Epi

B a s i n

Cairns

Flora Reef

Mellish
Reef

Éfaté

* PORT VILA

AUSTRALIA

Flinders
Reef

Lihou
Reef

Tregrosse
Reefs

North New Hebrides Trench

Erromango

Tanna

Great

Marion
Reef

Isles Loyaute

Lifou

Anatom

Townsville

145°

B a r r i e r

Isles
Chesterfield

Lane
Downe
Bank

New
Caledonia

Maré

20°

5

6

20°

Frederick
Reefs

Kenn
Reefs

Fairway
Reef

NOUMÉA *

Île des Pins

7

R e e f

150°

Wreck
Reefs

Rockhampton

Nova
Bank

Argo
Bank

Tropic of Capricorn

Lord Howe Seamount Chain

New Caledonia Trough

Norfolk Ridge

Cook Fracture Zone

8

Hervey
Bay

Sandy Cape

Recorder
Guyot

Kelso
Bank

25°

25°

Capel
Bank

Brisbane

Moreton
Seamount

Brisbane
Guyot

Gifford
Guyot

Dampier Ridge

9

Queensland
Guyot

Britannia
Guyots

Stradbroke
Seamount

165°

170°

Middleton
Reef

Norfolk Island

Coffs Harbour

30°

Elizabeth
Reef

30°

10

Derwent Hunter
Guyot

160°

155°

Lord Howe Island

**BATHYMETRIC
DEPTHS**

Feet	Meters
Sea level	Sea level
656	200
1640	500
3281	1000
6562	2000
9842	3000
13,123	4000
16,404	5000
19,685	6000
26,246	8000

Sea whip (left)
A diver enjoys the clear waters of the Coral Sea and admires an elegant sea whip or sea fan (*Gorgonia sp.*). The fan spreads itself across the prevailing current to maximize chances for its eight-armed polyps to catch small plankton.

GREAT BARRIER REEF

The Great Barrier Reef consists of more than 2,900 individual reefs and 900 islands and extends along Australia's east coast for 1,250 miles (2,000 km). At least 400 species of hard and soft corals form the reef. The animal life found here includes more than 1,500 species of fish; 125 species of sharks, stingrays, and skates; 30 species of whales, porpoises, and dolphins; 6 species of turtles; and 17 species of sea snakes. Some 1.5 million birds breed on its islands. Saltwater crocodiles live in mangrove and salt marshes near the coast, and most of the world's remaining dugong population is found on the reef where seagrasses are abundant.

THE FACTS	
Area	134,286 square miles (347,800 km²)
Length	1,250 miles (2,000 km)
Maximum width	95 miles (152 km)
Surface water temperature	75°–86°F (24°–30°C)
No. of hard coral species	More than 300
No. of fish species	More than 1,500
No. of sponge species	More than 400
No. of mollusk species	Approximately 4,000
No. of seaweed species	Approximately 500

Above the reef (right)
The Great Barrier Reef is the world's biggest single structure made by living organisms.

Crown-of-thorns starfish (below)
The crown-of-thorns starfish (*Acanthaster planci*) feeds on coral polyps, its venomous spines keeping predators at bay. On the Great Barrier Reef occasional population explosions have damaged entire reefs. Pollution and climate change have been suspected, but the reasons for these outbreaks are still unclear.

Coral bleaching

One of the main effects of global warming is an increase in ocean water temperatures. This can lead to coral bleaching, the loss of zooxanthellae—a symbiotic algae—from the polyps. A temperature increase of just 2.7–3.6°F (1.5–2°C) above normal can kill coral. In 2002, the Great Barrier Reef suffered the worst coral bleaching event on record for the reef. Almost 55 percent of the reef suffered some degree of bleaching. On the map, pink indicates abnormally high temperatures.

2002 coral bleaching

- Extreme bleaching (>60% of corals affected)
- Very high bleaching (30–60%)
- High bleaching (10–30%)
- Moderate bleaching (1–10%)
- No bleaching (<1% of corals affected)

Map based on actual surveys

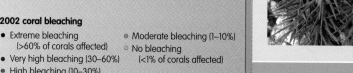

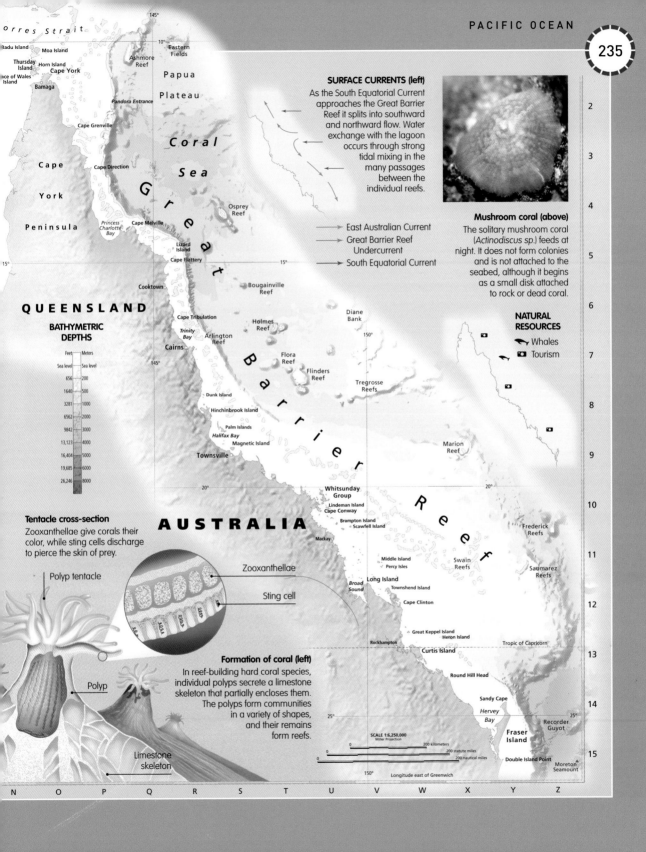

Torres Strait

Badu Island Moa Island
Thursday Island Horn Island Cape York
ace of Wales Island
Bamaga
Ashmore Reef
Eastern Fields
Papua Plateau
Cape Grenville
Pandora Entrance

Coral

Cape
York
Sea
Cape Direction
Cape Melville
Princess Charlotte Bay

Peninsula

Osprey Reef

Lizard Island
Cape Flattery

15°

Cooktown

Bougainville Reef

QUEENSLAND

Cape Tribulation
Holmes Reef
Diane Bank

Trinity Bay Arlington Reef
Cairns
Flora Reef
Flinders Reef

Dunk Island
Hinchinbrook Island
Tregrosse Reefs

Palm Islands
Halifax Bay Magnetic Island

Townsville

20°

Whitsunday Group

AUSTRALIA

Lindeman Island
Cape Conway
Brampton Island
Scawfell Island
Mackay

Marion Reef

Frederick Reefs

Middle Island
Percy Isles
Long Island
Broad Sound
Townshend Island
Cape Clinton

Swain Reefs

Saumarez Reefs

Great Keppel Island
Heron Island
Rockhampton
Curtis Island

Tropic of Capricorn

Round Hill Head

Sandy Cape
Hervey Bay

Recorder Guyot

Fraser Island

Double Island Point
Moreton Seamount

BATHYMETRIC DEPTHS

Feet	Meters
Sea level	Sea level
656	200
1640	500
3281	1000
6562	2000
9842	3000
13,123	4000
16,404	5000
19,685	6000
26,246	8000

SURFACE CURRENTS (left)
As the South Equatorial Current approaches the Great Barrier Reef it splits into southward and northward flow. Water exchange with the lagoon occurs through strong tidal mixing in the many passages between the individual reefs.

→ East Australian Current
→ Great Barrier Reef Undercurrent
→ South Equatorial Current

Mushroom coral (above)
The solitary mushroom coral (*Actinodiscus sp.*) feeds at night. It does not form colonies and is not attached to the seabed, although it begins as a small disk attached to rock or dead coral.

NATURAL RESOURCES
Whales
Tourism

Tentacle cross-section
Zooxanthellae give corals their color, while sting cells discharge to pierce the skin of prey.

Polyp tentacle

Zooxanthellae

Sting cell

Polyp

Limestone skeleton

Formation of coral (left)
In reef-building hard coral species, individual polyps secrete a limestone skeleton that partially encloses them. The polyps form communities in a variety of shapes, and their remains form reefs.

SCALE 1:6,250,000
Miller Projection
200 kilometers
200 statute miles
200 nautical miles

Longitude east of Greenwich

N O P Q R S T U V W X Y Z

TASMAN SEA

The Tasman Basin is open to the south but closed in the north and is thus influenced by the Southern Ocean at depth. The dominant surface feature is the fast-flowing and deep East Australian Current, the western boundary current of the South Pacific Subtropical Gyre. Islands in the Tasman Sea are home to the little penguin, the smallest of the world's 17 penguin species.

THE FACTS	
Area	1,545,000 square miles (4,001,530 km²)
Average depth	9,023 feet (2,750 m)
Maximum depth	17,000 feet (5,182 m)
Maximum width	1,400 miles (2,253 km)
Maximum length	1,243 miles (2,000 km)

Seahorse (right)
The pot-bellied seahorse (*Hippocampus abdominalis*) is at home in seagrass beds and mangroves of New Zealand and southeast Australia. It is found in rock pools at low tide among seaweed. Juveniles attach themselves to drifting seaweed by wrapping their tail around the stem.

SURFACE CURRENTS (left)
The East Australian Current with its eddies dominates the western Tasman Sea. On occasions it swings far to the south before turning back and heading toward New Zealand's North Cape. Broad water movement brings water from the Antarctic Circumpolar Current into the eastern Tasman Sea.

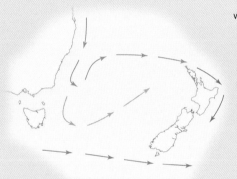

→ Circumpolar Current
→ East Auckland Current
→ East Australian Current
→ Most frequent flow

NATURAL RESOURCES
🐟 Fishing
🐋 Whales
🛢 Oil production
⬧ Gas production
▣ Tourism

⚡ Yellow-eyed penguin
Yellow-eyed penguins (*Megadyptes antipodes*) are the rarest of the world's penguins. They breed on the South Island and islands to the south of New Zealand and share their range with the little or fairy penguin (*Eudyptula minor*), a species also found in Australia.

SCALE 1:15,000,000
Miller Projection

400 kilometers
400 statute miles
400 nautical miles

BATHYMETRIC DEPTHS

Feet	Meters
Sea level	Sea level
656	200
1640	500
3281	1000
6562	2000
9842	3000
13,123	4000
16,404	5000
19,685	6000
26,246	8000

SEAFLOOR TOPOGRAPHY (right)

Near the southeast corner of mainland Australia the continental shelf is marked by a deep canyon. During winter, the water in shallow Bass Strait cools faster than in the Tasman Sea. Driven by its higher density, it flows down the canyon, forming an underwater waterfall.

VICTORIA
Melbourne
Bass Strait
TASMANIA
Hobart
Gascoyne Seamount
East Tasman Plateau
Tasman Abyssal Plain
Tasman Sea
Tasman Basin

4

5

6

7

8

Brisbane Guyot
Gifford Guyot
Queensland Guyot
Britannia Guyots
Middleton Reef
Elizabeth Reef
Stradbroke Seamount
D'awent Hunter Guyot
Lord Howe Island
Barcoo Bank
Taupo Bank
Balls Pyramid
Dampier Ridge
Lord Howe Seamounts
Lord Howe Rise
New Caledonia Basin
West Norfolk Ridge
Norfolk Ridge
Norfolk Island
Norfolk Basin
Three Kings Ridge
North Cape
160°
155°
165°
170°
175°
30°
30°

Brisbane

150°

145°

Sydney

35°

35°

A U S T R A L I A

Cape Howe
Gascoyne Seamount
Melbourne

Bass Strait

Tasmania

Hobart

East Tasman Plateau

145°

Tasman Sea

Tasman Abyssal Plain

Tasman Basin

Bellona Gap
Challenger Plateau
Cape Egmont
North Island
Auckland
WELLINGTON
Cook Strait
NEW ZEALAND
Christchurch
South Island
Dunedin
11
12
13
40°
45°
175°

N e w Z e a l a n d

45°
50°
Macquarie Ridge
Poysegor Trough
Solander Trough
Stewart Island
Campbell Plateau
Auckland Islands
Emerald Basin
170°
165°
160°
155°
50°

Longitude east of Greenwich

14

15

Sea anemones (above)

Sea anemones are predators that sting their prey by injecting a dose of poison on contact. The jewel anemone (*Corynactis australis*) lives in shaded spots on exposed coasts and entrances to caves in southeast Australia.

N O P Q R S T U V W X Y Z

CAMPBELL PLATEAU AND CHATHAM RISE

The Campbell Plateau, the Chatham Rise, and New Zealand once formed a microcontinent that separated from Antarctica. Today the major part of the Campbell Plateau is 1,200–3,000 feet (350–900 m) deep but breaks the surface in several places to form groups of islands, and rises to 270 feet (82 m) in the Campbell Rise. The plateau steers the Antarctic Circumpolar Current along its flanks, isolating the region from cold polar waters. Chatham Rise has depths of 600–1,800 feet (180–550 m), rising to 168 feet (51 m) at Mernoo Bank and breaking the surface at the Chatham Islands. The East Auckland Current brings warm subtropical water from the north and creates the Subtropical Front over the Chatham Rise.

John Dory (left)
The deep-sea predator, the John Dory (*Zeus faber*) is found at about 330 feet (100 m) along all coastal shelves except the Pacific east coast. A good table fish, it has been fished since the 1950s and supports a major commercial trawl fishery in New Zealand.

Snares crested penguin (above)
Snares crested penguin (*Eudyptes robustus*) breeds on The Snares, an island group off New Zealand's South Island. Its restricted distribution makes it a vulnerable species; the current population is estimated at around 30,000 breeding pairs. It feeds mainly on krill but occasionally takes squid and small fish.

White Island (left)
White Island, an active volcano in the Bay of Plenty off New Zealand's North Island, is known to Maori as Whakaari. It is 1.2 miles (2 km) wide and 1,053 feet (321 m) high. It was mined for sulfur until a landslide killed all 10 workers in 1914.

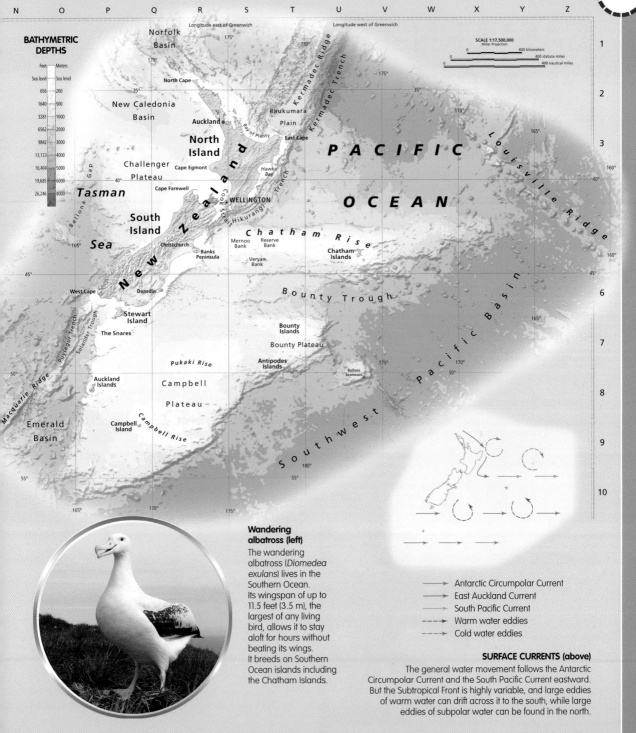

N   O   P   Q   R   S   T   U   V   W   X   Y   Z

BATHYMETRIC DEPTHS

Feet	Meters
Sea level	Sea level
656	200
1640	500
3281	1000
6562	2000
9842	3000
13,123	4000
16,404	5000
19,685	6000
26,246	8000

Longitude east of Greenwich   Longitude west of Greenwich

175°   180°   175°

170°   165°

SCALE 1:17,500,000
Miller Projection

0   400 kilometers
0   400 statute miles
0   400 nautical miles

Norfolk Basin

North Cape

35°

New Caledonia Basin

Auckland

North Island

Challenger Plateau

Cape Egmont

Cape Farewell

Bellona Gap

Tasman

South Island

Sea

165°

New Zealand

West Cape

Dunedin

Stewart Island

The Snares

Puysegur Trench

Solander Trough

Auckland Islands

Emerald Basin

Macquarie Ridge

Campbell Island

Campbell Rise

Campbell Plateau

Pukaki Rise

165°   170°   175°

Raukumara Plain

East Cape

Bay of Plenty

Hawke Bay

Cook Strait

Hikurangi Trench

WELLINGTON

Christchurch

Banks Peninsula

Mernoo Bank

Reserve Bank

Veryan Bank

Chatham Rise

Chatham Islands

Bounty Trough

Bounty Islands

Bounty Plateau

Antipodes Islands

180°

Southwest

55°

Kermadec Ridge

Kermadec Trench

PACIFIC

OCEAN

Louisville Ridge

35°

40°

45°

50°

Bollons Seamount

175°   170°   165°

Pacific Basin

50°

PACIFIC OCEAN (text within map)

1

2

3

40°

160°

45°

6

160°

7

8

9

10

Wandering albatross (left)
The wandering albatross (*Diomedea exulans*) lives in the Southern Ocean. Its wingspan of up to 11.5 feet (3.5 m), the largest of any living bird, allows it to stay aloft for hours without beating its wings. It breeds on Southern Ocean islands including the Chatham Islands.

⟶ Antarctic Circumpolar Current
⟶ East Auckland Current
⟶ South Pacific Current
- - -▶ Warm water eddies
- - -▶ Cold water eddies

SURFACE CURRENTS (above)
The general water movement follows the Antarctic Circumpolar Current and the South Pacific Current eastward. But the Subtropical Front is highly variable, and large eddies of warm water can drift across it to the south, while large eddies of subpolar water can be found in the north.

EASTERN TROPICAL PACIFIC OCEAN

The first chemosynthetic ecosystem around a hydrothermal vent was discovered in 1977 at the junction of the East Pacific Rise and the Galápagos Rift. Westward water movement dominates the region, interrupted by the eastward North Equatorial Countercurrent. Upwelling along the equator supports an important tuna fishery. The region contains some of the world's smallest nation states. Kiritimati (Christmas Island), the world's largest coral island, is home to millions of seabirds, and the waters of the uninhabited Phoenix Islands form the world's largest marine protected area.

Fanning Island (below)
Tabuaeran, also known as Fanning Island, is one of 32 atolls that belong to the island nation of Kiribati. The atolls, dispersed over 1.35 million square miles (3.5 million km²), are home to over 100,000 people. If the sea level rises, most of these low-lying islands will disappear.

Sunfish (right)
The sunfish (*Mola mola*), a resident of tropical and temperate waters, has a stocky body that ends just behind the vertical fins but can grow to 10 feet (3 m). It feeds on jellyfish and likes to sunbathe, lying sideways, flat at the sea surface.

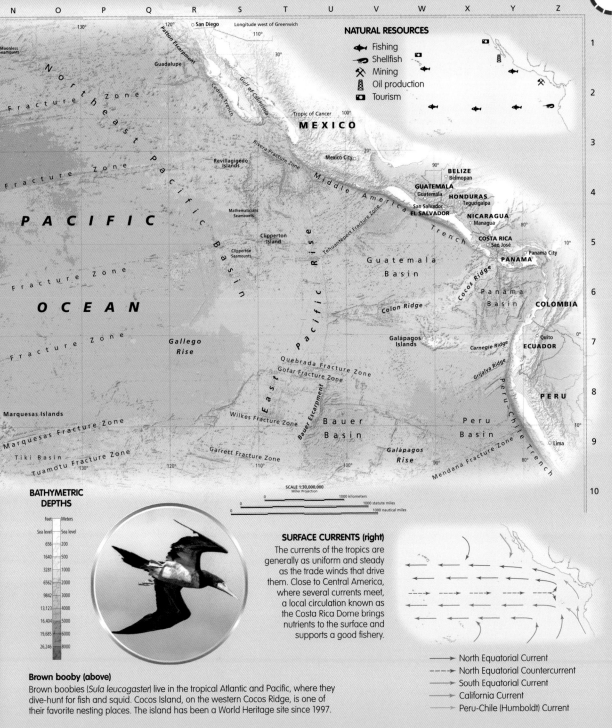

N O P Q R S T U V W X Y Z

130° 120° ○ San Diego Longitude west of Greenwich 110°

NATURAL RESOURCES

🐟 Fishing
🦐 Shellfish
⛏ Mining
🛢 Oil production
📷 Tourism

Moonless Seamounts

North east

Guadalupe

Fracture Zone

Fracture Zone

30°

Cedros Trench

Gulf of California

Tropic of Cancer   100°

MEXICO

Rivera Fracture Zone

Revillagigedo Islands

Mexico City   20°

Pacific

Mathematicians Seamounts

Middle America

90°

BELIZE
Belmopan

GUATEMALA
Guatemala

HONDURAS
Tegucigalpa

San Salvador
EL SALVADOR

NICARAGUA
Managua   80°

Clipperton Island

Clipperton Seamounts

P A C I F I C

Fracture Zone

Tehuantepec Fracture Zone

Guatemala Basin

COSTA RICA
San José   10°

Panama City
PANAMA

O C E A N

Fracture Zone

Colon Ridge

East Pacific Rise

Cocos Ridge

P a n a m a
B a s i n

COLOMBIA

Gallego Rise

Galápagos Islands

Quito   0°
ECUADOR

Carnegie Ridge

Quebrada Fracture Zone
Gofar Fracture Zone

Grijalva Ridge

Peru–Chile Trench

Marquesas Islands

Wilkes Fracture Zone

Bauer Escarpment

B a u e r
B a s i n

P e r u
B a s i n

PERU

8

Marquesas Fracture Zone

10°

Tiki Basin

Garrett Fracture Zone

Galápagos Rise

Lima   9

Tuamotu Fracture Zone   130°   120°   110°   100°   90°   Mendana Fracture Zone   80°

10

SCALE 1:30,000,000
Miller Projection

0   1000 kilometers
0   1000 statute miles
0   1000 nautical miles

BATHYMETRIC DEPTHS

Feet	Meters
Sea level	Sea level
656	200
1640	500
3281	1000
6562	2000
9842	3000
13,123	4000
16,404	5000
19,685	6000
26,246	8000

SURFACE CURRENTS (right)

The currents of the tropics are generally as uniform and steady as the trade winds that drive them. Close to Central America, where several currents meet, a local circulation known as the Costa Rica Dome brings nutrients to the surface and supports a good fishery.

→ North Equatorial Current
--→ North Equatorial Countercurrent
→ South Equatorial Current
→ California Current
→ Peru-Chile (Humboldt) Current

Brown booby (above)

Brown boobies (*Sula leucogaster*) live in the tropical Atlantic and Pacific, where they dive-hunt for fish and squid. Cocos Island, on the western Cocos Ridge, is one of their favorite nesting places. The island has been a World Heritage site since 1997.

GULF OF CALIFORNIA

Where the East Pacific Rise comes to the surface in the Baja California Peninsula, it creates a narrow sea with a rich and unique ecosystem, the Gulf of California, also known as the Sea of Cortez. Whales, turtles, and many other migratory species are regular visitors to the region. There are resident populations of sea lions and elephant seals. The more than 800 species of fish support the major part of Mexico's fishery. West of the peninsula and farther north, coastal upwelling creates one of the richest ecosystems in the world's oceans, where sea otters float among giant kelp, seaweed that grows 10 inches (27 cm) a day to reach 160 feet (50 m) at maturity.

THE FACTS	
Area	62,000 square miles (160,580 km²)
Average width	95 miles (153 km)
Maximum width (at mouth)	200 miles (320 km)
Maximum length	750 miles (1,200 km)

⚡ Californian sea otters

The endangered Californian sea otter (*Enhydra lutris*) forages for sea urchins, mollusks, and crustaceans, which it dislodges and opens using small rocks as tools. This mother and baby are wrapped in kelp to avoid floating away while resting.

Sea lions (below)
The highly intelligent Californian sea lion (*Zalophus californianus*) is a common sight at Moss Landing in Monterey Bay. Sea lions feed on squid and fish and have learned to wait for prey near fish ladders. During the non-breeding season, males and juveniles migrate north along the coast.

Kelp forests

Kelp occurs worldwide where the water temperature does not exceed 68°F (20°C). It requires high nutrient supply, mixing from wave action, and light. In the Californian upwelling region, giant kelp (*Macrocystis pyrifera*) grows into dense forests and provides habitat for many marine creatures. Supported by gas-filled bladders, its fronds grow straight up to the surface, where they form a dense canopy.

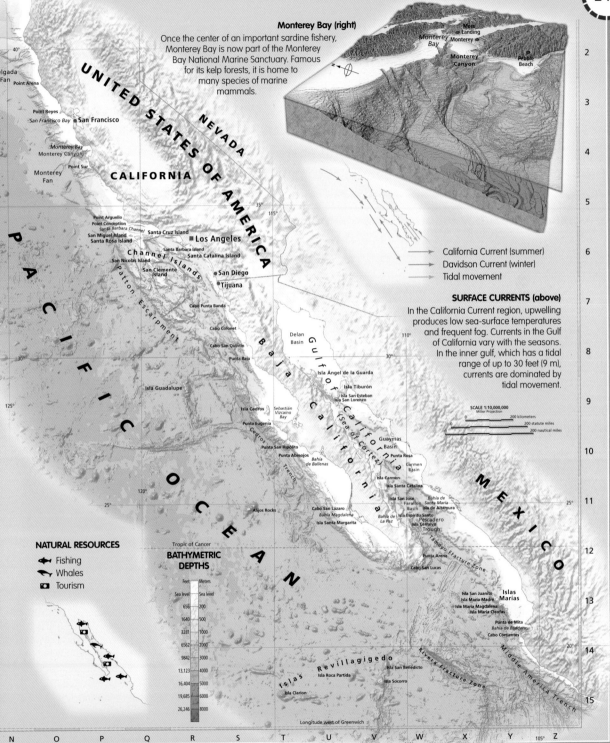

Monterey Bay (right)
Once the center of an important sardine fishery, Monterey Bay is now part of the Monterey Bay National Marine Sanctuary. Famous for its kelp forests, it is home to many species of marine mammals.

Moss Landing
Monterey
Monterey Bay
Monterey
Monterey Canyon
Pebble Beach

Delgada Fan
Point Arena

Point Reyes
San Francisco Bay   San Francisco

UNITED STATES OF AMERICA

NEVADA

Monterey Bay
Monterey Canyon
Point Sur

Monterey Fan

CALIFORNIA

Point Arguello
Point Conception
Santa Barbara Channel   Santa Cruz Island
San Miguel Island
Santa Rosa Island   Santa Barbara Island   Los Angeles
Santa Catalina Island
San Nicolas Island
San Clemente Island   San Diego
Tijuana

Channel Islands

P A C I F I C

Patton Escarpment

Cabo Punta Banda

Cabo Colonet

Cabo San Quintín

Punta Baja

Isla Guadalupe

Baja California

Delan Basin

Gulf of California (Sea of Cortez)

Isla Ángel de la Guarda
Isla Tiburón
Isla San Esteban
Isla San Lorenzo

Isla Cedros
Sebastián Vizcaíno Bay
Punta Eugenia
Cedros Trench

Punta San Hipólito
Punta Abreojos
Bahía de Ballenas

Guaymas Basin
Punta Rosa
Carmen Basin
Isla Carmen
Isla Santa Catalina

Alijos Rocks
Cabo San Lázaro
Bahía Magdalena
Isla Santa Margarita

Isla San José
Isla San Francisco   Bahía de Santa María   Basin
Isla de Altamura
Bahía de La Paz   Isla Espíritu Santo   Pescadero
Isla Cerralvo   Trough

MEXICO

California Current (summer)
Davidson Current (winter)
Tidal movement

SURFACE CURRENTS (above)
In the California Current region, upwelling produces low sea-surface temperatures and frequent fog. Currents in the Gulf of California vary with the seasons. In the inner gulf, which has a tidal range of up to 30 feet (9 m), currents are dominated by tidal movement.

SCALE 1:10,000,000
Miller Projection
0   200 kilometers
0   200 statute miles
0   200 nautical miles

O C E A N

Tropic of Cancer

Punta Arena Fracture Zone
Cabo San Lucas

Isla San Juanito
Isla María Madre   Islas Marías
Isla María Magdalena
Isla María Cleofas

Punta de Mita
Bahía de Banderas
Cabo Corrientes

NATURAL RESOURCES

🐟 Fishing
🐋 Whales
📷 Tourism

BATHYMETRIC DEPTHS

Feet	Meters
Sea level	Sea level
656	200
1640	500
3281	1000
6562	2000
9842	3000
13,123	4000
16,404	5000
19,685	6000
26,246	8000

Islas Revillagigedo
Isla Roca Partida
Isla San Benedicto
Isla Socorro
Isla Clarion

Rivera Fracture Zone

Middle America Trench

Longitude west of Greenwich

N   O   P   Q   R   S   T   U   V   W   X   Y   Z
115°   110°   105°

GALÁPAGOS ISLANDS

The Galápagos Archipelago was formed over a volcanic hot spot and contains some of the most active volcanoes in the world. Declared a World Heritage site in 1978, the islands' unique ecosystem gave Charles Darwin the observational material for his work *On the Origin of Species*. Lacking mammal predators, island life is characterized by reptiles, among them giant tortoises, and land and sea iguanas. The islands form an obstacle in the South Equatorial Current that produces a wake 600 miles (1,000 km) long. Upwelling in the wake brings cold water and nutrients to the surface, which provides ideal conditions for the Galápagos penguin, the world's northernmost penguin species.

Rocky shores (below)

Red rock crabs (*Grapsus grapsus*) live in swarms among rocks in the turbulent wave zone just above the limit of the sea spray, where they feed on algae and clean up carcasses. These crabs are common along the Pacific coast of Central and South America and on the Galápagos Islands.

Galápagos sea lions (above)

The Galápagos sea lion (*Zalophus wollebaeki*) is at home on the Galápagos Islands and on the Isla de la Plata off the coast of Ecuador. It is a social animal that loves to play, sunbathe, and perform acrobatics in the surf.

Marine iguana

Among the many unique lifeforms encountered by Charles Darwin on his visit to the Galápagos, the marine iguana (*Amblyrhynchus cristatus*) is certainly the most specially adapted creature. It grazes on algae in cold water, yet being cold-blooded it can remain under water for only half an hour before it has to return to shore. There it basks in the sun to raise its body temperature again.

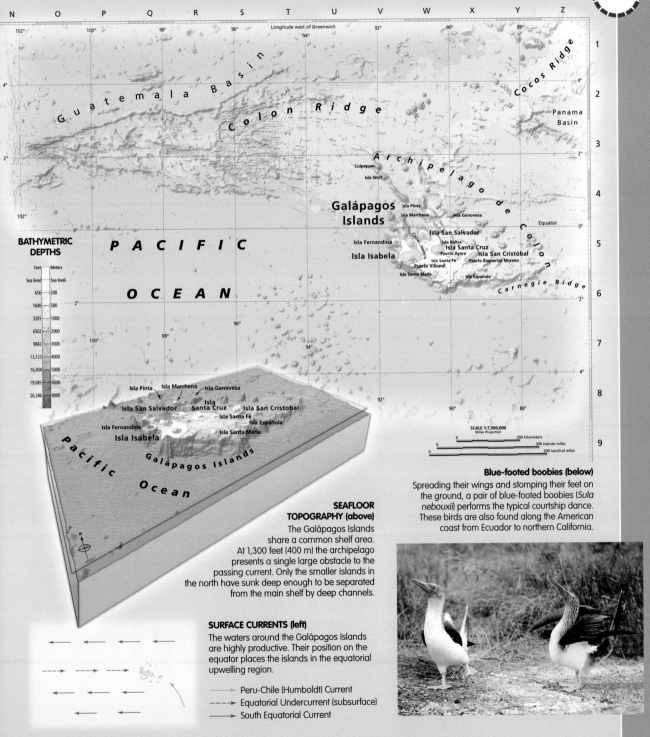

N O P Q R S T U V W X Y Z

Longitude west of Greenwich

102° 100° 98° 96° 94° 92° 90° 88°

Guatemala Basin

Colon Ridge

Cocos Ridge

Panama Basin

Culpepper

Isla Wolf

Archipelago de Colon

Galápagos Islands

Isla Pinta

Isla Marchena   Isla Genovesa

Isla Fernandina   **Isla San Salvador**

                       Isla Baltra

                       Isla Santa Cruz

Isla Isabela   Puerto Ayora **Isla San Cristóbal**

                       Isla Santa Fé   Peurto Baquerizo Moreno

                       Puerto Villamil

Isla Santa María   Isla Española

Carnegie Ridge

Equator

PACIFIC OCEAN

BATHYMETRIC DEPTHS

Feet	Meters
Sea level	Sea level
656	200
1640	500
3281	1000
6562	2000
9842	3000
13,123	4000
16,404	5000
19,685	6000
26,246	8000

Isla Pinta   Isla Marchena   Isla Genovesa

Isla San Salvador   **Isla Santa Cruz**   Isla San Cristobal

Isla Fernandina   Isla Santa Fé

                         Isla Española

                 Isla Santa Maria

Isla Isabela

Galápagos Islands

Pacific Ocean

N

SCALE 1:7,500,000
Miller Projection

200 kilometers

200 statute miles

200 nautical miles

SEAFLOOR TOPOGRAPHY (above)

The Galápagos Islands share a common shelf area. At 1,300 feet (400 m) the archipelago presents a single large obstacle to the passing current. Only the smaller islands in the north have sunk deep enough to be separated from the main shelf by deep channels.

Blue-footed boobies (below)

Spreading their wings and stomping their feet on the ground, a pair of blue-footed boobies (*Sula nebouxii*) performs the typical courtship dance. These birds are also found along the American coast from Ecuador to northern California.

SURFACE CURRENTS (left)

The waters around the Galápagos Islands are highly productive. Their position on the equator places the islands in the equatorial upwelling region.

⟶ Peru-Chile (Humboldt) Current

⇢ Equatorial Undercurrent (subsurface)

⟶ South Equatorial Current

SOUTHEASTERN PACIFIC OCEAN

Few shipping lanes cross the southeastern Pacific and the region remains among the world's least explored. Its waters are low in nutrients, their deep blue contrasting with the white sands and green vegetation of the islands. Coastal upwelling beside Chile and Peru supports the world's largest fishery and feeds millions of seabirds responsible for guano deposits. Disruption of the upwelling during El Niño years causes mass mortality among fish and birds, and upheaval in fishing villages and towns.

I   J   K   L   M

140°

Line Islands

Marquesas Islands

Marquesas Fracture Zon

Tuamotu Archipelago

Society Archipelago   Tahiti

Tubuai Island

President Thiers Seamount

Austral Islands

Southwest Pacific Basin

Eftanin

BATHYMETRIC DEPTHS

Feet	Meters
Sea level	Sea level
656	200
1640	500
3281	1000
6562	2000
9842	3000
13,123	4000
16,404	5000
19,685	6000
26,246	8000

Easter Island

Isolated in the vast South Pacific, Easter Island, a World Heritage site, is located 2,237 miles (3,600 km) west of mainland Chile. Between 1250 and 1500, its Polynesian inhabitants, the Rapanui, created hundreds of large monolithic statues called moai. In the eighteenth and nineteenth centuries all moai were overthrown, probably during conflict between clans. Some 50 statues have been re-erected.

Great barracuda (below)

The great barracuda (*Sphyraena barracuda*), a voracious predator of all tropical oceans, grows to 6 feet (1.8 m). It waits in reefs to ambush its prey, attacking with short bursts of speed up to 25 mph (40 km/h).

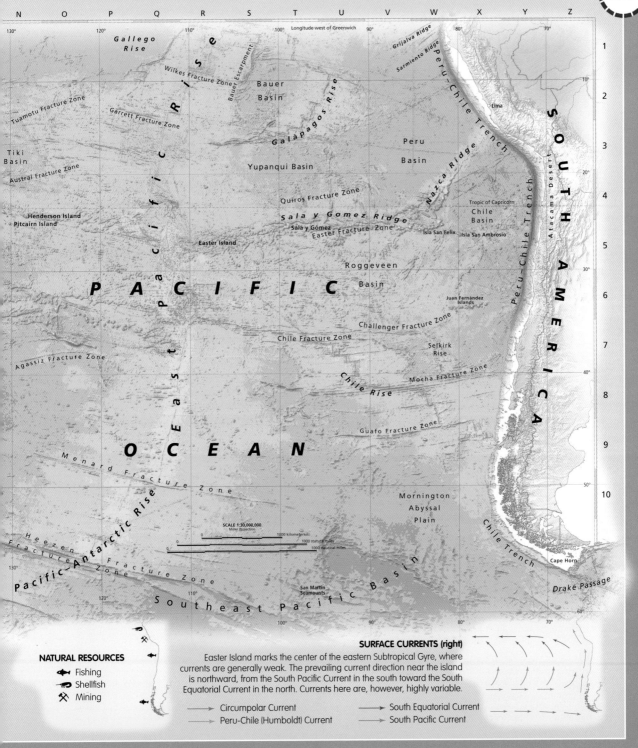

N O P Q R S T U V W X Y Z

130° 120° 110° 100° Longitude west of Greenwich 90° 80° 70°

Gallego Rise

Wilkes Fracture Zone

Bauer Escarpment

Bauer Basin

Grijalva Ridge

Sarmiento Ridge

Peru–Chile Trench

Tuamotu Fracture Zone

Garrett Fracture Zone

Galápagos Rise

Lima

Tiki Basin

Austral Fracture Zone

Yupanqui Basin

Peru Basin

Quiros Fracture Zone

**Henderson Island
Pitcairn Island**

Easter Island

Sala y Gomez Ridge

Sala y Gómez

Easter Fracture Zone

Nazca Ridge

Chile Basin

Isla San Felix

Isla San Ambrosio

Tropic of Capricorn

Atacama Desert

P A C I F I C

Roggeveen Basin

Juan Fernández Islands

Peru–Chile Trench

O C E A N

Challenger Fracture Zone

Selkirk Rise

Chile Fracture Zone

Agassiz Fracture Zone

Chile Rise

Mocha Fracture Zone

Guafo Fracture Zone

Menard Fracture Zone

Mornington Abyssal Plain

Heezen Fracture Zone

Pacific–Antarctic Rise

Fracture Zone

San Martin Seamounts

Chile Trench

Cape Horn

Southeast Pacific Basin

Drake Passage

S O U T H   A M E R I C A

East Pacific Rise

SCALE 1:30,000,000
Miller Projection

1000 kilometers
1000 statute miles
1000 nautical miles

130° 120° 110° 100° 90° 80° 70° 60°

1
10°
2
3
20°
4
5
30°
6
7
40°
8
9
50°
10

NATURAL RESOURCES

🐟 Fishing
🦐 Shellfish
⚒ Mining

SURFACE CURRENTS (right)

Easter Island marks the center of the eastern Subtropical Gyre, where currents are generally weak. The prevailing current direction near the island is northward, from the South Pacific Current in the south toward the South Equatorial Current in the north. Currents here are, however, highly variable.

→ Circumpolar Current
→ Peru-Chile (Humboldt) Current
→ South Equatorial Current
→ South Pacific Current

POLYNESIAN ISLANDS

Several hot spots created the many island chains of the South Pacific. Young islands such as Tahiti have volcanic cones surrounded by fringing reefs. As the islands drift away from their place of formation, they sink back into the ocean crust while their coral fringes grow into barrier reefs. Eventually the islands disappear into the sea, leaving coral atolls as their legacy. The islands' reefs support a diverse ecosystem that provides for the island communities, whose diet depends on fish. Cyclones are a rare occurrence, and the fresh breezes that moderate the region's temperature make it a tourist destination.

School of bannerfish (left)
A school of longfin bannerfish (*Heniochus acuminatus*) moves through a lagoon. Bannerfish, also known as butterflyfish, occur in several species on reefs of the Indian and Pacific Oceans with water temperatures of 77–82°F (25–28°C).

Three types of volcanic islands

The Leeward Islands demonstrate the development from volcano to atoll. Huahine, Raiatea, and Tahaa (bottom right and center in the photo) are tall volcanic islands with fringing reefs. Bora Bora's volcano (center left) has started to sink, a lagoon has opened around the island, and the reef has become a barrier reef. At Tupai (top left) the island has sunk below the surface, leaving an atoll and an enclosed lagoon.

SEAFLOOR TOPOGRAPHY (below)

The underwater topography of these islands in the Society Islands group reveals their character as dormant volcanoes on a common platform, created by the slow movement of the Pacific Plate over a hot spot.

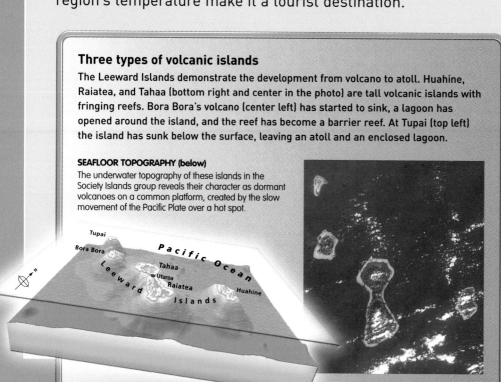

→ South Equatorial Current

SURFACE CURRENTS (above)
Most Polynesian Islands are under the trade wind and in the path of the South Equatorial Current. South of 20°S, currents are weak and variable, but the prevailing water movement is northward.

Coral trout (right)
A coral trout (*Cephalopholis miniata*) hovers in a coral niche among sponges, soft corals, and sea fans. The abundance of sedentary plankton-feeders is an indication that the area is bathed in plankton-rich current. Coral trout are common in reefs of the tropical Pacific.

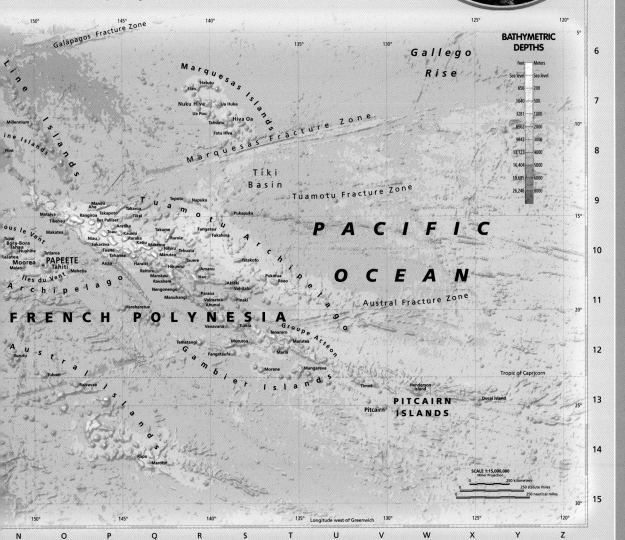

BATHYMETRIC DEPTHS

Feet	Meters
Sea level	Sea level
656	200
1640	500
3281	1000
6562	2000
9842	3000
13,123	4000
16,404	5000
19,685	6000
26,246	8000

Galápagos Fracture Zone

Gallego Rise

Line Islands

ine Islands

Millennium

Flint

Marquesas Islands

Hatutu
Eiao
Nuku Hiva   Ua Huka
Ua Pou
Tahuata   Hiva Oa
Fatu Hiva

Marquesas Fracture Zone

Tíki Basin

Tuamotu Fracture Zone

P A C I F I C

O C E A N

Austral Fracture Zone

Tepoto   Napuka
Manihi
Ahe   Takaroa
Mataiva   Takapoto
Rangiroa   Tikei
Tikehau   Îles Palliser
Makatea   Aratika
Toau   Kauehi
Niau   Takume
Fakarava   Raraka   Raroia
Tupai   Faaite   Katiu   Makemo   Fakahina
Bora-Bora   Tahaa   Tahanea   Nihiru
Huahine   Marutea
Raiatea   Tetiaroa   Anaa   Haraiki   Hikueru   Tauere
Moorea   Reitoru   Tatakoto
Maiao   Mehetia   Marokau
PAPEETE   Hao   Amanu
Tahiti   Ravahere
Nengonengo   Pukarua
Manuhangi   Akiaki   Réao
Paraoa   Vahitahi
Vairaatea   Pinaki
Ahunui
Hereheretue

Pukapuka

Fangataufa
Fangatau

Îles du Vent
Archipelago

F R E N C H   P O L Y N E S I A

Austral Islands

Rurutu

Tubuai

Raivavae

Rapa   Marotiri

Vanavana   Tureia
Tematangi   Tenararo
Groupe Acteon
Mururoa   Marutea
Fangataufa   Maria
Morane   Mangareva
Gambier Islands
Timoe

Henderson Island

Tropic of Capricorn

Ducie Island

PITCAIRN ISLANDS
Pitcairn

SCALE 1:15,000,000
Miller Projection

0   250 kilometers
0   250 statute miles
0   250 nautical miles

Longitude west of Greenwich

N   O   P   Q   R   S   T   U   V   W   X   Y   Z

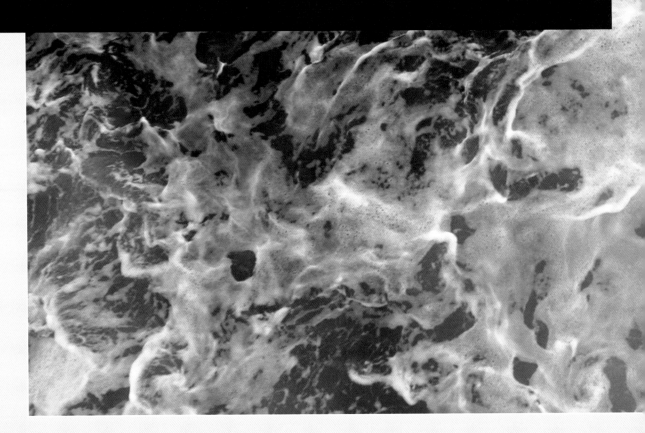

REFERENCE

Fascinating world
The global sea is a vast, diverse, and surprisingly fragile natural world. Despite centuries of marine exploration and avid human use of marine resources, the depths continue to reveal new wonders, pose new challenges, and spark the imagination and curiosity of each new generation.

OCEAN FACTFILE

NAMES OF OCEANS AND SEAS	AREA square miles (km²)	AVERAGE DEPTH feet (m)	GREATEST KNOWN depth: feet (m)	LENGTH miles (km)	WIDTH miles (km)	VOLUME cubic miles (km³)
Planet Earth				(Equatorial circ.)*	(Polar circ.)*	
Planet Earth	196,930,000 (510,000,000)	–	–	24,902 (40,077)*	24,820 (39,942)*	–
The Continents (29.2% area of Earth)	57,510,000 (148,940,000)	–	–	–	–	–
The World Ocean (70.8% of Earth)	139,420,000 (361,060,000)	12,430 (3,790)	36,201 (11,034)	–	–	329,070,000 (1,370,740,000)
The three main ocean basins						
Pacific Ocean including marginal seas and Pacific section of the Southern Ocean	69,380,000 (179,680,000)	13,220 (4,030)	36,201 (11,034)	10,106 (16,264)	to 11,185 (to 18,000)	173,770,000 (723,840,000)
Atlantic Ocean including marginal seas (Black, Mediterranean, Caribbean, etc), the Arctic Ocean and the Atlantic section of the Southern Ocean	41,110,000 (106,460,000)	10,920 (3,330)	27,493 (8,380)	13,360 (21,500)	to 4,909 (7,900)	85,200,000 (354,900,000)
Indian Ocean including marginal seas and the Indian Ocean section of the Southern Ocean	28,930,000 (74,920,000)	12,790 (3,890)	24,460 (7,455)	6,351 (10,220)	to 6,338 (10,200)	70,100,000 (292,000,000)
The oceans						
Pacific Ocean, including marginal seas	65,590,000 (169,852,000)	13,127 (4,001)	36,201 (11,034)	8,637 (13,900)	to 11,185 (18,000)	163,100,000 (679,614,000)
Atlantic Ocean, including marginal seas	33,560,000 (86,915,000)	11,828 (3,605)	28,233 (8,605)	8,774 (14,120)	to 4,909 (7,900)	75,200,000 (313,352,500)
Indian Ocean, including marginal seas)	26,980,000 (69,876,000)	12,645 (3,854)	24,460 (7,455)	5,841 (9,400)	to 6,338 (10,200)	64,720,000 (269,302,000)
Southern Ocean, including marginal seas	7,850,000 (20,327,000)	14,450 (4,500)	23,736 (7,235)	to 13,360 (21,500)	249–1,678 (400–2,700)	21,950,000 (91,471,500)
Arctic Ocean, including marginal seas	5,440,000 (14,090,000)	4,690 (1,430)	18,456 (5,625)	to 3,107 (5,000)	to 1,988 (3,200)	4,100,000 (17,000,000)

THE OCEANS AND SUBDIVISIONS IHO 23-4th: Limits of Oceans and Seas, Special Publication 23, 4th Edition June 2002, published by the International Hydrographic Bureau of the International Hydrographic Organization.

IHO	Names of oceans and seas	Area square miles (km²)	Average depth feet (m)	Greatest known depth: feet (m)	Length miles (km)	Width miles (km)	Volume cubic miles (km³)
				North Atlantic Ocean and subdivisions			
1	North Atlantic Ocean	–	–	28,233 (8,605)	4,636 (7,460)	to 4,909 (7,900)	–
1.1	Skaggerak	12,970 (33,600)	1,312 (400)	1,969 (600)	150 (240)	80–90 (130–145)	3,225 (13,440)
1.2	North Sea	222,100 (575,200)	308 (94)	2,165 (660)	621 (1,000)	93–373 (150–600)	12,974 (54,069)
1.3	Inner Seas (off West Coast Scotland)	4,630 (12,000)	82 (25)	266 (81)	174 (280)	43–62 (70–100)	72 (300)
1.4	Irish Sea	40,000 (100,000)	125 (38)	576 (175)	130 (210)	150 (240)	912 (3,800)
1.5	Bristol Channel	1,160 (3,000)	36 (11)	98 (30)	93 (150)	3–24 (5–40)	8 (33)
1.6	Celtic Sea	61,780 (160,000)	180 (55)	236 (72)	249 (400)	249 (400)	2,112 (8,800)
1.7	English Channel	34,700 (89,900)	272 (83)	394 (120)	249 (400)	21–112 (31–180)	1,726 (7,192)
1.7.1	Dover Strait	950 (2,450)	46 (14)	180 (55)	43 (70)	18–25 (30–40)	8 (34)
1.8	Bay of Biscay	86,000 (223,000)	7,874 (2,400)	15,525 (4,735)	317 (510)	342 (550)	128,419 (535,200)
1.9	Gulf of Guinea	324,360 (840,000)	12,796 (3,900)	16,405 (5,000)	435 (700)	746 (1,200)	786,064 (3,276,000)
1.10	Caribbean Sea	1,049,500 (2,718,200)	8,685 (2,647)	25,218 (7,686)	1,678 (2,700)	360–840 (600–1,400)	1,726,430 (7,195,075)
1.11	Gulf of Mexico	615,000 (1,592,800)	4,874 (1,486)	12,425 (3,787)	1,100 (1,770)	800 (1,287)	567,929 (2,366,901)
1.12	Straits of Florida	48,270 (125,000)	1,148 (350)	1,641 (500)	311 (500)	155 (250)	10,498 (43,750)
1.13	Bay of Fundy	3,600 (9,300)	328 (100)	656 (200)	94 (151)	32 (52)	223 (930)
1.14	Gulf of St. Lawrence	62,530 (162,000)	197 (60)	656 (200)	280 (450)	261 (420)	2,332 (9,720)
1.15	Labrador Sea	222,030 (575,000)	6,562 (2,000)	12,468 (3,800)	to 870 (1,400)	to 492 (820)	275,938 (1,150,000)

IHO	Names of oceans and seas	Area square miles (km²)	Average depth feet (m)	Greatest known depth: feet (m)	Length miles (km)	Width miles (km)	Volume cubic miles (km³)
Other subdivisions of the North Atlantic Ocean							
–	Bay of Campeche	65,640 (170,000)	1,476 (450)	10,499 (3,200)	441 (710)	205 (330)	18,356 (76,500)
–	Block Island Sound	190 (500)	59 (18)	66 (20)	20 (32)	10 (16)	2 (9)
–	Cabot Strait	1,450 (3,750)	1,148 (350)	3,281 (1,000)	155 (250)	60–372 (100–320)	315 (1,313)
–	Canarias Sea	90,360 (234,000)	5,906 (1,800)	6,562 (2,000)	373 (600)	249 (400)	101,065 (421,200)
–	Cape Cod Bay	830 (2,150)	82 (25)	115 (35)	31 (50)	27 (43)	13 (54)
–	Chaleur Bay	1,680 (4,350)	82 (25)	164 (50)	90 (145)	15–25 (24–40)	26 (109)
–	Chesapeake Bay	5,800 (15,000)	23 (7)	80 (24)	193 (311)	3–25 (5–40)	25 (105)
–	Delaware Bay	970 (2,500)	23 (7)	70 (21)	52 (84)	6–25 (10–40)	4 (18)
–	Denmark Strait	54,060 (140,000)	3,281 (1,000)	8,203 (2,500)	300 (483)	180 (290)	33,592 (140,000)
–	Gulf of Cadiz	14,480 (37,500)	1,969 (600)	3,281 (1,000)	93 (150)	200 (320)	5,399 (22,500)
–	Gulf of Venezuela	10,190 (26,400)	8,203 (2,500)	9,843 (3,000)	75 (120)	150 (240)	15,836 (66,000)
–	Gulf of Honduras	30,890 (80,000)	2,953 (900)	8,203 (2,500)	249 (400)	9–240 (15–400)	17,276 (72,000)
–	Gulf of Maine	90,700 (235,000)	492 (150)	1,237 (377)	323 (520)	280 (450)	8,458 (35,250)
–	Long Bay	4,630 (12,000)	49 (15)	131 (40)	78 (125)	62 (100)	43 (180)
–	Long Island Sound	1,180 (3,056)	82 (25)	328 (100)	90 (145)	3–20 (5–32)	18 (76)
–	Massachusetts Bay	820 (2,123)	115 (35)	295 (90)	31 (50)	26 (42)	18 (74)
–	Mona Passage	8,500 (22,000)	656 (200)	3,281 (1,000)	112 (180)	68–87 (110–145)	1,056 (4,400)
–	Nantucket Sound	1,000 (2,600)	59 (18)	131 (40)	43 (70)	25 (40)	11 (47)
–	North Channel	2,320 (6,000)	328 (100)	656 (200)	124 (200)	11–36 (18–60)	144 (600)
–	Onslow Bay	5,790 (15,000)	66 (20)	164 (50)	103 (165)	62 (100)	72 (300)
–	Rhode Island Sound	580 (1,500)	23 (7)	33 (10)	25 (40)	24 (38)	3 (11)
–	St. George's Channel	4,250 (11,000)	148 (45)	203 (62)	99 (160)	47 (76)	119 (495)
–	Sargasso Sea	1,448,020 (3,750,000)	16,405 (5,000)	21,005 (6,402)	1,864 (3,000)	994 (1,600)	4,498,990 (18,750,000)
–	Windward Passage	3,480 (9,000)	3,281 (1,000)	5,545 (1,690)	68 (110)	50 (80)	2,160 (9,000)
–	Yucatan Channel	16,600 (43,000)	3,281 (1,000)	6,693 (2,040)	135 (217)	124 (200)	10,318 (43,000)
Baltic Sea and subdivisions (North Atlantic Ocean)							
2	Baltic Sea	163,000 (422,200)	180 (55)	1,380 (421)	795 (1,280)	24–324 (40–540)	5,572 (23,221)
2.1	Central Baltic Sea	46,340 (120,000)	164 (50)	656 (200)	373 (600)	186 (300)	1,440 (6,000)
2.2	Gulf of Bothnia	45,200 (117,000)	200 (60)	965 (295)	450 (725)	48–150 (80–240)	1,684 (7,020)
2.2.1	Bothnian Sea	19,110 (49,500)	246 (75)	656 (200)	205 (330)	48–132 (80–220)	891 (3,713)
2.2.2	Bay of Bothnia	9,270 (24,000)	246 (75)	656 (200)	249 (400)	9–75 (15–125)	432 (1,800)
2.3	Gulf of Finland	11,600 (30,000)	85 (26)	377 (115)	249 (400)	12–80 (19–130)	187 (780)
2.4	Sound Sea	25,100 (65,000)	82 (25)	164 (50)	186 (300)	137 (220)	390 (1,625)
2.5	Gulf of Riga	7,000 (18,000)	131 (40)	144 (44)	109 (175)	24–72 (40–120)	173 (720)
2.6	The Sound	390 (1,000)	131 (40)	164 (50)	68 (110)	3–9 (5–14)	10 (40)
2.7	The Great Belt	460 (1,200)	85 (26)	164 (50)	47 (75)	9–12 (15– 20)	7 (31)
2.8	The Little Belt	420 (1,100)	85 (26)	164 (50)	37 (60)	9–24 (15– 40)	7 (29)
2.9	Kattegat	9,840 (25,485)	84 (26)	164 (50)	137 (220)	37–88 (60–142)	159 (663)
Other subdivisions of the Baltic Sea (North Atlantic Ocean)							
–	Gulf of Gdansk	1,660 (4,296)	180 (55)	197 (60)	62 (100)	43 (70)	57 (236)
–	Kiel Bay	970 (2,500)	131 (40)	131 (40)	50 (80)	22 (35)	24 (100)
–	Mecklenburger Bay	1,000 (2,600)	131 (40)	125 (38)	47 (75)	18–27 (30–45)	25 (104)
–	Pomeranian Bay	930 (2,400)	66 (20)	164 (50)	43 (70)	31 (50)	12 (48)
Mediterranean Sea and subdivisions (North Atlantic Ocean)							
3.1	Mediterranean Sea	969,000 (2,510,000)	4,920 (1,500)	16,897 (5,150)	2,500 (4,000)	497 (800)	860,636 (3,586,790)
3.1.1	Mediterranean Sea, Western Basin	328,220 (850,000)	-	12,000 (3,658)	1,250 (2,000)	497 (800)	-
3.1.1.1	Strait of Gibraltar	290 (750)	1,200 (365)	3,117 (950)	36 (58)	8 (13)	66 (274)
3.1.1.2	Alboran Sea	18,530 (48,000)	1,969 (600)	3,872 (1180)	249 (400)	48–120 (80–200)	6,910 (28,800)
3.1.1.3	Balearic Sea	123,560 (320,000)	2,461 (750)	4,987 (1,520)	497 (800)	120–420 (200–700)	57,587 (240,000)
3.1.1.4	Ligurian Sea	13,510 (35,000)	4,265 (1,300)	9,300 (2,850)	155 (250)	106 (170)	10,918 (45,500)
3.1.1.5	Tyrrhenian Sea	46,340 (120,000)	9,515 (2,900)	11,897 (3,626)	475 (760)	60–300 (97–483)	83,501 (348,000)

IHO	Names of oceans and seas	Area square miles (km²)	Average depth feet (m)	Greatest known depth: feet (m)	Length miles (km)	Width miles (km)	Volume cubic miles (km³)
	Mediterranean Sea and subdivisions (North Atlantic Ocean) – continued						
3.1.2	Mediterranean Sea, Eastern Basin	640,990 (1,660,000)	-	16,897 (5,150)	1,250 (2,000)	497 (800)	-
3.1.2.1	Adriatic Sea	52,220 (135,250)	1,457 (444)	4,035 (1,324)	497 (800)	99 (160)	14,409 (60,051)
3.1.2.2	Strait of Sicily	19,310 (50,000)	328 (100)	1,969 (600)	311 (500)	93 (150)	1,200 (5,000)
3.1.2.3	Ionian Sea	104,260 (270,000)	12,796 (3,900)	16,000 (4,900)	373 (600)	120–360 (200–600)	252,663 (1,053,000)
3.1.2.4	Aegean Sea	83,000 (214,000)	1,969 (600)	11,627 (3,543)	380 (611)	186 (399)	30,809 (128,400)
3.2	Sea of Marmara	4,430 (11,474)	1,620 (494)	4,446 (1,355)	175 (280)	50 (80)	1,360 (5,668)
3.3	Black Sea	196,000 (508,000)	4,062 (1,240)	7,365 (2,245)	730 (1,175)	160 (260)	151,147 (629,920)
3.4	Sea of Azov	14,500 (37,555)	23 (7)	45 (13)	210 (340)	85 (135)	63 (263)
	Other subdivisions of the Mediterranean Sea (North Atlantic Ocean)						
–	Dardanelles	100 (250)	180 (55)	300 (92)	38 (61)	0.75–4 (1.2–6.5)	3.3 (13.8)
–	Gulf of Lion	11,580 (30,000)	246 (75)	276 (84)	93 (150)	60–138 (100–230)	540 (2,250)
–	Gulf of Venice	2,010 (5,200)	98 (30)	128 (39)	60 (95)	37 (60)	37 (156)
–	Bosporus	40 (105)	98 (30)	408 (124)	19 (30)	2.3 (3.7)	0.8 (3.2)
–	Sea of Crete	27,800 (72,000)	6,562 (2,000)	10,000 (3,294)	249 (400)	130 (210)	34,552 (144,000)
–	Thracian Sea	3,480 (9,000)	246 (75)	328 (100)	93 (150)	50 (80)	162 (675)
	Southern Atlantic Ocean and subdivisions						
4	South Atlantic Ocean	–	–	27,651 (8,428)	4,139 (6,660)	to 4,680 (to 7,800)	–
4.1	River Plate	12,740 (33,000)	20 (6)	70 (21)	186 (300)	9 to 120 (15 to 200)	48 (198)
4.2	Scotia Sea	348,000 (900,000)	11,500 (4,500)	27,651 (8,428)	870 (1,400)	497 (800)	755,830 (3,150,000)
4.3	Drake Passage	308,910 (800,000)	11,000 (3,400)	15,600 (4,800)	497 (800)	621 (1,000)	652,653 (2,720,000)
	Other subdivisions of the South Atlantic Ocean						
–	San Jorge Gulf	15,450 (40,000)	115 (35)	262 (80)	99 (160)	137 (220)	336 (1,400)
–	San Matias Gulf	6,950 (18,000)	98 (30)	230 (70)	99 (160)	24–90 (40–150)	130 (540)
–	Strait of Magellan	2,240 (5,800)	66 (20)	98 (30)	350 (560)	2–20 (3–32)	28 (116)
	Indian Ocean and subdivisions						
5	Indian Ocean	26,500,000 (68,600,000)	12,644 (3,854)	23,376 (7,125)	5,800 (9,400)	6,300 (10,200)	64,720,000 (269,302,104)
5.1	Mozambique Channel	432,470 (1,120,000)	8,531 (2,600)	9,843 (3,000)	1,000 (1,600)	250–600 (400–950)	698,723 (2,912,000)
5.2	Gulf of Suez	4,050 (10,500)	82 (25)	295 (90)	180 (290)	15–35 (24–56)	63 (263)
5.3	Gulf of Aqaba	1,480 (3,840)	2,625 (800)	6,070 (1,850)	99 (160)	12–17 (19–27)	737 (3,072)
5.4	Red Sea	169,100 (438,000)	1,608 (490)	9,974 (3,040)	1,398 (2,250)	220 (355)	51,602 (215,058)
5.5	Gulf of Aden	205,000 (530,000)	4,922 (1,500)	17,586 (5,360)	920 (1,480)	300 (480)	190,757 (795,000)
5.6	Persian Gulf	96,911 (251,000)	164 (50)	344 (119)	615 (989)	35 (56)	1,957 (8,155)
5.7	Strait of Hormuz	4,630 (12,000)	213 (65)	2,953 (900)	99 (160)	35–60 (55–95)	187 (780)
5.8	Gulf of Oman	65,640 (170,000)	3,937 (1,200)	9,843 (3,000)	350 (560)	200 (320)	48,949 (204,000)
5.9	Arabian Sea	1,500,000 (3,900,000)	9,022 (2,750)	15,262 (4,652)	to 1,243 (2,000)	1,490 (2,400)	2,533,521 (10,558,708)
5.10	Lakshadweep Sea	289,600 (750,000)	7,874 (2,400)	14,765 (4,500)	to 932 (1,500)	to 620 (1,000)	431,903 (1,800,000)
5.11	Gulf of Mannar	11,740 (30,400)	3,281 (1,000)	5,906 (1,800)	99 (160)	80–170 (130–275)	7,294 (30,400)
5.12	Palk Strait and Palk Bay	5,780 (14,960)	98 (30)	295 (90)	85 (136)	40–85 (64–137)	108 (449)
5.13	Bay of Bengal	838,613 (2,172,000)	8,500 (2,600)	15,400 (4,694)	1,300 (2,090)	1,000 (1,610)	1,355,648 (5,649,800)
5.14	Andaman Sea	308,000 (797,700)	2,854 (870)	12,392 (3,777)	750 (1,200)	400 (645)	166,522 (693,999)
5.15	Timor Sea	235,000 (615,000)	459 (140)	10,800 (3,300)	609 (980)	435 (700)	20,659 (86,100)
5.15.1	Joseph Bonaparte Gulf	19,310 (50,000)	197 (60)	328 (100)	99 (160)	225 (360)	720 (3,000)
5.16	Arafura Sea	250,990 (650,000)	230 (70)	12,000 (3,660)	to 620 (1,000)	to 435 (700)	10,918 (45,500)
5.16.1	Gulf of Carpentaria	120,000 (310,000)	164 (50)	230 (70)	544 (875)	120–390 (200–650)	3,719 (15,500)
5.17	Great Australian Bight	366,830 (950,000)	7,218 (2,200)	14,765 (4,500)	1,740 (2,800)	to 620 (1,000)	501,487 (2,090,000)
	Other subdivisions of the Indian Ocean						
–	Gulf of Bahrain	3,280 (8,500)	98 (30)	131 (40)	106 (170)	12–57 (20–95)	61 (255)
–	Strait of Tiran	440 (1,150)	262 (80)	400 (122)	31 (50)	16 (25)	22 (92)

IHO	Names of oceans and seas	Area square miles (km²)	Average depth feet (m)	Greatest known depth: feet (m)	Length miles (km)	Width miles (km)	Volume cubic miles (km³)
	South China and Eastern Archipelagic Seas (Pacific Ocean)						
6	South China and Eastern Archipelagic Seas	–	–	–	–	–	–
6.1	South China Sea	895,400 (2,319,000)	5,419 (1,652)	16,456 (5,016)	to 1,182 (1,970)	to 840 (1,400)	919,231 (3,830,988)
6.2	Gulf of Tonkin	46,340 (120,000)	246 (75)	230 (70)	311 (500)	150 (250)	2,160 (9,000)
6.3	Gulf of Thailand	123,553 (320,000)	148 (45)	262 (80)	450 (724)	350 (563)	3,455 (14,400)
6.4	Natuna Sea	135,150 (350,000)	148 (45)	328 (100)	559 (900)	60–390 (100–650)	3,779 (15,750)
6.5	Malacca Strait	25,000 (65,000)	90 (27)	656 (200)	497 (800)	40–155 (65–249)	421 (1,755)
6.6	Singapore Strait	1,000 (2,600)	131 (40)	164 (50)	65 (105)	10–18 (16–30)	25 (104)
6.7	Sunda Strait	4,440 (11,500)	131 (40)	164 (50)	103 (165)	16–70 (26–110)	110 (460)
6.8	Java Sea	167,000 (433,000)	151 (46)	689 (210)	900 (1,450)	261 (420)	4,779 (19,918)
6.9	Makassar Strait	81,090 (210,000)	2,625 (800)	6,562 (2,000)	497 (800)	80–230 (130–370)	40,311 (168,000)
6.10	Bali Sea	15,830 (41,000)	197 (60)	1,805 (550)	311 (500)	75 (120)	590 (2,460)
6.11	Flores Sea	93,000 (240,000)	6,890 (2,100)	16,860 (5,140)	435 (700)	108–360 (180–600)	120,933 (504,000)
6.12	Sumba Strait	6,490 (16,800)	328 (100)	2,461 (750)	130 (210)	36–60 (60–100)	403 (1,680)
6.13	Savu Sea	41,000 (105,000)	8,859 (2,700)	11,385 (3,470)	404 (650)	155 (250)	68,025 (283,500)
6.14	Aru Sea	30,890 (80,000)	6,562 (2,000)	11,484 (3,500)	311 (500)	78–102 (130–170)	38,391 (160,000)
6.15	Banda Sea	181,000 (470,000)	14,765 (4,500)	24,409 (7,440)	652 (1,050)	228–330 (380–550)	507,486 (2,115,000)
6.16	Gulf of Bone	12,740 (33,000)	6,562 (2,000)	9,843 (3,000)	186 (300)	36–102 (60–170)	15,836 (66,000)
6.17	Ceram Sea	31,280 (81,000)	7,218 (2,200)	11,484 (3,500)	360 (580)	68–120 (110–200)	42,758 (178,200)
6.18	Gulf of Berau	4,250 (11,000)	230 (70)	328 (100)	137 (220)	12–42 (20–70)	185 (770)
6.19	Halmahera Sea	28,570 (74,000)	2,461 (750)	3,281 (1,000)	186 (300)	186 (300)	13,317 (55,500)
6.20	Molucca Sea	77,000 (200,000)	9,187 (2,800)	15,780 (4,810)	373 (600)	150–258 (250–430)	134,370 (560,000)
6.21	Gulf of Tomini	23,170 (60,000)	3,937 (1,200)	4,922 (1,500)	261 (420)	60–123 (100–205)	17,276 (72,000)
6.22	Celebes Sea	110,000 (280,000)	13,780 (4,200)	20,406 (6,220)	420 (675)	520 (837)	282,177 (1,176,000)
6.23	Sulu Sea	100,000 (260,000)	11,484 (3,500)	18,400 (5,600)	490 (790)	375 (603)	218,351 (910,000)
	Other subdivisions of the South China and Eastern Archipelagic Seas						
–	Luzon Sea	81,090 (210,000)	2,953 (900)	9,843 (3,000)	466 (750)	217 (350)	45,350 (189,000)
–	Luzon Strait	46,340 (120,000)	2,953 (900)	6,562 (2,000)	217 (350)	249 (400)	25,914 (108,000)
–	Karimata Strait	52,130 (135,000)	492 (150)	656 (200)	280 (450)	120–228 (200–380)	4,859 (20,250)
–	Yapen Strait	6,180 (16,000)	3,281 (1,000)	3,281 (1,000)	155 (250)	40 (65)	3,839 (16,000)
–	Cenderawasih Bay	18,150 (47,000)	2,297 (700)	3,281 (1,000)	174 (280)	54–252 (90–420)	7,894 (32,900)
	North Pacific Ocean and subdivisions						
7	North Pacific Ocean	–	–	36,201 (11,034)	4,499 (7,240)	to 10,800 (18,000)	–
7.1	Philippine Sea	1,776,230 (4,600,000)	19,700 (6,000)	34,578 (10,539)	to 1,800 (3,000)	to 1,200 (2,000)	6,622,513 (27,600,000)
7.2	Taiwan Strait	21,240 (55,000)	197 (60)	230 (70)	286 (460)	100–174 (160–280)	792 (3,300)
7.3	East China Sea	284,000 (735,800)	574 (175)	8,913 (2,717)	684 (1,100)	435 (700)	30,897 (128,765)
7.4	Yellow Sea	180,000 (466,200)	131 (40)	338 (103)	600 (960)	435 (700)	4,475 (18,648)
7.4.1	Bo Hai	30,890 (80,000)	82 (25)	164 (50)	217 (350)	72–192 (120–320)	480 (2,000)
7.4.2	Liaodong Gulf	8,110 (21,000)	82 (25)	164 (50)	112 (180)	75 (120)	126 (525)
7.5	Inland Sea of Japan	8,500 (22,000)	121 (37)	197 (60)	233 (375)	6–105 (10–175)	195 (814)
7.6.1	Tatar Strait	23,940 (62,000)	246 (75)	3,281 (1,000)	311 (500)	78 (125)	1,116 (4,650)
7.7	Sea of Okhotsk	613,800 (1,589,700)	2,749 (838)	12,001 (3,658)	to 1,020 (1,700)	to 780 (1,300)	319,369 (1,332,169)
7.8	Bering Sea	884,900 (2,291,900)	5,075 (1,547)	15,659 (4,773)	1,490 (2,397)	990 (1,593)	850,746 (3,545,569)
7.8.1	Gulf of Anadyr	37,070 (96,000)	246 (75)	492 (150)	200 (320)	250 (400)	1,728 (7,200)
7.9	Bering Strait	29,350 (76,000)	133 (40)	164 (50)	236 (380)	60–180 (100–300)	729 (3,040)
7.10	Gulf of Alaska	592,000 (1,533,000)	8,203 (2,500)	16,405 (5,000)	to 1,200 (2,000)	to 240 (400)	919,594 (3,832,500)
7.11	Coastal Waters of Southeast Alaska and British Colombia	13,900 (36,000)	9,843 (3,000)	12,468 (3,800)	932 (1,500)	to 99 (160)	25,914 (108,000)
7.12	Gulf of California	62,000 (160,580)	3,937 (1,200)	10,000 (3,050)	750 (1,200)	200 (320)	44,054 (183,600)
7.13	Gulf of Panama	8,570 (22,200)	246 (75)	328 (100)	99 (160)	115 (185)	400 (1,665)

IHO	Names of oceans and seas	Area square miles (km²)	Average depth feet (m)	Greatest known depth: feet (m)	Length miles (km)	Width miles (km)	Volume cubic miles (km³)
	Other subdivisions of the North Pacific Ocean						
–	Amurskiy Liman	2,160 (5,600)	82 (25)	164 (50)	87 (140)	12–39 (20–65)	34 (140)
–	Bristol Bay	18,530 (48,000)	82 (25)	164 (50)	200 (320)	to 180 (300)	288 (1,200)
–	Cheju Strait	3,860 (10,000)	246 (75)	328 (100)	103 (165)	37 (60)	180 (750)
–	Gulf of Tehuantepec	12,160 (31,500)	984 (300)	3,281 (1,000)	326 (525)	75 (120)	2,267 (9,450)
–	Gulf of Santa Catalina	3,670 (9,500)	394 (120)	656 (200)	68 (110)	62 (100)	274 (1,140)
–	Hecate Strait	7,920 (20,500)	1,476 (450)	3,281 (1,000)	160 (257)	40–60 (64–129)	2,214 (9,225)
–	Strait of La Perouse	4,830 (12,500)	246 (75)	328 (100)	130 (210)	27–51 (45–85)	225 (938)
–	Korea Bay	13,900 (36,000)	98 (30)	164 (50)	165 (265)	121 (195)	259 (1080)
–	Korea Strait	2,510 (6,500)	295 (90)	328 (100)	62 (100)	30–48 (50–80)	140 (585)
–	Queen Charlotte Sound	7,410 (19,200)	1,575 (480)	3,281 (1,000)	124 (200)	75 (120)	2,211 (9,216)
–	Sakhalin Gulf	2,900 (7,500)	98 (30)	164 (50)	47 (75)	36–96 (60–160)	54 (225)
–	Santa Barbara Channel	2,320 (6,000)	1,312 (400)	1,641 (500)	75 (120)	31 (50)	576 (2,400)
–	San Pedro Channel	770 (2,000)	394 (120)	656 (200)	28 (45)	28 (45)	58 (240)
–	Sea of Japan	377,600 (978,000)	5,748 (1,752)	12,276 (3,742)	1,740 (2,800)	to 540 (900)	411,137 (1,713,456)
–	Strait of Georgia	1,450 (3,750)	328 (100)	1,200 (370)	138 (222)	17 (28)	90 (375)
–	Strait of Juan de Fuca	1,310 (3,400)	394 (120)	900 (275)	80–100 (130–160)	16 (25)	98 (408)
–	Gulf of Shelikhova	69,500 (180,000)	410 (125)	1,624 (495)	420 (670)	185 (300)	5,399 (22,500)
	South Pacific Ocean and subdivisions						
8	South Pacific Ocean	–	–	35,704 (10,882)	4,139 (6,660)	to 10,800 (18,000)	–
8.1	Bismarck Sea	194,227 (503,000)	6,600 (2,000)	8,200 (2,500)	497 (800)	249 (400)	241,386 (1,006,000)
8.2	Solomon Sea	278,019 (720,000)	14,765 (4,500)	29,988 (9,140)	621 (1,000)	497 (800)	777,425 (3,240,000)
8.3	Coral Sea	1,849,000 (4,788,888)	7,870 (2,398)	25,134 (7,661)	1,400 (2,250)	1,500 (2,414)	2,758,421
8.3.1	Torres Strait	10,430 (27,000)	246 (75)	328 (100)	130 (210)	80 (130)	486 (2,025)
8.3.2	Great Barrier Reef	134,286 (347,800)	197 (60)	328 (100)	1,250 (2,000)	30–95 (50–152)	3,599 (15,000)
8.3.3	Gulf of Papua	14,670 (38,000)	213 (65)	328 (100)	95 (150)	225 (360)	593 (2,470)
8.4	Tasman Sea	1,545,000 (4,001,530)	9,023 (2,750)	17,000 (5,182)	1,243 (2,000)	1,400 (2,253)	2,639,407
8.4.1	Bass Strait	28,950 (75,000)	210 (60)	262 (80)	224 (360)	150 (240)	1,080 (4,500)
	Other subdivisions of the South Pacific Ocean						
–	Bay of Plenty	3,090 (8,000)	328 (100)	820 (250)	99 (160)	37 (60)	192 (800)
–	Cook Strait	2,120 (5,500)	420 (128)	3,445 (1,050)	81 (130)	14 (23)	169 (704)
–	Foveaux Strait	970 (2,500)	98 (30)	164 (50)	43 (70)	22 (35)	18 (75)
–	Gulf of Guayaquil	5,410 (14,000)	82 (25)	197 (60)	124 (200)	87 (140)	84 (350)
	Arctic Ocean and subdivisions						
9	Arctic Ocean	5,440,000 (14,090,000)	4,690 (1,430)	18,455 (5,625)	to 3,100 (5,000)	to 2,000 (3,200)	4,834,603 (20,148,700)
9.1	East Siberian Sea	361,000 (936,000)	328 (100)	510 (155)	777 (1,250)	497 (800)	22,459 (93,600)
9.2	Laptev Sea	250,900 (649,800)	1,896 (578)	9,774 (2,980)	528 (850)	497 (800)	90,120 (375,584)
9.3	Kara Sea	340,000 (880,000)	417 (127)	2,034 (620)	932 (1,500)	559 (900)	26,816 (111,760)
9.4	Barents Sea	542,000 (1,405,000)	750 (229)	1,969 (600)	808 (1,300)	650 (1,050)	77,201 (321,745)
9.5	White Sea	36,680 (95,000)	200 (60)	1,115 (340)	261 (420)	249 (400)	1,368 (5,700)
9.6	Greenland Sea	353,320 (915,000)	4,750 (1,450)	16,000 (4,800)	808 (1,300)	621 (1,000)	318,349 (1,326,750)
9.7	Norwegian Sea	328,220 (850,000)	5,254 (1,600)	13,020 (3,970)	870 (1,400)	684 (1,100)	326,327 (1,360,000)
9.8	Iceland Sea	111,980 (290,000)	3,701 (1,128)	9,843 (3,000)	404 (650)	280 (450)	78,491 (327,120)
9.9	Davis Strait	115,840 (300,000)	1,476 (450)	4,922 (1,500)	404 (650)	200–400 (322–644)	32,393 (135,000)
9.10	Hudson Strait	37,070 (96,000)	1,641 (500)	3,090 (942)	497 (800)	40–150 (65–240)	11,517 (48,000)
9.11	Hudson Bay	475,800 (1,232,300)	420 (128)	600 (183)	590 (950)	590 (950)	37,848 (157,734)

IHO	Names of oceans and seas	Area square miles (km²)	Average depth feet (m)	Greatest known depth: feet (m)	Length miles (km)	Width miles (km)	Volume cubic miles (km³)
			Arctic Ocean and subdivisions – continued				
9.12	Baffin Bay	266,000 (689,000)	6,234 (1,900)	7,000 (2,100)	900 (1,450)	68–400 (110–650)	314,113 (1,309,100)
9.13	Lincoln Sea	57,920 (150,000)	2,461 (750)	9,394 (2,863)	249 (400)	236 (380)	26,994 (112,500)
9.14	Northwestern Passages	–	492 (150)	656 (200)	–	–	–
9.15	Beaufort Sea	184,000 (476,000)	3,239 (1,004)	15,360 (4,682)	684 (1100)	404 (650)	114,671 (477,904)
9.16	Chukchi Sea	225,000 (582,000)	253 (77)	7,218 (2,200)	559 (900)	435 (700)	10,753 (44,814)
			Other subdivisions of the Arctic Ocean				
–	Fox Basin	55,600 (144,000)	492 (150)	656 (200)	280 (450)	249 (400)	5,183 (21,600)
–	James Bay	30,890 (80,000)	164 (50)	230 (70)	275 (443)	135 (217)	960 (4,000)
–	Kane Basin	7,720 (20,000)	492 (150)	656 (200)	124 (200)	62 (100)	720 (3,000)
–	Pechora Sea	34,750 (90,000)	20 (6)	689 (210)	249 (400)	162 (260)	130 (540)
–	Wandel Sea	28,960 (75,000)	1,148 (350)	1,955 (596)	186 (300)	155 (250)	6,299 (26,250)
			Southern Ocean and subdivisions				
10	Southern Ocean	7,850,000 (20,327,000)	14,750 (4,500)	23,736 (7,235)	to 12,900 (21,500)	240–1,620 (400–2,700)	21,948,232 (91,471,500)
10.1	Weddell Sea	1,080,000 (2,800,000)	13,124 (4,000)	16,405 (5,000)	to 1,200 (to 2,000)	to 1,200 (2,000)	2,687,397 (11,200,000)
10.2	Lazarev Sea	185,350 (480,000)	11,484 (3,500)	13,124 (4,000)	497 (800)	373 (600)	403,109 (1,680,000)
10.3	Riiser-Larsen Sea	260,640 (675,000)	12,468 (3,800)	13,124 (4,000)	559 (900)	404 (650)	615,462 (2,565,000)
10.4	Cosmonauts Sea	386,140 (1,000,000)	14,108 (4,300)	16,405 (5,000)	621 (1,000)	621 (1,000)	1,031,768 (4,300,000)
10.5	Cooperation Sea	386,140 (1,000,000)	9,515 (2,900)	13,124 (4,000)	621 (1,000)	621 (1,000)	695,844 (2,900,000)
10.6	Davis Sea	347,520 (900,000)	6,562 (2,000)	9,843 (3,000)	621 (1,000)	559 (900)	431,903 (1,800,000)
10.6.1	Tryoshnikova Gulf	34,750 (90,000)	6,562 (2,000)	9,843 (3,000)	280 (450)	to 240 (400)	43,190 (180,000)
10.7	Mawson Sea	96,530 (250,000)	6,562 (2,000)	9,843 (3,000)	311 (500)	311 (500)	119,973 (500,000)
10.8	Dumont d'Urville Sea	185,350 (480,000)	5,906 (1,800)	13,124 (4,000)	497 (800)	373 (600)	207,313 (864,000)
10.9	Somov Sea	100,400 (260,000)	6,562 (2,000)	6,562 (2,000)	404 (650)	249 (400)	124,772 (520,000)
10.10	Ross Sea	370,000 (960,000)	656 (200)	2,625 (800)	684 (1,100)	621 (1,000)	46,070 (192,000)
10.10.1	McMurdo Sound	3,860 (10,000)	3,281 (1,000)	3,281 (1,000)	92 (148)	46 (74)	2,399 (10,000)
10.11	Amundsen Sea	297,330 (770,000)	6,562 (2,000)	9,843 (3,000)	684 (1,100)	435 (700)	369,517 (1,540,000)
10.12	Bellingshausen Sea	173,760 (450,000)	6,562 (2,000)	9,843 (3,000)	435 (700)	404 (650)	215,952 (900,000)
10.13	Drake Passage	308,910 (800,000)	11,000 (3,400)	15,600 (4,800)	497 (800)	621 (1,000)	652,653 (2,720,000)
10.14	Bransfield Strait	26,260 (68,000)	1,148 (350)	1,641 (500)	249 (400)	106 (170)	5,711 (23,800)
			Inland Seas (salt lakes not seas)				
–	Caspian Sea	152,239 (394,299)	591 (180)	3,104 (946)	746 (1,200)	102–270 (170–450)	17,030 (70,974)
–	Aral Sea	13,000 (33,800)	52 (16)	223 (68)	266 (428)	176 (284)	130 (541)
–	Dead Sea	394 (1,020)	313 (96)	1,310 (399)	48 (78)	10 (15)	23 (97)
–	Salton Sea	344 (890)	30 (9)	51 (16)	30 (48)	10 (16)	2 (8)
–	Sea of Galilee	64 (166)	79 (24)	157 (48)	13 (21)	7 (11)	1 (4)
			Largest subdivisions of the oceans by surface area				
8.3	Coral Sea	1,849,000 (4,790,000)	7,870 (2,400)	25,134 (7,661)	1,400 (2,250)	1,500 (2,414)	2,758,421 (11,496,000)
7.1	Philippine Sea	1,776,230 (4,600,000)	19,700 (6,000)	34,578 (10,539)	to 1,800 (3,000)	to 1,200 (2,000)	6,622,513 (27,600,000)
8.4	Tasman Sea	1,545,000 (4,000,000)	9,023 (2,750)	17,000 (5,200)	1,243 (2,000)	1,400 (2,250)	2,639,407 (11,000,000)
5.9	Arabian Sea	1,491,000 (3,862,000)	8,970 (2,734)	16,405 (5,000)	to 1,243 (2,000)	to 1,320 (2,200)	2,533,521 (10,558,708)
–	Sargasso Sea	1,448,020 (3,750,000)	16,405 (5,000)	21,005 (6,402)	1,864 (3,000)	994 (1,600)	4,498,990 (18,750,000)
10.1	Weddell Sea	1,080,000 (2,800,000)	13,124 (4,000)	16,405 (5,000)	to 1,200 (2,000)	to 1,200 (2,000)	2,687,397 (11,200,000)
1.10	Caribbean Sea	1,049,500 (2,718,200)	8,685 (2,647)	25,218 (7,686)	1,678 (2,700)	360–840 (600–1,400)	1,726,430 (7,195,075)
3.1	Mediterranean Sea	969,000 (2,510,000)	4,688 (1,429)	16,897 (5,150)	2,500 (4,000)	500 (800)	860,636 (3,586,790)
6.1	South China Sea	895,400 (2,319,075)	5,419 (1,652)	16,456 (5,015)	to 1,182 (1,902)	to 840 (1,352)	919,231 (3,830,988)
7.8	Bering Sea	884,900 (2,291,880)	5,075 (1,547)	15,659 (4,773)	990 (1,593)	1,490 (2,397)	850,746 (3,545,569)
5.13	Bay of Bengal	839,000 (2,173,000)	8,500 (2,600)	15,400 (4,694)	1,056 (1,700)	994 (1,600)	1,355,648 (5,649,800)
1.11	Gulf of Mexico	615,000 (1,592,800)	4,874 (1,486)	12,425 (3,787)	1,100 (1,770)	800 (1,287)	567,929 (2,366,901)
7.7	Sea of Okhotsk	611,000 (1,582,483)	2,818 (859)	11,063 (3,742)	1,530 (2,463)	932 (1,500)	319,649 (1,332,169)
7.10	Gulf of Alaska	592,000 (1,533,273)	7,976 (2,431)	16,500 (5,029)	1,200 (2,000)	240 (400)	919,594 (3,832,500)
9.4	Barents Sea	542,000 (1,405,000)	750 (229)	2,000 (600)	800 (1,300)	650 (1,050)	77,201 (321,745)

IHO	Names of oceans and seas	Area square miles (km²)	Average depth feet (m)	Greatest known depth: feet (m)	Length miles (km)	Width miles (km)	Volume cubic miles (km³)
			Largest subdivisions of the oceans by surface area – continued				
9.11	Hudson Bay	475,800 (1,232,300)	420 (128)	600 (183)	590 (950)	590 (950)	37,848 (157,734)
5.1	Mozambique Channel	432,470 (1,120,000)	8,531 (2,600)	10,000 (3,000)	1,000 (1,600)	250–600 (400–950)	698,723 (2,912,000)
10.4	Cosmonauts Sea	386,140 (1,000,000)	14,108 (4,300)	16,405 (5,000)	621 (1,000)	621 (1,000)	1,031,768 (4,300,000)
10.5	Cooperation Sea	386,140 (1,000,000)	9,515 (2,900)	13,124 (4,000)	621 (1,000)	621 (1,000)	695,844 (2,900,000)
–	Sea of Japan	377,600 (977,979)	5,748 (1,751)	12,276 (3,742)	1,740 (2,800)	to 540 (900)	411,137 (1,713,456)
10.10	Rose Sea	370,000 (960,000)	656 (200)	2,625 (800)	684 (1,100)	621 (1,000)	46,070 (192,000)
5.17	Great Australian Bight	366,830 (950,000)	7,218 (2,200)	14,765 (4,500)	1,740 (2,800)	to 620 (1,000)	501,487 (2,090,000)
9.1	East Siberian Sea	361,000 (936,000)	328 (100)	510 (155)	777 (1,250)	497 (800)	22,459 (93,600)
9.6	Greenland Sea	353,320 (915,000)	4,750 (1,450)	16,000 (4,800)	808 (1,300)	621 (1,000)	318,349 (1,326,750)
4.2	Scotia Sea	348,000 (900,000)	11,500 (3,500)	27,651 (8,428)	870 (1,400)	497 (800)	755,830 (3,150,000)
10.6	Davis Sea	347,520 (900,000)	6,562 (2,000)	9,843 (3,000)	621 (1,000)	559 (900)	431,903 (1,800,000)
9.3	Kara Sea	340,000 (880,000)	417 (127)	2,034 (620)	932 (1,500)	559 (900)	26,816 (111,760)
9.7	Norwegian Sea	328,220 (850,000)	5,254 (1,600)	13,020 (3,970)	870 (1,400)	684 (1,100)	326,327 (1,360,000)
1.9	Gulf of Guinea	324,360 (840,000)	12,796 (3,900)	16,405 (5,000)	435 (700)	746 (1,200)	786,064 (3,276,000)
10.13 + 4.3	Drake Passage	308,910 (800,000)	11,000 (3,400)	15,600 (4,800)	497 (800)	621 (1,000)	652,653 (2,720,000)
5.14	Andaman Sea	308,000 (797,700)	2,854 (870)	12,392 (3,777)	750 (1,200)	400 (645)	166,522 (693,999)
10.11	Amundsen Sea	297,330 (770,000)	6,562 (2,000)	9,843 (3,000)	684 (1,100)	435 (700)	369,517 (1,540,000)
5.10	Lakshadweep Sea	289,600 (750,000)	7,874 (2,400)	14,765 (4,500)	to 932 (1,500)	to 620 (1,000)	431,903 (1,800,000)
7.3	East China Sea	284,000 (735,800)	574 (175)	8,913 (2,717)	684 (1,100)	435 (700)	30,897 (128,765)
8.2	Solomon Sea	278,019 (720,000)	14,765 (4,500)	29,988 (9,140)	621 (1,000)	497 (800)	777,425 (3,240,000)
9.12	Baffin Bay	266,000 (689,000)	6,234 (1,900)	7,000 (2,100)	900 (1,450)	70–400 (110–650)	314,113 (1,309,100)
10.3	Riiser-Larsen Sea	260,640 (675,000)	12,468 (3,800)	13,124 (4,000)	559 (900)	404 (650)	615,462 (2,565,000)
5.16	Arafura Sea	250,990 (650,000)	230 (70)	12,000 (3,660)	to 620 (1,000)	to 435 (700)	10,918 (45,500)
9.2	Laptev Sea	250,900 (649,800)	1,896 (578)	9,774 (2,980)	528 (850)	497 (800)	90,120 (375,584)
5.15	Timor Sea	235,000 (615,000)	459 (140)	10,800 (3,300)	609 (980)	435 (700)	20,659 (86,100)
9.16	Chukchi Sea	225,000 (582,000)	253 (77)	7,218 (2,200)	559 (900)	435 (700)	10,753 (44,814)
1.2	North Sea	222,100 (575,200)	308 (94)	2,165 (660)	621 (1,000)	93–373 (150–600)	12,974 (54,069)
1.15	Labrador Sea	222,030 (575,000)	6,562 (2,000)	12,468 (3,800)	to 870 (1,400)	to 492 (820)	275,938 (1,150,000)
5.5	Gulf of Aden	205,000 (530,000)	4,922 (1,500)	17,586 (5,360)	920 (1,480)	300 (480)	190,757 (795,000)
8.1	Bismarck Sea	194,227 (503,000)	6,600 (2,000)	8,200 (2,500)	497 (800)	249 (400)	241,386 (1,006,000)
10.2	Lazarev Sea	185,350 (480,000)	11,484 (3,500)	13,124 (4,000)	497 (800)	373 (600)	403,109 (1,680,000)
10.8	Dumont d'Urville Sea	185,350 (480,000)	5,906 (1,800)	13,124 (4,000)	497 (800)	373 (600)	207,313 (864,000)
9.15	Beaufort Sea	184,000 (476,000)	3,239 (1,004)	15,360 (4,682)	684 (1,100)	404 (650)	114,671 (477,904)
6.15	Banda Sea	181,000 (470,000)	14,765 (4,500)	24,409 (7,440)	652 (1,050)	228–330 (380–550)	507,486 (2,115,000)
7.4	Yellow Sea	180,000 (466,200)	131 (40)	338 (103)	600 (960)	435 (700)	4,475 (18,648)
10.12	Bellingshausen Sea	173,760 (450,000)	6,562 (2,000)	9,843 (3,000)	435 (700)	404 (650)	215,952 (900,000)
5.4	Red Sea	169,100 (438,000)	1,611 (491)	9,974 (3,040)	1,200 (1,930)	190 (305)	51,602 (215,058)
6.8	Java Sea	167,000 (433,000)	151 (46)	689 (210)	900 (1,450)	260 (420)	4,779 (19,918)
2	Baltic Sea	163,000 (422,200)	180 (55)	1,380 (421)	795 (1,280)	324 (540)	5,572 (23,221)

UNESCO Marine Heritage sites

UNESCO World Heritage sites are designated as part of the United Nations International World Heritage Programme. All have exceptional natural or cultural features. Like other natural areas recognized by UNESCO, the growing number of marine sites must possess remarkable natural beauty or have extraordinary ecological importance.

Major oceanographic research centers

The numerous centers of oceanographic research and study throughout the world attest to the importance of the sea in human affairs. Their discoveries have applications both for understanding and protecting the marine world, as well as for finding environmentally friendly methods of harnessing marine resources.

1	Península Valdés, Argentina
2	Great Barrier Reef, Australia
3	Shark Bay, Australia
4	Macquarie Island, Australia
5	Belize Barrier Reef Reserve System
6	Lord Howe Island Group, Australia
7	Brazilian Atlantic Islands
8	Cocos Island National Park, Costa Rica
9	Area de Conservacion, Guanacaste, Costa Rica
10	Desembarco de Granma National Park, Cuba
11	Ilulissat Ice Fjord, Denmark
12	Galápagos Islands, Ecuador
13	High Coast/Kvarken Archipelago, Finland and Sweden
14	The lagoons of New Caledonia
15	Gulf of Porto, Corsica
16	Isole Aolie (Aeolian Islands), Italy
17	Surtsey, Iceland
18	Shiretoko, Hokkaido, Japan
19	MacDonald and Heard Islands, Australia
20	Gulf of California, Mexico, Islands, and Protected Areas
21	Sian Ka'an, Mexico
22	West Norwegian Fjords, Norway
23	El Vizcaino Whale Sanctuary, Mexico
24	New Zealand Sub-Antarctic Islands
25	Tewahipounamu, Southwest New Zealand
26	Coiba National Park, Panama
27	Tubbataha Reef Marine Park, Philippines
28	Natural System of Wrangel Island Reserve, Russian Federation
29	Pitons Management Area, St Lucia
30	Aldabra Atoll, Seychelles
31	East Rennell, Solomon Islands
32	Dorset & East Devon Coast, UK
33	Giants Causeway and Causeway Coast, UK
34	Gough and Inacccessible Islands, UK
35	Henderson Island, UK
36	Hawaii Volcanoes National Park, Hawaii, USA
37	Ha Long Bay, Vietnam
38	Socotra Archipelago, Yemen
39	Papahanaumokuakea, USA
40	Rock Islands Southern Lagoon, Palau
41	Phoenix Islands, Kiribati
42	Ogasawara Islands, Japan
43	The Wadden Sea, Germany and the Netherlands
44	Ningaloo Coast, Australia

1	National Oceanic and Atmospheric Administration (NOAA), USA
2	Massachusetts Institute of Technology, USA
3	Virginia Institute of Marine Science, USA
4	Duke Marine Laboratory, USA
5	Moss Landing Marine Laboratories, USA
6	Rosenstiel School of Marine Science, USA
7	University of Rhode Island School of Marine Science, USA
8	University of Washington School of Marine Science, USA
9	Monterey Bay Aquarium Research Institute, USA
10	University of California, Scripps Institution of Oceanography, USA
11	University of Hawaii, School of Ocean and Earth Science and Technology, USA
12	Woods Hole Oceanographic Institution, USA
13	Bedford Institute of Oceanography, Ocean Sciences Division, Canada
14	Memorial University of Newfoundland, Ocean Sciences Center, Canada
15	Southampton Oceanography Centre, UK
16	Plymouth Marine Laboratory, UK
17	University of East Anglia, UK
18	Dunstuffnage Marine Laboratory, UK
19	Ghent University, Belgium
20	Netherlands Institute for Sea Research, Netherlands
21	University of Kiel, Institute of Marine Research, Germany
22	Alfred Wegener Institute for Polar and Marine Research, Germany
23	Consejo Superior de Investigaciones Científicas (CSIC), Spain
24	French Research Institute for Exploitation of the Sea, France
25	Université de Bretagne Occidentale, Institut Universitaire Européen de la Mer, France
26	Shirshov Institute of Oceanology, Russia
27	Ocean University of Qingdao, China
28	University of Hong Kong, Swire Institute of Marine Science, China
29	Japan Agency for Marine-Earth Science and Technology, Japan
30	University of Tokyo, Ocean Research Institute, Japan
31	University of Otago, Department of Marine Science, New Zealand
32	National Institute of Water and Atmospheric Research, New Zealand
33	CSIRO Marine Laboratories, Australia
34	University of Tasmania, Australia
35	University of Cape Town, Center for Marine Studies, South Africa
36	Universidad Catolica de Valparaiso, Escuela de Ciencias del Mar, Chile
37	University of São Paulo, Oceanographic Institute, Brazil

GLOSSARY

Abyssal plain
The flat area of an ocean basin between the continental slope and the mid-ocean ridge.

Abyssal zone
Ocean depths between 13,120 and 19,680 feet (4,000 and 6,000 m).

Adaptation
A change in an animal's behavior or body that allows it to survive and breed in new conditions.

Algae
Simple plant-like organisms that are found as single cells or as seaweeds.

Antarctic circle
The line of latitude at 66°33'S marking the northern limit of the Antarctic region.

Aphotic zone
The part of the ocean where no surface light can penetrate.

Archipelago
A group of islands or an area that contains many small islands.

Arctic circle
The line of latitude at 66°33'N marking the southern limit of where the sun does not set in June or rise at December solstices.

Ascidians
The sea squirts—a group of invertebrates that produce larvae with a primitive backbone.

Astrolabe
An early navigation instrument that was the forerunner of the sextant.

Atoll
A coral reef that has formed around a central lagoon.

Austral
Relating to the southern hemisphere.

AUV
Autonomous Underwater Vehicle—an unmanned, self-contained submersible.

Backwash
The water retreating down the shore after an incoming wave.

Baleen plates
Plates with frayed edges made out of keratin, the same material as hair and fingernails. Found in the mouths of certain whales instead of teeth, they are used for filter feeding.

Bar
A submerged or emerged mound of sand, gravel, or shell material built on the ocean floor in shallow water by waves and currents.

Barrier island
A ridge of sand, or gravel, that lies parallel to a coast.

Barrier reef
A coral reef around islands or along continental coasts, separated from the land by a deep lagoon.

Bathymetry
Study of the depth contours of all or part of an undersea area.

Bathypelagic zone
The ocean between 656 and 13,120 feet (200 and 4,000 m) deep.

Bathyscaphe
The earliest form of manned submersible.

Bay
A recess in the shore or an inlet of a sea between two capes or headlands, not as large as a gulf but larger than a cove.

Beach
The region of the shore where loose material, sand, mud, or pebbles, are deposited between high and low watermarks.

Benthic zone
The upper layers of the seabed and the water layer immediately above the seabed.

Berm
A horizontal ridge of sand or shingle running parallel to the shore, at the limit of wave action.

Biodiversity
The variety of plant and animal species found in a habitat on land or in the sea.

Bioluminescence
The generation of light by living organisms using the enzyme luciferin.

Bivalve
A mollusk, such as an oyster or a mussel, that has two shells that are joined at a hinge.

Bloom
The sudden increase in phytoplankton numbers, usually associated with seasonal changes or pollution.

Brash ice
Accumulations of floating ice made up of fragments not more than 6.6 feet (2 m) across; the wreckage of other forms of ice.

Cap rock
A hard, impervious rock that forms a layer above another rock and, as a result, seals it.

Carapace
The upper part of the shell of a turtle or tortoise.

Cephalopod
An advanced group of mollusks that includes the squids, octopuses, and cuttlefish.

Cetaceans
Whales and dolphins.

Channel
A body of water that connects two larger bodies of water (like the English Channel). A channel is also a part of a river or harbor that is deep enough to let ships sail through.

Chronometer
A watch or clock able to maintain its accuracy on long sea voyages.

Coelenterates
Gelatinous invertebrates with radial symmetry and sting cells.

Cold seep
Cold seawater, rich in methane, hydrogen sulfide, and hydrocarbons, issuing from the seafloor.

Comet
A small astronomical body composed of ice and dust that orbits the Sun on an elongated path.

Continental drift
The theory that the present distribution of continents is the result of the fragmentation of one or more pre-existing supercontinents that have drifted apart.

Continental rise
The gently sloping base of the continental slope.

Continental shelf
The shallow, gently sloping edge of a continental landmass where it meets the sea.

Continental slope
The steeply inclined edge of continental plate below the continental shelf.

Copepod
One of a number of tiny freshwater and marine crustaceans.

Coral bleaching
The loss of color affecting coral reefs when the algae that live in them are killed or forced out. Rising sea temperatures are a leading cause.

Coriolis effect
The apparent tendency of a freely moving object to follow a curved path in relation to the rotating surface of Earth, similar to the apparent path of a ball thrown from a merry-go-round. Movement is to the right in the northern hemisphere and to the left in the southern hemisphere.

Crustaceans
Invertebrates with jointed limbs and hard chalky shells, such as lobsters, crabs, shrimps, and copepods.

Crustal plate
A segment of Earth's surface. Continental plates are about 25 miles (40 km) thick and oceanic plates 3 miles (5 km) thick.

Current
A flow of water in the sea, generated by wind, tides, or thermohaline circulation.

Cyclone
An intense tropical wind system around a low pressure center with winds that move counterclockwise in the northern hemisphere, and clockwise in the southern hemisphere. A cyclone has maximum sustained winds of 74 miles per hour (120 km/h) or greater. Also known as hurricanes or typhoons.

Deep-sea hydrothermal vent
A spring of superheated, mineral-rich water found on some ridges deep in the ocean.

Deep-sea trench
A long, narrow, steep-sided depression in the seafloor. Trenches occur at subduction zones, where one crustal plate sinks beneath another.

Density
The mass of a substance for a given volume.

Delta
A layer of sediment deposited at the mouth of a slow-moving river and protruding beyond the coastline.

Diatom
One of many kinds of tiny algae in marine and freshwater environments.

Dinoflagellate
One of many kinds of one-celled aquatic and mostly microscopic organisms bearing two dissimilar flagellae (long whip-like structures that let them turn, maneuver, and spin around), and having characteristics of both plants and animals.

Dune
An accumulation of windblown sand often found above the high tide mark on sand shores.

Ebb tide
The period of tide between high water and low water. A falling tide.

Echinoderms
Exclusively marine invertebrates with five-way symmetry and a water vascular system, including starfish, sea cucumbers, and brittle stars.

Echiurans
A group of soft-bodied non-segmented worms found from the shore down to the bottom of ocean trenches.

Echolocation
The use of sound by whales and dolphins to sense objects.

Ecosystem
An interacting system of organisms and the environment to which they are adapted.

Eddy
A circular movement in the water produced by flows around obstructions or by interacting currents.

El Niño
The periodic warming of the surface waters in the east Pacific Ocean that stops upwelling of nutrients.

Endemic
A species, or other taxon, found only in one habitat or region.

Erosion
The wearing away of land by the action of natural forces. On a beach, the carrying away of beach material by wave action, tidal currents, littoral currents, or wind.

Estuary
A semi-enclosed area of water where the salinity departs strongly from ocean salinity, either from mixing with river water or from excessive evaporation.

Euphotic zone
The upper layers where there is sufficient light for photosynthesis.

Fast ice
Ice that is anchored to the shore or ocean bottom and does not move with the winds or currents.

Fetch
The distance over water in which waves are generated by a wind having a rather constant direction and speed.

Filter feeder
An animal that obtains food by straining small prey from seawater.

Flood tide
The period of tide between low water and high water. A rising tide.

Fossil fuels
Carbon-based materials, such as oil, coal, and natural gas, formed from the fossils of ancient plants and animals, and burned to produce energy and electricity.

Frazil ice
Frazil ice, a form of sea ice, refers to small ice crystals that form in the surface water when it reaches freezing temperature.

Fringing reef
A coral reef that forms around the shore of an island and gradually extends out to sea.

Gas bladder
The gas-filled buoyancy organ found in most bony fish.

Ghost net
A fishing net that has become detached from the vessel that set it and so floats freely in the sea, where it may entangle marine life.

Gill
A structure used by aquatic animals to exchange dissolved gases and salts between their body fluids and the water.

Glacier
A mass of ice that moves over the underlying surface.

Global ocean conveyor belt
A circulation pattern that is driven by the sinking of cold water of high salinity in the North Atlantic and connects all oceans. Water moves into the Antarctic at depth and from there into the Indian and Pacific Oceans, from where it returns to the North Atlantic at intermediate depth.

Gondwana
The southern supercontinent fragment comprising New Zealand, Antarctica, Australia, South America, Africa, and India. It existed as a separate landmass from 650 million years ago and began to break up 130 million years ago.

Greenhouse effect
The warming of the lower layers of the atmosphere caused by the trapping of solar radiation by carbon dioxide and other gases.

Gulf
Part of the ocean or sea that is partly surrounded by land, usually on three sides; it is usually larger than a bay.

Gulf stream
The strong western boundary current flowing up the east coast of North America.

Guyot
A flat-topped seamount.

Gyre
A circular motion in a body of water.

Hadal zone
The ocean zone below 19,680 feet (6,000 m).

Headland
An area of high elevation more resistant to erosion than surrounding areas and less susceptible to flooding. Headlands can supply sand and gravel to beaches.

Hermatypic coral
Species living in tropical waters able to secrete sufficient calcium carbonate to form reefs.

High tide
The maximum elevation reached by each rising tide.

Holdfast
The multi-branched structure anchoring seaweeds to hard surfaces.

Holoplankton
Animals that live out their entire lifecycles floating in the water column.

Hot spot
In volcanology, local areas of high volcanic activity that do not occur at the edges of tectonic plates.

Hurricane
The name used for cyclones in the Atlantic and eastern Pacific Oceans.

Hydrological cycle
The endless cycling of water between land, ocean, and atmosphere.

Hydrothermal vent
A spring of superheated, mineral-rich water found on some ocean ridges.

Ice age
A cold phase in the climatic history of Earth during which large areas of land were covered by ice.

Ice sheet
The largest type of glacier.

Ice shelf
An area of floating ice, once part of a glacier, that is still attached to land.

Iceberg
A floating piece of ice broken off from a glacier or ice sheet.

Intertidal zone
The area of a seashore that is washed by tides. It is covered by water at high tide and exposed to the air at low tide.

Invertebrate
A multicellular animal without a true backbone.

Kelps
A group of large, fast-growing brown seaweeds.

Krill
A shrimp-like crustacean abundant in polar waters that is the principal food of baleen whales.

La Niña
Periods of unusually cold ocean temperatures in the equatorial Pacific that occur between El Niño events. An episode of La Niña brings these conditions for a minimum of five months.

Lagoon
A shallow body of water, as a pond or lake, usually connected to the sea.

Latitude
A measure of north–south location, relative to the equator at 0°.

Laurasia
One of the two continents that formed when the supercontinent Pangea separated. It includes Europe, North America, and Asia (not India). Similarity of plants and animals of these countries is explained by this former connection.

Littoral zone
The seashore between high and low tide marks.

Longitude
A measure of east–west location relative to the Prime Meridian (0°) that runs through the Greenwich Observatory, London, UK.

Longshore drift
The movement of beach material parallel to the coastline by combined wind and wave action.

Lophophore
The brush-like feeding organ of sea mats, horseshoe worms, and lamp shells.

Low tide
The minimum elevation reached by each falling tide.

Magma
Molten rock found below Earth's crust that is ejected by volcanoes and emerges at ocean ridges as lava.

Mangrove
Flowering shrubs and trees tolerant of salt water, found on low-lying tropical coasts and estuaries.

Mantle
The layer of Earth between the crust and the core.

Mariculture
The intensive cultivation of marine organisms in cages in coastal areas, or on land in seawater ponds.

Medusa
The free-living bell or disc-like form of many coelenterates.

Meroplankton
The young stages of marine organisms that spend time in the plankton, before developing into non-planktonic adults.

Mid-ocean ridge
A region of the ocean floor where magma rises to the surface to create new ocean floor on either side of a central rift valley.

Migration
The movement of an animal from one place to another, often over long distances. Sea turtles, whales, seabirds, and many fish migrate through and above Earth's oceans.

Mollusks
A group of soft-bodied non-segmented invertebrates that includes sea snails, bivalves, and cephalopods.

Navigation
The science of position fixing and course plotting, using astronomical and other observations.

Neap tides
Tides with much smaller ranges than spring tides, that occur while the gravitational pulls of the Moon and the Sun on the oceans work against each other.

Neritic zone
The zone from high tide to the continental shelf break.

Nilas ice
A smooth, thin sheet of sea ice formed of frazil sea ice crystals.

Ocean
One of the five great bodies of seawater defined by continental margins, the equator, and other arbitrary divisions.

Ocean desert
An ocean region devoid of nutrients and therefore particularly high water clarity.

Oceanography
The scientific study of all aspects of the oceans.

Ore
A mineral or rock that contains a metal in a concentration that is high enough to make its extraction commercially viable. Hematite and iron ore are examples.

Osmoregulation
The regulation of the concentration of body fluids by aquatic animals.

Overfishing
The commercial fishing of natural populations so that breeding does not replenish what is removed.

Ozone
A gas that absorbs most of the harmful ultraviolet rays from the Sun and also prevents some heat loss from Earth; it occurs naturally in a thin layer in the stratosphere and is also an ingredient in photochemical smog.

Ozone layer
The thin layer of ozone gas, located roughly 15 miles (24 km) above Earth's surface, which shields us from ultraviolet rays generated by the Sun.

Pack ice
Sea ice that forms around the permanent ice sheets of polar regions in winter and which thins and retreats in summer.

Pancake ice
Uneven plate shapes of sea ice that occur when seawater movement disturbs newly melded ice crystals or nilas ice.

Pangea
The ancient supercontinent that once contained all of Earth's continents. It began to break up about 200 million years ago into Gondwana and Laurasia.

Pelagic zone
The water column above the benthic zone.

Photophores
Light-producing organs, especially common in deep-sea fish.

Photosynthesis
The biological conversion of carbon dioxide and water into sugars using solar energy.

Phytoplankton
Single-celled algae and other photosynthetic organisms floating in the surface layers of the oceans.

Piedmont glacier
A lobe of ice formed when a valley glacier emerges from a mountain and spreads on to a plain.

Pinnipeds
Seals, walruses, and sea lions.

Plastron
The bottom part of the shell of a turtle or tortoise.

Plate tectonics
The processes by which the plates that form Earth's surface are formed, moved, and destroyed.

Polar regions
The cold zones between the poles and either the Arctic or Antarctic circles.

Pollutant
A harmful substance or heat energy introduced into an ecosystem by human activities.

Polychaetes
A group of marine segmented worms.

Polynesia
A large group of Pacific islands extending from the Hawaiian Islands south to New Zealand and east to Easter Island.

Polynyas
Areas of open water surrounded by sea ice, often of a large enough extent to make them navigable. Also spelled polynia.

Polyp
The sedentary body form of coelenterates, notably corals.

Predator
An animal that feeds by capturing and eating other animals.

Primary production
The biological conversion of inorganic carbon (carbon dioxide) into living material (organic carbon).

Projection
The system used to translate the three-dimensional form of Earth onto a two-dimensional map.

Radar
Radio Detection and Ranging; the use of pulsed radio waves to follow moving objects by analysing changes in reflected radio signals.

Remote sensing
The use of airborne or satellite sensors to map Earth's surface in space and time.

Reverse osmosis
The use of pressure to force water through semi-permeable membrane, leaving behind any dissolved salts. Used to obtain freshwater from seawater.

Roaring Forties
Areas of ocean either side of the equator between 40° and 50° N or S latitude, noted for high winds and rough seas.

Rogue wave
An unusually high wave created by the constructive interference of two or more smaller waves.

ROV
A Remotely Operated Vehicle; an unmanned submersible controlled and powered from the surface by an umbilical cord.

Salt marsh
An area of soft, wet land periodically covered by salt water, in temperate zones generally treeless with characteristic salt-tolerant plants such as reeds and samphire.

Sandbar
A low ridge of sand in shallow water close to a shore.

Scuba
Self-Contained Underwater Breathing Apparatus; the combination of a pressure-compensated regulator or demand valve and high-pressure compressed air cylinders for diving without an air supply from the surface.

Sea
A division of an ocean or a large body of salt water partially enclosed by land. The term is also used for large, usually saline, lakes that lack a natural outlet, such as the Caspian Sea and the Aral Sea. The term is used in a less geographically precise manner as synonymous with ocean.

Sea ice
Ice that forms when the surface of the ocean freezes.

Sea stack
A rocky tower or spire close to shore that has formed due to the erosion of a nearby headland by wave action, or by the collapse of a natural rock arch.

Seamount
A steep-sided circular or elliptical projection from the seafloor that is more than 0.6 miles (1 km) in height.

Seasonality
The timing of major biological events cued by changes in light intensity and water temperature, associated with the seasons in temperate latitudes.

Seawall
A vertical, wall-like coastal-engineering structure built parallel to the beach or duneline and usually located at the back of the beach or the seaward edge of the dune.

Sediment
Fine organic or mineral particles deposited on the seafloor, originating from the weathering of rocks and transported, suspended in, or deposited by air, water, or ice, or by other natural agents such as chemical precipitation.

Seismic survey
The use of high-intensity sound waves to examine deep geological structures.

Sextant
A navigational instrument used to measure the angles between the Moon, Sun, stars, and other objects such as the horizon.

Shear
The difference in speed of water movement in adjacent regions or layers, creating friction and turbulence.

Shelf sea
The shallow but often highly productive seas over continental shelves.

Side-scan sonar
High-resolution sound-imaging of the seabed.

Soft corals
Coral species that do not have a hard outer blanket of calcium carbonate. Soft corals do not form reefs.

Sonar
Sound Navigation and Ranging; the detection of objects in or on water using pulsed sound waves and their reflected echoes.

Sponges
Invertebrates that consist of complex aggregations of cells, bound together by protein fibers and mineral spicules.

Spray zone
The area along a shore that is above the normal high-tide zone.

Spring tide
A tide that occurs at or near the time of a new or full moon with a large tidal rise and fall.

Strait
A narrow channel of water that connects two larger bodies of water, and thus lies between two landmasses.

Subduction zone
The area where one crustal plate is forced under another plate, giving rise to volcanic activity and earthquakes. These zones are usually marked by deep trench systems in the oceans.

Submersible
A small underwater vehicle designed for deep-sea research and other tasks.

Sunlight zone
The upper layer of the ocean where enough sunlight reaches to support the growth of phytoplankton.

Symbiosis
The close beneficial feeding relationship between two species.

Tethys Sea
The body of water partially enclosed by the C-shaped Pangean supercontinent. It was closed when Pangea split into Laurasia and Gondwana.

Thermohaline circulation
Water movement caused by differences in density produced by salinity and/or temperature changes.

Tide
The regular rising and falling of the sea that results from gravitational attraction of the Moon, Sun, and other astronomical bodies acting upon rotating Earth.

Tide pool
A depression on a shore, usually rocky, that remains filled with seawater when exposed at low tide.

Tidewater glacier
A glacier that flows into the sea, producing icebergs as pieces break off.

Trade winds
The steady winds that blow from east to west, toward the equator to replace hot air rising from the equatorial region.

Transit time
The time it takes a water particle to travel through a described region. Also the time it takes to empty and replace all water in a described region.

Transport
The amount of water carried by a current in mass or volume per unit time.

Trench
A narrow, deep depression in the ocean floor, often associated with the subduction of an oceanic plate at a continental margin.

Trophic web
The complex feeding relationships between plants and animals in a habitat.

Tropics
The zone between the Tropic of Cancer (23°27'N) and the Tropic of Capricorn (23°27'S) which approximates to the area of the ocean where water temperatures remain above 69°F (20°C).

Tsunami
A huge wave created by an earthquake or volcanic explosion that can cause massive destruction in coastal areas. Mistakenly called a "tidal wave."

Typhoon
The name used for cyclones in the western Pacific Ocean, including the China Sea.

Upwelling
The rising of deep, cold nutrient-laden waters into the surface layers, close to continental coasts.

Water budget
The balance sheet of water entering and leaving a region; includes the effect of currents, rainfall, evaporation, and rivers.

Water lens
A body of water wedged between two other layers of water and kept together in lens-shaped form.

Wave
The disturbance in water caused by the movement of energy through the water.

Zooplankton
Small animals that spend all or part of their lifecycles floating in the surface layers of the ocean, either grazing on phytoplankton or preying on other zooplankton.

Zooxanthellae
Single-celled photosynthetic organisms that live in coral tissues in a symbiotic relationship.

GAZETTEER

Glossary of foreign terms

Archipièlag	archipelago
Bahía	bay
Baja, Bajo	shoal
Boca	channel, river
Bocche, Bogazi	strait
Cabo, Cap, Capo	cape
Cayo	key
Dao	island
Damagheh	cape
Dawhat	bay, cove, inlet
Denizi	sea
Ensenada	bay, cove
Golfe, Golfo	gulf
Île, Isla, Isola	island
Jazirat, Jazireh	islands
Kepulauan	archipelago islands
Ko, Koh	island
Khawr, Khowr	bay, channel, inlet
Kólpos, Körfezi	gulf
Laguna	lagoon
Mui	cape, point
Mys	cape, point
Peñón	point, rock
Punta	point
Ra´s, Ras, Râs	cape
Selat, Stretto	strait
Tanjung	cape, point
Teluk	bay

A

Abbot Ice Shelf, Sou.	140	L-12
Abd al Kuri, Ind.	186	M-8
Abrolhos Bank, Atl.	169	N-6
Abruka, Atl.	153	U-8
Abu al Jirab, Ind.	189	V-9
Abu Musa, Ind.	189	W-7
Abu Shawk Reefs, Ind.	185	S-8
Academician Berg Seamount, Pac.	210	H-2
Acklins Island, Atl.	159	Q-2
Adak Island, Pac.	207	T-8
Adana Trough, Atl.	165	X-8
Adare Seamounts, Sou.	143	W-13
Adelaide Island, Sou.	141	N-7
Adi, Pac.	225	Y-11
Admiralty Island, Pac.	209	W-4
Admiralty Islands, Pac.	227	T-9
Adonara, Pac.	225	S-13
Adriatic Sea, Atl.	165	P-4
Adventure Bank, Atl.	165	P-8
Aegean Sea, Atl.	165	U-7
Aegir Ridge, Arc.	132	K-11
Afanasy Nikitin Seamount, Ind.	195	O-5
Afognak Island, Pac.	209	P-3
Africana II Seamount, Ind.	198	H-11
Agassiz Fracture Zone, Pac.	247	N-7
Agatti, Ind.	187	V-8
Agattu Island, Pac.	207	Q-8
Agattu Strait, Pac.	207	Q-7
Agrihan, Pac.	227	T-2
Agulhas Bank, Ind.	191	O-11
Agulhas Basin, Ind.	191	P-13
Agulhas Plateau, Ind.	191	P-12
Agulhas Ridge, Ind.	191	N-12
Ahe, Pac.	249	P-9
Ahunui, Pac.	249	R-11
Air Force Island, Arc.	135	S-10
Aitutaki, Pac.	248	K-11
Akademii Nauk Rise, Pac.	213	S-8
Akiaki, Pac.	249	S-11
Akkeshi-wan, Pac.	215	Y-8
Akuseki-shima, Pac.	217	U-8
Akutan Island, Pac.	207	W-7
Al Hanish al Kabir, Ind.	186	I-7
Al Jazirah, Ind.	189	T-7
Al Qaffay, Ind.	189	T-9
Al Yasat, Ind.	189	T-9
Alamagan, Pac.	227	T-2
Åland, Atl.	153	T-6
Ålands Hav, Atl.	153	S-6
Alaska Peninsula, Pac.	209	N-4
Albatross Bay, Pac.	231	W-11
Alboran Ridge, Atl.	164	J-8
Alboran Sea, Atl.	164	I-8
Aldabra Islands, Ind.	193	W-1
Alderney, Atl.	163	W-2
Alenuihaha Channel, Pac.	211	W-7
Aleutian Basin, Pac.	207	R-5
Aleutian Islands, Pac.	207	P-7
Aleutian Rise, Pac.	207	P-7
Aleutian Trench, Pac.	207	Q-8
Alexander Archipelago, Pac.	209	V-3
Alexander Island, Sou.	141	O-8
Alexandra Land, Arc.	133	R-6
Algerian Basin, Atl.	164	L-8
Alijos Rocks, Pac.	243	S-11
Alor, Pac.	225	S-14
Alpha Ridge, Arc.	131	R-7
Alula-Fartak Trench, Ind.	191	U-3
Amakusa-nada, Pac.	215	P-15
Amakusa-Shimo-shima, Pac.	215	P-15
Amami-O-shima, Pac.	217	U-9
Amanu, Pac.	249	R-10
Amazon Cone, Atl.	168	L-1
Ambelau, Pac.	225	U-11
Ambon, Pac.	225	U-11
Ambrym, Pac.	233	Y-5
Amchitka Island, Pac.	207	S-8
Amchitka Pass, Pac.	207	S-8
American-Antarctic Ridge, Atl.	169	Q-14
Amery Ice Shelf, Sou.	139	W-7
Amindivi Islands, Ind.	187	V-8
Amini, Ind.	187	W-8
Amirante Islands, Ind.	191	T-6
Amirante Trench, Ind.	191	U-6
Amlia Island, Pac.	207	U-7
Ampere Seamount, Atl.	149	S-8
Amsterdam Fracture Zone, Ind.	199	O-12
Amsterdam Island, Ind.	199	P-12
Amukta Pass, Pac.	207	V-8
Amund Ringnes Island, Arc.	135	O-5
Amundsen Abyssal Plain, Sou.	139	N-9
Amundsen Coast, Sou.	143	S-2
Amundsen Gulf, Arc.	134	I-7
Amundsen Ridges, Sou.	139	P-9
Amundsen Sea, Sou.	139	P-8
Anaa, Pac.	249	P-10
Anatahan, Pac.	227	T-2
Anatolian Trough, Atl.	166	L-8
Anatom, Pac.	233	Y-6
Anaximander Mountains, Atl.	165	V-8
Andaman Basin, Ind.	183	W-11
Andaman Islands, Ind.	183	W-9
Andaman Sea, Ind.	183	X-11
Andreanof Islands, Pac.	207	T-8
Andros Island, Atl.	159	N-1
Andrott, Ind.	187	W-8
Anegada, Atl.	159	W-4
Ängesön, Atl.	153	T-4
Angola Abyssal Plain, Atl.	173	O-2
Angola Basin, Atl.	173	O-1
Anguilla, Atl.	159	W-4
Anguilla Cays, Atl.	157	Y-6
Anholt, Atl.	153	O-9
Anjouan, Ind.	193	V-3
Annobón, Atl.	171	W-7
Antalya Basin, Atl.	165	W-8
Antarctic Canyon, Sou.	141	U-9
Antarctic Peninsula, Sou.	141	P-6
Antigua, Atl.	159	X-5
Antipodes Islands, Pac.	239	S-7
Anvers Island, Sou.	141	O-5
Anxious Bay, Ind.	197	X-3
Ao Ban Don, Pac.	223	P-7
Ao Sawi, Pac.	223	P-6
Apalachee Bay, Atl.	157	W-2
Apulian Plateau, Atl.	165	R-7
Aquarius Seachannel, Pac.	209	O-7
Arabian Basin, Ind.	187	R-7
Arabian Sea, Ind.	187	R-5
Arafura Sea, Pac.	231	R-8
Arafura Shelf, Pac.	231	R-9
Aratika, Pac.	249	P-10
Archipelago de Colon, Pac.	245	V-3
Archipelago de los Canarreos, Atl.	158	L-2
Archipelago of the Recherche, Ind.	197	Q-4
Archipiélago de Camagüey, Atl.	159	N-2
Archipiélago de los Jardines de la Reina, Atl.	159	N-3
Archipiélago de Sabana, Atl.	158	M-1
Ardasier Reefs, Pac.	221	T-9
Argentine Abyssal Plain, Atl.	168	K-11
Argentine Basin, Atl.	168	K-10
Argo Bank, Pac.	233	U-7
Argo Fracture Zone, Ind.	191	W-8
Argolikos Basin, Atl.	165	T-8
Argonaut Seamount, Pac.	211	N-2
Ariaga, Pac.	225	T-6
Arlington Reef, Pac.	235	R-7
Arnhem Land, Pac.	231	R-8
Arthur, Arc.	133	S-6
Aru Basin, Pac.	225	Y-12
Arzanah, Ind.	189	U-8
As Sa´diyat, Ind.	189	V-9
Ascension, Atl.	169	S-3
Ascension Fracture Zone, Atl.	169	R-3
Ashizuri-misaki, Pac.	215	S-14
Ashmore Reef, Pac.	235	Q-1
Assumption Island, Ind.	193	W-1
Astove Island, Ind.	193	Y-2
Astrid Ridge, Sou.	139	T-3
Asuncion, Pac.	227	T-1
Atauro, Pac.	225	T-14
Atchafalaya Bay, Atl.	157	R-3
Atiu, Pac.	248	K-11
Atka Island, Pac.	207	U-7
Atlantic Ocean, Atl.	147	C-14
Atlantic-Indian Basin, Sou.	139	T-2
Atlantic-Indian Ridge, Ind.	191	N-14
Atlantis Fracture Zone, Atl.	148	M-8
Atlantis II Deep, Ind.	185	R-8
Atlantis II Fracture Zone, Ind.	191	V-11
Attu Island, Pac.	207	Q-7
Aua Island, Pac.	227	S-9
Auckland Islands, Pac.	239	P-8
Augustine Island, Pac.	205	T-3
Aur, Pac.	221	O-11
Aurora Canyon, Sou.	141	S-5
Austral Fracture Zone, Pac.	247	N-4
Austral Islands, Pac.	249	N-12
Australian-Antarctic Basin, Ind.	195	Q-14
Avalon Peninsula, Atl.	155	Y-5
Awaji-shima, Pac.	215	S-13
Awa-shima, Pac.	215	V-11
Axel Heiberg Island, Arc.	135	P-4
Az Zuqur, Ind.	186	H-7
Azores, Atl.	149	Q-7
Azores-Biscay Rise, Atl.	149	Q-6

Guaymas Basin, Pac. 243 V-10
Gudaut'a Bank, Atl. 167 X-5
Guernsey, Atl. 163 V-2
Guguan, Pac. 227 T-2
Guiana Basin, Atl. 148 M-11
Guimaras, Pac. 225 R-3
Guinea Basin, Atl. 169 U-1
Gulf of Aden, Ind. 185 W-13
Gulf of Alaska, Pac. 209 T-5
Gulf of Anadyr, Pac. 207 T-3
Gulf of Aqaba, Ind. 185 Q-4
Gulf of Bahrain, Ind. 189 R-7
Gulf of Boothia, Arc. 135 O-9
Gulf of Bothnia, Atl. 153 S-5
Gulf of California, Pac. 243 U-8
Gulf of Carpentaria, Pac. 231 V-11
Gulf of Darién, Atl. 159 O-9
Gulf of Finland, Atl. 153 V-7
Gulf of Gdansk, Atl. 153 S-11
Gulf of Genoa, Atl. 165 O-5
Gulf of Guinea, Atl. 171 T-4
Gulf of Kachchh, Ind. 187 U-2
Gulf of Khambhat, Ind. 187 V-4
Gulf of Maine, Atl. 155 O-9
Gulf of Mannar, Ind. 183 O-12
Gulf of Martaban, Ind. 183 Y-7
Gulf of Mexico, Atl. 157 Q-6
Gulf of Oman, Ind. 187 P-2
Gulf of Panama, Atl. 159 N-10
Gulf of Papua, Pac. 231 Z-8
Gulf of Paria, Atl. 159 X-9
Gulf of Riga, Atl. 153 V-8
Gulf of Salûm, Atl. 165 U-10
Gulf of Sirte, Atl. 165 S-10
Gulf of St. Lawrence, Atl. 155 R-4
Gulf of Suez, Ind. 185 O-3
Gulf of Taganrog, Atl. 167 V-1
Gulf of Thailand, Ind. 195 R-3
Gulf of Thailand, Pac. 223 R-6
Gulf of Tongking, Pac. 221 Q-3
Gulf of Venezuela, Atl. 159 S-8
Gulf of Venice, Atl. 165 P-4
Gulf St. Vincent, Ind. 197 Z-4
Gunungapi, Pac. 225 U-13

H

Haaheo Seamount, Pac. 211 N-4
Habibas Escarpment, Atl. 164 K-8
Hachijo-jima, Pac. 215 W-14
Hailuoto, Atl. 153 V-2
Hainan Strait, Pac. 221 R-3
Hainan, Pac. 221 Q-4
Haitan Dao, Pac. 217 P-11
Haizhou Wan, Pac. 217 P-5
Hajiki-zaki, Pac. 215 U-11
Halul, Ind. 189 T-7
Halifax Bay, Pac. 235 R-9
Hall, Arc. 133 T-6
Hall Islands, Pac. 227 W-6
Hall Peninsula, Arc. 135 U-12
Halmahera, Pac. 225 V-8
Halmahera Basin, Pac. 225 V-9
Halmahera Sea, Pac. 225 V-9
Halong Bay, Pac. 221 Q-3

Halten Bank, Arc. 133 N-13
Hamilton Bank, Atl. 148 L-4
Hangzhou Wan, Pac. 217 Q-8
Hanöbukten, Atl. 153 Q-10
Hao, Pac. 249 R-11
Haraiki, Pac. 249 Q-10
Harmil, Ind. 185 T-11
Harris Seamount, Pac. 205 S-5
Hartog Ridge, Ind. 195 S-10
Hateruma-jima, Pac. 217 R-12
Hatteras Abyssal Plain,
   Atl. 148 J-9
Hatteras Canyon, Atl. 160 L-2
Hatteras Island, Atl. 160 L-1
Hatton Bank, Atl. 149 Q-4
Hatutu, Pac. 249 R-7
Havelock Island, Ind. 183 W-10
Havre Trough, Pac. 229 U-7
Hawaii, Pac. 211 V-8
Hawaiian Islands, Pac. 211 P-2
Hawaiian Ridge, Pac. 211 N-5
Hawaiian Trough, Pac. 211 W-8
Hawke Bay, Pac. 239 S-4
Haydn Seamount, Pac. 211 T-4
Hayes Fracture Zone, Atl. 161 Y-2
Hazel Holme Bank, Pac. 229 S-3
Hazen Strait, Arc. 134 M-5
Head of Bight, Ind. 197 V-2
Heard Island, Ind. 199 O-15
Hearst Island, Sou. 141 Q-7
Hebridean Shelf, Atl. 151 N-5
Hecate Strait, Pac. 209 X-5
Heezen Fracture Zone,
   Pac. 247 N-11
Helgoländer Bucht, Atl. 151 X-10
Hellenic Trench, Atl. 165 T-9
Helodrano Antongila, Ind. 193 Z-6
Henashi-zaki, Pac. 215 V-9
Henderson Island, Pac. 249 W-13
Hendorabi, Ind. 189 U-6
Henry Ice Rise, Sou. 141 R-13
Herdman Seamount, Atl. 169 V-11
Hereheretue, Pac. 249 Q-11
Herma Ness, Atl. 151 Q-3
Hermit Islands, Pac. 227 T-9
Hero Fracture Zone, Atl. 175 S-10
Herodotus Abyssal Plain,
   Atl. 165 U-9
Herodotus Basin, Atl. 165 V-9
Herodotus Rise, Atl. 165 T-9
Herodotus Trough, Atl. 165 S-9
Heron Island, Pac. 235 W-13
Hervey Bay, Pac. 235 X-14
Hess Rise, Pac. 205 P-7
Hess Tablemount, Pac. 203 P-7
Hiiumaa, Atl. 153 U-8
Hikueru, Pac. 249 Q-10
Hikurangi Trench, Pac. 239 S-5
Hillary Canyon, Sou. 143 S-13
Hillary Coast, Sou. 143 W-8
Hinchinbrook Island
   (Aust.), Pac. 235 R-8
Hinchinbrook Island
   (USA), Pac. 209 S-2
Hispaniola, Atl. 161 N-7

Hispaniola Trough, Atl. 159 R-3
Hiva Oa, Pac. 249 S-7
Hokkaido, Pac. 215 X-7
Hollick-Kenyon
   Peninsula, Sou. 141 P-7
Holmes Reef, Pac. 235 S-6
Holy Island, Atl. 151 O-5
Home Bay, Arc. 135 T-10
Hon Khoai, Pac. 223 V-8
Hon Rai, Pac. 223 V-6
Honshu, Pac. 215 U-13
Hooker, Arc. 133 S-6
Hopen, Arc. 133 Q-9
Horizon Deep, Pac. 229 V-6
Horizon Ridge, Ind. 195 S-7
Hormoz, Ind. 189 Y-6
Horn Island, Pac. 231 X-10
Horseshoe Seamounts,
   Atl. 149 R-7
Hotspur Fracture Zone,
   Atl. 169 R-5
Hotspur Seamount, Atl. 169 O-5
Howland Island, Pac. 203 P-9
Hoy, Atl. 151 P-5
Huahine, Pac. 249 N-10
Hudson Bay, Arc. 130 K-8
Hudson Strait, Arc. 135 U-13

I

Iberian Abyssal Plain, Atl. 149 R-7
Ibiza, Atl. 164 L-7
Iceland, Atl. 149 Q-2
Iceland Basin, Atl. 149 Q-3
Iceland-Faeroe Rise, Atl. 149 R-2
Icelandic Plateau, Arc. 132 K-10
Icy Bay, Pac. 209 T-2
Ie-jima, Pac. 217 U-10
Ifalik, Pac. 227 T-6
Igneada Burnu, Atl. 167 O-6
Ihavandhippolhu Atoll,
   Ind. 187 V-10
Iheya-jima, Pac. 217 U-10
IJsselmeer, Atl. 151 V-11
Iki, Pac. 217 V-6
Iki-suido, Pac. 215 P-14
Île Brion, Atl. 155 S-5
Île d'Anticosti, Atl. 155 S-3
Île d'Oléron, Atl. 163 X-7
Île d'Ouessant, Atl. 163 S-4
Île d'Yeu, Atl. 163 W-6
Île de l'Est, Atl. 155 S-5
Île de Jerba, Atl. 165 P-9
Île de la Gonâve, Atl. 159 Q-4
Île de la Tortue, Atl. 159 R-3
Île de Noirmoutier, Atl. 163 W-6
Île de Ré, Atl. 163 X-7
Île des Pins, Pac. 233 X-7
Île du Harve Aubert, Atl. 155 R-6
Île Europa, Ind. 193 S-10
Île Juan de Nova, Ind. 193 U-7
Île Lamèque, Atl. 155 Q-5
Île Tromelin, Ind. 191 U-8
Îles Barren, Ind. 193 V-8
Îles Chausey, Atl. 163 X-3

Îles de la Madeleine, Atl. 155 R-5
Îles de Mingan, Atl. 155 R-3
Îles du Vent, Pac. 249 N-10
Îles Glorieuses, Ind. 193 X-3
Îles Kerguelen, Sou. 139 Z-5
Îles Kerkenah, Atl. 165 P-9
Îles Maria, Pac. 248 M-12
Îles Palliser, Pac. 249 P-9
Îles Sous le Vent, Pac. 248 M-10
Ilha Benguérua, Ind. 193 P-10
Ilha da Trindade, Atl. 169 P-6
Ilha do Bazaruto, Ind. 193 P-10
Ilha Puga Puga, Ind. 193 S-6
Ilhas Martin Vas, Atl. 169 P-5
Îls de Groix, Atl. 163 U-5
Imarssuak Channel, Atl. 149 O-3
Ince Burun, Atl. 167 T-5
Independence Fjord, Arc. 131 R-10
Indian-Antarctic Ridge,
   Ind. 195 X-13
Indispensable Reefs, Pac. 233 V-3
Indomed Fracture Zone,
   Ind. 191 S-13
Indus Cone, Ind. 187 S-4
Instituta Okeanologii
   Rise, Pac. 213 T-6
Interview Island, Ind. 183 V-9
Inubō-zaki, Pac. 215 W-12
Investigator Group, Ind. 197 W-3
Investigator Ridge, Ind. 199 S-6
Ionian Basin, Atl. 165 R-8
Ionian Islands, Atl. 165 S-8
Ionian Sea, Atl. 165 R-7
Iro-zaki, Pac. 215 V-13
Irabu-jima, Pac. 217 S-11
Irbe Strait, Atl. 153 U-9
Ireland, Atl. 149 S-4
Irian Jaya, Pac. 231 S-5
Iriomote-jima, Pac. 217 R-12
Irish Sea, Atl. 149 T-4
Irminger Basin, Atl. 149 O-3
Isakov Seamount, Pac. 204 L-8
Iselin Bank, Sou. 143 T-12
Iselin Seamount, Sou. 139 S-11
Ise-wan, Pac. 215 U-13
Ishigaki-jima, Pac. 217 S-11
Ishikari-wan, Pac. 215 W-7
Isla Ángel de la Guarda,
   Pac. 243 U-8
Isla Aracena, Atl. 175 P-3
Isla Baltra, Pac. 245 W-5
Isla Beata, Atl. 159 R-5
Isla Blanquilla, Atl. 159 W-8
Isla Carmen, Pac. 243 V-11
Isla Cedros, Pac. 243 S-9
Isla Cerralvo, Pac. 243 W-11
Isla Clarence, Atl. 175 O-3
Isla Clarion, Pac. 243 T-15
Isla Coiba, Atl. 158 L-10
Isla Dawson, Atl. 175 P-3
Isla de Altamura, Pac. 243 W-11
Isla de Bioco, Atl. 171 X-4
Isla de Cozumel, Atl. 157 U-8
Isla de Guanaja, Atl. 158 J-5
Isla de la Juventud, Atl. 157 W-7

R

Raas, Pac.	221	T-15
Raiatea, Pac.	249	N-10
Raijua, Pac.	225	Q-5
Raippaluoto, Atl.	153	T-4
Raita Bank, Pac.	211	O-4
Raivavae, Pac.	249	O-13
Rangiroa, Pac.	249	O-9
Rapa, Pac.	249	Q-14
Raraka, Pac.	249	P-10
Raroia, Pac.	249	Q-10
Rarotonga, Pac.	229	Y-5
Ras at Tarfa', Ind.	185	U-10
Ras Abu Qumayyis, Ind.	189	S-9
Ras Abu Madd, Ind.	185	Q-6
Ras Abu Shagara, Ind.	185	R-8
Ras Abu Sôma, Ind.	185	P-5
Ras al 'Allak, Ind.	189	T-8
Ras al Hadd, Ind.	187	Q-3
Ras al Ard, Ind.	189	O-3
Ras al Kalb, Ind.	186	L-7
Ras al Katib, Ind.	185	U-12
Ras al Khafji, Ind.	189	P-4
Ras al Matbakh, Ind.	189	S-7
Ras al Madrakah, Ind.	187	P-5
Ras al Mish'ab, Ind.	189	P-4
Ras al Qulay'ah, Ind.	189	P-4
Ras al Saffaniyah, Ind.	189	P-5
Ras az Zawr, Ind.	189	Q-5
Ras Bab al Mandab, Ind.	186	H-7
Ras Banâs, Ind.	185	Q-6
Ras Baridi, Ind.	185	R-6
Ras Bu Kuskayshah, Ind.	189	V-9
Ras Caluula, Ind.	186	L-8
Ras Caseyr, Ind.	186	M-8
Ras Fartak, Ind.	186	M-6
Ras Hanyurah, Ind.	189	V-8
Ras Hardârba, Ind.	185	R-7
Ras Hatibah, Ind.	185	S-7
Ras Jaddi, Ind.	187	R-2
Ras Jagin, Ind.	187	P-2
Ras Kaboudia, Atl.	165	P-9
Ras Kasar, Ind.	185	S-10
Ras Khansiir, Ind.	185	W-14
Ras Khumays, Ind.	189	T-9
Ras Laffan, Ind.	189	S-7
Ras Lma', Ind.	189	Y-7
Ras Macbar, Ind.	186	M-9
Ras Manrec, Ind.	185	T-11
Ras Masturah, Ind.	185	R-7
Ras Mirbat, Ind.	187	N-6
Ras Momi, Ind.	187	N-7
Ras Muari, Ind.	187	T-2
Ras Muhammad, Ind.	185	P-4
Ras Musandam, Ind.	189	Y-7
Ras Naws, Ind.	187	O-5
Ras Nuh, Ind.	187	R-2
Ras Ormara, Ind.	187	S-2
Ras osh Shatt, Ind.	189	R-3
Ras Sajir, Ind.	187	N-6
Ras Sallan, Ind.	189	Y-9
Ras Sawqirah, Ind.	187	O-5
Ras Sharbithat, Ind.	187	O-5
Ras Surud, Ind.	185	X-13
Ras Tanaqib, Ind.	189	P-5
Ras Tannurah, Ind.	189	R-6
Ras Xaafuun, Ind.	186	M-8
Ras-e Barkan, Ind.	189	Q-2
Ras-e Halileh, Ind.	189	R-4
Ras-e Meydani, Ind.	187	P-2
Ras-e Shir, Ind.	189	Z-7
Ras-e Shenas, Ind.	189	W-6
Ra's Barim al Mandab, Ind.	185	V-12
Rat Island, Pac.	207	S-8
Rat Islands, Pac.	207	S-8
Raukumara Plain, Pac.	239	T-2
Ravahere, Pac.	249	Q-11
Réao, Pac.	249	T-11
Rebun-to, Pac.	215	W-6
Recorder Guyot, Pac.	233	T-8
Red Rocks Point, Ind.	197	T-2
Red Sea, Ind.	185	R-6
Redang, Pac.	223	T-11
Reed Bank, Pac.	225	O-3
Reitoru, Pac.	249	Q-10
Renaud Island, Sou.	141	O-6
Rennell, Pac.	233	U-3
Researcher Seamount, Atl.	161	O-5
Reserve Bank, Pac.	239	S-5
Resolution Island, Arc.	135	V-13
Réunion, Ind.	198	L-9
Reykjanes Basin, Arc.	132	E-9
Reykjanes Ridge, Arc.	132	F-11
Rhodes Basin, Atl.	165	V-8
Rhodes, Atl.	165	V-8
Rhône Fan, Atl.	164	M-5
Richards Inlet, Sou.	143	U-4
Rifleman Bank, Pac.	221	S-9
Riiser-Larsen Ice Shelf, Sou.	139	R-5
Riiser-Larsen Sea, Sou.	139	T-4
Rimatara, Pac.	248	M-12
Rinca, Pac.	225	P-14
Rio Grande Fracture Zone, Atl.	169	S-7
Rio Grande Gap, Atl.	169	N-8
Rio Grande Rise, Atl.	169	O-8
Rishiri-to, Pac.	215	W-6
Ritchie's Archipelago, Ind.	183	W-10
Rivera Fracture Zone, Pac.	241	S-3
Robbie Ridge, Pac.	229	V-3
Robert Island, Atl.	175	X-11
Robertson Bay, Sou.	143	X-13
Robertson Island, Sou.	141	Q-5
Rockall Bank, Atl.	149	R-4
Rockall Plateau, Atl.	149	R-4
Rockall Trough, Atl.	149	R-4
Rocky Point, Atl.	173	T-3
Rodrigues Island, Ind.	191	W-8
Roggeveen Basin, Pac.	247	V-5
Rokko-zaki, Pac.	215	U-11
Roma, Pac.	225	U-13
Romanche Gap, Atl.	169	Q-2
Ronne Entrance, Sou.	141	N-10
Ronne Ice Shelf, Sou.	141	Q-12
Roosevelt Island, Sou.	143	R-6
Rosalind Bank, Atl.	158	M-5
Rosario Bank, Atl.	158	J-4
Ross Bank, Sou.	143	U-9
Ross Canyon, Sou.	143	Q-11
Ross Ice Shelf, Sou.	143	R-6
Ross Island, Sou.	143	V-8
Ross Sea, Sou.	143	Q-10
Röst Bank, Arc.	133	O-12
Rota, Pac.	227	T-3
Rote, Pac.	225	S-15
Rothschild Island, Sou.	141	N-8
Rottnest Island, Ind.	196	L-2
Round Hill Head, Pac.	235	X-13
Rousay, Atl.	151	P-5
Rowley Island, Arc.	135	Q-10
Rowley Shelf, Ind.	195	U-7
R.S.A. Seamount, Atl.	169	T-9
Rudolf Land, Arc.	133	S-6
Rugged Island, Atl.	175	V-12
Ruhnu, Atl.	153	U-8
Rum Cay, Atl.	159	Q-1
Rurutu, Pac.	249	N-12
Rutland Island, Ind.	183	W-10
Ryberg Peninsula, Sou.	141	N-10
Ryukyu Islands, Pac.	217	U-11

S

Saaremaa, Atl.	153	U-8
Saba, Atl.	159	W-4
Sable Island, Atl.	155	T-8
Sabtang, Pac.	221	W-3
Sadoga-shima, Pac.	215	U-11
Sagami-nada, Pac.	215	V-13
Saganthif Kyun, Pac.	223	N-4
Sagittarius Seachannel, Pac.	209	N-7
Saharan Seamounts, Atl.	149	Q-9
Sahul Banks, Pac.	225	S-15
Sahul Shelf, Ind.	195	V-7
St. Anna Trough, Arc.	133	T-5
St. Austell Bay, Atl.	163	U-1
St. Barthélémy, Atl.	159	X-4
St. Croix, Atl.	159	V-5
St. Eusatius, Atl.	159	W-5
St. George Island, Atl.	157	V-3
St. George Island, Pac.	207	W-6
St. Georges Bay, Atl.	155	S-7
St. Helena Bay, Atl.	173	W-10
St. Helena Fracture Zone, Atl.	169	R-5
St. Helena, Atl.	169	U-5
St. John, Atl.	159	V-4
St. Joseph Island, Atl.	157	O-4
St. Kitts, Atl.	159	X-5
St. Lawrence Island, Pac.	207	V-3
St. Lawrence, Atl.	155	N-4
St. Lucia Channel, Atl.	159	X-6
St. Martin, Atl.	159	W-4
St. Mary's Bay, Atl.	155	X-6
St. Matthew Island, Pac.	207	T-4
St. Matthias Group, Pac.	227	V-9
St. Paul Fracture Zone, Atl.	169	P-1
St. Paul Island, Atl.	155	S-6
St. Paul Island, Ind.	199	P-12
St. Paul Island, Pac.	207	V-6
St.-Pierre, Atl.	155	W-6
St. Rogatien Bank, Pac.	211	Q-5
St. Thomas, Atl.	159	V-4
St. Vincent Island, Atl.	157	V-3
St. Vincent Passage, Atl.	159	X-7
St. Vincent, Atl.	159	Y-7
Saipan, Pac.	227	T-3
Sakarya Canyon, Atl.	167	Q-6
Sakhalin, Pac.	213	Q-7
Sakhalinskiy Zaliv, Pac.	213	P-6
Sakishima-shoto, Pac.	217	R-11
Sala y Gomez Ridge, Pac.	247	T-5
Sala y Gómez, Pac.	247	T-5
Salawati, Pac.	225	W-9
Salibabu, Pac.	225	T-7
Salisbury, Arc.	133	S-6
Salisbury Island, Arc.	135	S-13
Salm, Arc.	133	T-6
Salmon Bank, Pac.	210	K-3
Samar, Pac.	225	S-2
Samoa, Pac.	229	V-3
Samoa Basin, Pac.	229	W-4
Samos, Atl.	165	U-8
Samotharaki, Atl.	166	M-7
Samothraki Plateau, Atl.	165	U-6
Samsun Ridge, Atl.	167	V-5
San Clemente Island, Pac.	243	Q-6
San Cristobel, Pac.	233	V-3
San Francisco Bay, Pac.	243	O-3
San Martin Canyon, Sou.	141	S-7
San Martin Seamounts, Pac.	247	T-12
San Miguel Island, Pac.	243	P-6
San Nicolas Island, Pac.	243	P-6
San Salvador, Atl.	160	L-6
Sanak Islands, Pac.	207	Y-7
Sanday, Atl.	151	Q-5
Sandwich Bay, Atl.	173	U-5
Sandy Cape, Pac.	235	X-14
Sandy Cay, Ind.	187	V-8
Sangeang, Pac.	225	P-13
Sangir, Pac.	225	T-7
Sanibel Island, Atl.	157	W-5
Sant Lazarus Bank, Ind.	193	T-3
Santa Barbara Channel, Pac.	243	P-6
Santa Barbara Island, Pac.	243	Q-6
Santa Catalina Island, Pac.	243	R-6
Santa Cruz Island, Pac.	243	Q-6
Santa Cruz Islands, Pac.	233	X-2
Santa Isabel, Pac.	233	U-1
Santa Rosa Island, Pac.	243	P-6
Santander Canyon, Atl.	163	U-9
Santaren Channel, Atl.	157	Y-6
Santos Plateau, Atl.	168	M-7
São Pedro e São Paulo, Atl.	149	P-12
São Tomé, Atl.	171	V-6
Sapudi, Pac.	221	T-15

INDEX

ACKNOWLEDGMENTS

Key: t = top; c = center; b = bottom; l = left; r = right.

Photo credits

GI = Getty Images; iS = istockphoto.com; N = NASA; N_EO = NASA Earth Observatory; N_ES = NASA Earth from Space; N_G = Great Images in NASA; N_GS = NASA Goddard Space Flight Center; N_J = NASA Jet Propulsion Laboratory; N_L = NASA Landsat; N_V = Visible Earth; NRCS_VA = Natural Resources Conservation Service Virginia; SH = Shutterstock; USAP = U.S. Antarctic Program.

1 iS/Perry Kroll; **2–3** SH/Wollertz; **6**t SH/Soygirl53; ct SH/Levent Konuk; cb SH/Ethan Daniels; b iS; **14–15** SH/Chen Min Chun; **17**tr SH; tcr SH/bradlifestyle; bcr SH/Richard Whitcombe; br SH/Powell'sPoint; **18**cl N; cr SH/Nejron Photo; **19**bc SH/Matt Ragen; c SH; tc SH/kongsak sumano; **20**bl N_V; **23** SH/Rob Bayer; **26**bl OAR/National Undersea Research Program (NURP); br SH; **27**tl National Oceanic and Atmospheric Administration; br SH/Doug Lemke; **28–29** SH/paulista; **30**bl SH/iurii; **32**c SH/Roman Vukolov; **33**br SH/Federico Rostagno; bl SH/chuyuss; **34**bc National Oceanic and Atmospheric Administration; br iS; **35**bl National Oceanic and Atmospheric Administration; br Christian M. Caldwell/U.S. Navy; **36–7** SH/Peter Rimkus; **38**cl SH; **39**tl, tr N_V; bl, bc, br SH; **41**cr, br N; **43**bl iS; bc, br N_L; **45**t TOPEX/Poseidon; bl SH/Mikhail Kochiev; bc SH/mikeledray; br N_G; **47**cr SH/Jason Pruden; **48**cl SH/Steve Heap; **49**br SH; bc SH/Kees Zwanenburg; br SH/Ethan Daniels; **50**cl iS; **51**c National Oceanic and Atmospheric Administration; bl iS; **53**tl N_V; tr N_EO; cr SH/Richard Whitcombe; br SH; **55**tr, tl, br N_VE; **56**cr iS; br SH; **57**cr iS; **58–9** SH/Sphinx Wang; **60**cl SH/Shane Gross; cr SH/Beth Swanson; bl SH/Jubal Harshaw; bc SH/feathercollector; br SH/Dmytro Pylypenko; **62**bl, br National Oceanic and Atmospheric Administration; **64**br National Oceanic and Atmospheric Administration; **65**tr, bl, br National Oceanic and Atmospheric Administration; **66**c, cr iS; **67**tl SH/Trudy Simmons; tr SH/Matt Haeger; bl N_V; **68**cl, c, cr SH; **69**t SH; **70**tr, cl, cc, cr iS; **71**cl, bl iS; **73**bl SH/John A. Anderson; bc SH/bikeriderlondon; cr SH/LHamilton; **74**bl SH; **75**cl SH/davidpstephens; bc SH/John A. Anderson; br SH/Luiz A. Rocha; **77**tl National Park Service; ctl Mila Zinkova; ccl SH/Incredible Arctic; cbl, bl SH; **78**cr SH/Matthew Jacques; **79**cr SH/Graceson; **80**c SH/trekandshoot; br SH/City of Angels; bl SH/shunfa Teh; **81**tl SH/Matt Tilghman; tr SH/Martin Mecnarowski; **82**cr, bc, br iS; cl SH; **83**tr N; cl N_V; cr iS; br SH/iliuta goean; **84–5** SH/BlueOrange Studio; **86**cl Uwe Kils; br SH/Amelie Koch; **87**bl N_E; bcl N_J; bcr, br N_V; **89**tl Lamiot; cl Hans Hillewaert; bl Prof. Gordon T. Taylor, Stony Brook University; rt–b N; **90**cl SH/scubaluna; cr SH/Sascha Janson; bl SH/Fiona Ayerst; **91**tl SH/Daniel Huebner; cr SH/Sarawut Kundej; bl SH/Yusran Abdul Rahman; **92**tr Luis Miguel Bugallo Sánchez; cl SH/OPIS Zagreb; bl SH/worldswildlifewonders; br Mike Baird from Morro Bay, USA; **93**tr Kirt L. Onthank; **94**cl Hans Hillewaert; cr N_E; bl SH/Amanda Nicholls; **95**cl iS; cr SH; **96**cr iS; br SH/Daleen Loest; **97**cl SH/Rich Carey; cr SH/Shane Gross; bl SH/Andrii Slonchak; br SH/Brian Lasenby; **98**cl SH/Tory Kallman; cr SH/Ivan Kuzmin; **99**tl SH/Ondrej Prosicky; tr SH/windcoast; **100**bc SH/kikujungboy; **101**bl SH/Paul S. Wolf; br SH/Dray van Beeck; **102**cl GI/Solvin Zankl; br GI/Norbert Wu/Minden Pictures; **103**tl GI/Norbert Wu; tr National Oceanic and Atmospheric Administration; cl Gervais et Boulart; **105**cl SH/Michael Toh; bl SH/Tony Brindley; cr SH/critterbiz; br SH/Ken C. Moore; **106**tr N_VE; c US Fish and Wildlife; cbr SH/Heiko Kiera; bc SH/mangojuicy; **107**cr SH/Eric Krouse; **108**tr Dorothy Birch; br SH/Jana Shea; **109**tl SH/AndreAnita; ct SH/Lauren Rodgers; cl SH/Christopher Boswell; bl SH/Fiona Ayerst; cr iS; **110–11** SH/Andrea Izzotti; **112**bl iS; br National Oceanic and Atmospheric Administration; **113**cr SH; **114**cr iS; **115**c SH; bl SH/Richard Whitcombe; **116**c NRCS_VA; **117**cl SH/smspsy; c SH; cr iS; cbl National Oceanic and Atmospheric Administration; **118**cl SH/Barbara Tripp; bl SH/Yongyut Kumsri; **119**cl SH/Oleksandr Koretskyi; cr SH/Brady Barrineau; **120**c iS; **121**tl, cr iS; tc SH; tr SH/Marat Dupri; br SH/Ben Grasser; **122**cl N_L; **123**cr SH/Ethan Daniels; **124**cr SH/Lano Lan; bl SH/VisionDive; br SH/Kichigin; **125**ct SH/Steve Meese; lt U.S. Fish and Wildlife Service Southeast Region; c SH/Jamesplay; lc SH/David Littman; b diliff; **126**cl Philip Colla; cc, cr National Oceanic and Atmospheric Administration; br Forest and Kim Starr; **127**c SH/tororo reaction; bl, bcl, bcr iS; br SH/Ethan Daniels; **128–9** SH/Florida Stock; **130**br iS; **131**tr SH; **132**cl iS; tr SH; **133**br iS; **134**bl iS; br National Oceanic and Atmospheric Administration; **135**tr SH; bl SH/Vladimir Melnik; **136–7** SH/Thelma Amaro Vidales; **138**cr SH/Mariusz Potocki; **140**cl, br iS; cl SH; **141**br iS; **142**bl iS; br, cl National Oceanic and Atmospheric Administration; tr SH/BMJ; **143**tr National Oceanic and Atmospheric Administration; **144–5** SH/Vladimir Kogan Michael; **148**cl SH/Luca85; br SH/Mark Caunt; **150**bl iS; cl SH; **151**bl, tr iS; **152**cr iS; bl N_EO; cl SH; **153**tl, br iS; **154**cr N_V; cl SH; **155**br SH/Photogrape; **156**bl SH/Christopher Meder; **157**br N_V; **158**bl SH; **159**br SH; **160**bl GI/Robert F. Sisson; br SH/Ethan Daniels; **162**cl, bc iS; cr SH; **163**tl, bl iS; **164**cl iS; bl N_EO; **165**tr SH/burnel1; **166**c, bl SH; tr SH/Iakov Filimonov; br SH/Antonio Martin; **168**c SH/Sergey Uryadnikov; **169**br SH/Tomas Kotouc; **170**cl iS; bl SH/Susana_Martins; **171**br SH/Seaphotoart; **172**tr, bl, bc SH; cr iS; **174**bl N_EO; cc SH; cr SH/Ondrej Prosicky; **175**cl SH/Ondrej Prosicky; **176–7** SH/Willyam Bradberry; **178**bl SH/Andrey Armyagov; **180**c SH/Rich Carey; **181**bl SH; br SH/divedog; **182**br SH; tr N_V; **183**tl N_J; tr SH/Jeremy Brown; **184**br SH; cl SH/vkilikov; cc SH/Rich Carey; **185**tr SH; **186**c SH/Laura Dinraths; br iS; **187**bl SH; **188**c iS; bl N_V; **189**tr, bc, br iS; **190**bl N_GS; cl SH; **191**tl SH/Don Mammoser; **192**bl N; cl SH; br SH/AlessandroZocc; **193**br iS; **194**cl SH/Michael Warwick; bc SH/Krzysztof Odziomek; bl SH/Stringer Image; **196**cl SH; cr SH/dirkr; **197**br SH/Ken C Moore; **198**cl SH; **199**tc SH/wildestanimal; **200–1** SH/Tomas Kotouc; **202**bl iS; bc SH; **204**bl SH/Birdiegal; **205**bl, br SH; **206**l SH/Christopher Meder; **207**cl Sasha Isachenko; bc SH/Doptis; **208**c N_V; br SH; **209**br SH/Johnny Adolphson; **210**bl SH/Benny Marty; bc iS; br N_V; **211**br SH/Timothy Ewing; **212**bl SH; cr N_V; **213**bl SH/DPS; br SH/Dmytro Pylypenko; **214**tr SH/Mutsuko Kawamura; bl SH/Muellek Josef; **216**br SH/dexterous simpson; bl N_V; **217**br SH/Vishnevskiy Vasily;

Illustration credits

Maps and graphs